Tea

Chemistry
Precision & Design

Second Edition

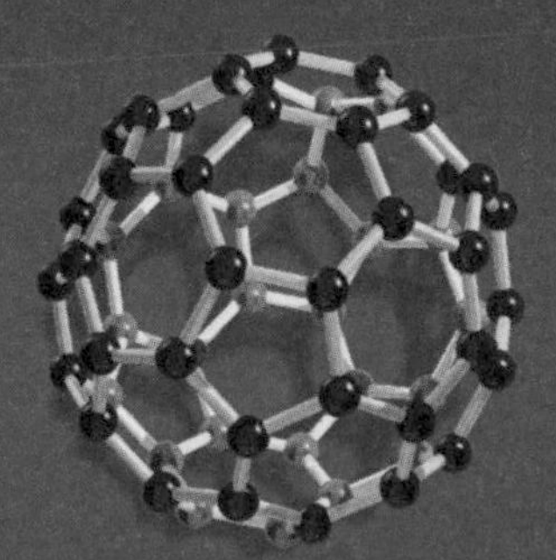

A Beka Book® Pensacola, FL 32523-9100
an affiliated ministry of PENSACOLA CHRISTIAN COLLEGE®

Correlated Materials

Chemistry: Precision and Design

Teacher Guide

Student Tests and Teacher Key

Student Quizzes and Teacher Key

Lab Manual and Teacher Key

Science in Action: A Science Project Guide

Optional

Video Lab Demonstrations—First Semester

Video Lab Demonstrations—Second Semester

Supplement for Advanced Studies

Teacher Guide for *Chemistry: Precision and Design*

Second Edition

Staff Credits

Editors: Gregory Parker, Shane Smith, Rebecca Ross, Brian Ashbaugh
Daily Pacing: Rebecca Ross
Teacher Notes: Gregory Parker, Verne Biddle

Photos: Cover—Digital Vision (glassware), Lockheed Martin Tactical Aircraft Systems (plane), Corbis Images (chemist, shuttle), Corel Corp. (balloons); inside cover—Corel Corp.; page i—Lockheed Martin Tactical Aircraft Systems.

A Beka Book, a Christian textbook ministry affiliated with Pensacola Christian College, is designed to meet the need for Christian textbooks and teaching aids. The purpose of this publishing ministry is to help Christian schools reach children and young people for the Lord and train them in the Christian way of life.

Contents

General Information

Daily Pacing, Teacher Notes, Answer Keys (by chapter)

Scope and Sequence

Weeks	Chapters (from *Chemistry: Precision and Design*)	Tests/Quizzes (from *Chemistry* Tests and Quizzes)	Labs (from Lab Manual)	Science Project (from *Science in Action*)
First Quarter				
1–4	1 Chemistry: An Introduction 2 Matter: The Substance of Chemistry	Quizzes 1–3 **Test 1** (Ch 1–2)	**Lab 1:** Laboratory Regulations and Safety Rules: A Demonstration **Lab 2:** Laboratory Techniques I **Lab 3:** Laboratory Techniques II **Lab 4:** Paper Chromatography of Pigments and Dyes (teacher demonstration) **Lab 5:** Observation of Elements, Compounds, and Mixtures **Lab 6:** Physical and Chemical Changes I	•Topic Selection •Investigation Background (bibliography cards) •Investigation Background (tentative outline)
5–7	3 Stoichiometry: Elements and Compounds 4 Stoichiometry: Chemical Reactions	Quizzes 4–8 **Test 2** (Ch 3–4)	**Lab 7:** Physical and Chemical Changes II **Lab 8:** Stoichiometry of a Single Displacement Reaction **Lab 9:** Stoichiometry of a Double Displacement Reaction	•Investigation Background (note cards) •Investigation Background (first draft and rewritten draft) •Investigation Background (final draft)
8–9	5 Gases	Quiz 9 **Test 3** (Ch 1–5)	**Lab 10:** Charles's Law	•Problem Selection •Investigation Plan (first draft)
Second Quarter				
10–11	6 Chemical Thermodynamics	Quiz 10 **Test 4** (Ch 6)	**Lab 11:** Analysis of Household Chemicals **Lab 12:** Calorimetry: Specific Heat of a Metal	•Investigation Plan (revised draft) •Investigation Plan (final draft) •Investigation begins
12–14	7 Light, Electrons, and Atomic Structure 8 The Periodic Table	Quizzes 11–13 **Test 5** (Ch 7–8)	**Lab 13:** Flame Tests (teacher demonstration) **Lab 14:** The Periodic Law	•First journal check (four entries) •Second journal check (6 entries) •Third journal check (10 entries)
15–17	9 The Chemical Bond and Intermolecular Forces	Quizzes 14–15 **Test 6** (Ch 1–9)	**Lab 15:** Molecular Models and Polarity **Lab 16:** Crystal Structures	•Fourth journal check (12 entries) •Fifth journal check (14 entries)

Scope and Sequence (cont.)

Weeks	Chapters (from *Chemistry: Precision and Design*)	Tests/Quizzes (from *Chemistry* Tests and Quizzes)	Labs (from Lab Manual)	Science Project (from *Science in Action*)
Third Quarter				
18–20	**10** Selected Nonmetals and Their Compounds **11** Selected Metals and Semimetals	Quizzes 16–17 **Test 7** (Ch 10–11)	**Lab 17:** Preparation and Properties of Oxygen **Lab 18:** Allotropes of Sulfur	•Investigation complete •Journal complete •Investigation Followup (first draft) •Investigation Followup (final draft)
21–24	**12** Solutions and Colloids **13** Chemical Kinetics	Quizzes 18–20 **Test 8** (Ch 12–13)	**Lab 19:** Colligative Properties: Determination of Boiling Point Elevation **Lab 20:** Colloids **Lab 21:** Chemical Kinetics: A Clock Reaction	•Oral Presentation with Exhibit
25	**14** Chemical Equilibrium	Quiz 21 **Test 9** (Ch 10–14)	**Lab 22:** Equilibrium: Le Châtelier's Principle	
Fourth Quarter				
26–28	**15** Acids, Bases, and Salts	Quiz 22 **Test 10** (Ch 15)	**Lab 23:** pH Measurement **Lab 24:** Acid-Base Titrations	
29–31	**16** Oxidation-Reduction Reactions and Electrochemistry **17** Nuclear Chemistry	Quizzes 23–25 **Test 11** (Ch 16–17)	**Lab 25:** Electrochemistry: Corrosion of Iron **Lab 26:** Electrochemistry: The Voltaic Cell **Lab 27:** Nuclear Chemistry (teacher demonstration) **Lab 28:** Radioactive Nuclear Decay and Half-Life	
32–34	**18** Organic Chemistry	Quizzes 26–27 **Test 12** (Ch 1–18)	**Lab 29:** Observation of Substituted Hydrocarbons **Lab 30:** Oxidation of an Aldehyde	

Chemistry in Christian Perspective

Christian Perspective

Chemistry: Precision and Design is written from a Christian perspective. Basic to this perspective is the conviction that God is the Creator and Sustainer of the universe. The Christian perspective gives the student of science several advantages:

- it gives him greater insight as he studies the brilliant order and design of God's creation;
- it enables him to study the physical creation without the hindrance of false philosophies such as evolution; and
- it gives him an infallible source of truth—the Bible—with which to compare his observations.

Insight into Creation

Only when the student of science acknowledges the hand of God in creation can he truly appreciate the intelligent design of the universe. Such a student recognizes that in science, one is merely "thinking God's thoughts after Him." *Chemistry: Precision and Design* explores the many branches of chemistry with the goal of discovering the thoughts of the Creator through the ingenious structure and orderly function of his creation (Ps. 19:1).

Knowledge of the Beginning

The Christian perspective of *Chemistry: Precision and Design* naturally rejects the unproven hypothesis of evolution, recognizing special creation as the reasonable explanation for the origin and design of the universe. The Bible confirms what nature clearly reveals—that "in the beginning, God created . . ." Although chemistry as an empirical science has been less permeated by evolutionary doctrine than biology or geology, one's view of origins *does* affect both how he approaches the science of chemistry and how he applies chemical principles to societal issues.

The Goal of Science

Chemistry: Precision and Design also recognizes God's command for man to have dominion over the creation (Gen. 1:28–30). Thus, the purpose of science is not merely knowledge for its own sake, but the *application* of that knowledge for the benefit of mankind. In every area of chemistry, the goal is to learn how man might extend his "dominion" and make better and wiser use of the physical creation. To this end, *Chemistry: Precision and Design* seeks to not only give the student a solid foundation in chemical principles, but also seeks to help the student understand the *practical application* of these principles.

Conservative Conservation

Although many other chemistry texts promote the views of radical environmentalists, *Chemistry: Precision and Design* supports the more balanced concept of responsible conservation. The Christian should be a good steward of God's creation; with man's dominion over the earth comes a responsibility to tend, manage, and conserve resources. But the ultimate purpose of the physical creation must not be forgotten—the earth was made for man to inhabit, and its resources for man to use. To help the student better understand current environmental issues, the text provides a balanced conservative perspective on topics such as ozone depletion, acid rain, global warming, and nuclear power, examining facets of the issues that are often ignored or glossed over by other textbooks.

Foundational Truths

Chemistry: Precision and Design lays a firm foundation for future studies in chemistry, physics, and other fields while teaching students a Christian perspective of science. With the academic knowledge students gain through this course, they will also find a greater appreciation for God's physical creation and an increased interest in science that will propel many toward more advanced courses in years to come.

Special Features of this Teacher Guide

This Teacher Guide is designed to help you, the teacher, use *Chemistry: Precision and Design* in the classroom. Following this introductory material, which includes a scope and sequence and helpful teaching suggestions, a teaching guide is provided for each chapter. Each guide includes these features:

Daily Pacing. The daily plans suggest what pages to teach and review each day. They also schedule labs and lab demonstrations, tests, quizzes, and science project deadlines. The questions for the unannounced homework reading quizzes are included in the daily plans. The other scheduled quizzes and tests are available separately. Altogether, the daily pacing for chapters 1– 18 provides a complete curriculum for 170 lesson plans.

Teacher Notes. The teacher notes contain a wide variety of information that you may find useful as you teach. These notes are intended primarily to provide you with

- *in-depth explanation* of principles and issues that are beyond the scope of student text, but which you may find useful in your teaching or personal study;
- *interesting facts* that you may wish to share with your class to enhance students' interest in chemistry; and
- *background information* on various topics.

Lecture Demonstrations. Explanations of lecture demonstrations and object lessons are included that you can use in your teaching. If properly used, lecture demonstrations can increase both student interest and student understanding of chemical concepts.

Resource Lists. In many chapters, lists of additional resources are provided for your reference. These include useful books, periodical articles, Internet resources, and even molecular visualization software (chapter 18).

Suggestions for Classroom Management

Suggested Daily Schedule

Each lesson plan in the Daily Pacing is designed for a 50-minute class period. Many science teachers have found the following schedule for a typical science class to be helpful:

1. **Check attendance** before the class bell rings, using your seating chart. (Later, you could have a reliable student do this.) Have students prepare for class by taking out their homework and passing it to the front of their row for you to check. Distribute any graded quizzes you wish to return to the students.
2. **Open with prayer** (1–2 minutes).
3. **Give any written quizzes** (8–10 min.). The Daily Pacing schedules an average of one or more written quizzes per chapter. These quizzes are provided in the *Chemistry: Precision and Design* Quizzes book. (See the Scope and Sequence for an overview of the written quizzes.) Answers and guidelines for giving and grading quizzes are given in the Teacher Key. Administer quizzes before reviewing previous lessons.

   Give any oral "pop" quizzes (3–5 min.). Beginning with chapter 2, one or two unannounced reading quizzes are given each week in addition to the written quizzes to keep students accountable for their reading assignments. These quizzes are provided with answers in the Daily Pacing for each chapter.
4. **Check and discuss homework** (2–3 min.). It is a good idea to give students an assignment to do while you check homework. Walk across the front of the room, checking each row's papers for completeness. Occasionally check for proper headings and neatness. Discuss answers after you have checked the homework.
5. **Review material taught in previous lessons** (3–5 min.). Review is an important element of the science class, for it helps students connect new concepts with principles previously taught. Review should be fast-paced, interesting, and varied.
6. **Teach the lesson** (30–35 min.). Each chapter is broken down into teachable lessons in the Daily Pacing. When you introduce a chapter, give the students an overview of the content. In addition, highlight illustrations and other special features to whet their interest. On the chalkboard, list important terms from the reading. Before you teach, study the lesson and gather any materials you may need for demonstrations and activities.

   As you teach the lesson, maintain your students' attention by asking questions and encouraging discussion. The Critical Thinking and Application questions from the Section Reviews in the text are especially good for class discussion. These questions encourage students to practice their higher thinking skills.
7. **Review the new material** (2–3 min.). Highlight the principles and applications covered in the lesson.
8. **Give and preview tomorrow's assignment** (2–3 min.). Each student should have an assignment pad in which to record his homework assignments. Repeat the assignment twice. Preview the assignment by mentioning a few important things you want the students to notice in their reading. If the assignment includes any difficult terms or names, you may want to write them on the chalkboard and pronounce them. Each lesson in the Daily Pacing includes a homework assignment.

Review Methods

Before you teach any new material, review the material previously taught in that chapter. After you teach the new material, review it as well. Consider these suggested methods for review:

1. Use the Section Review questions in the text.
2. Prepare questions of your own for a quick review drill.
3. Make a list of terms for the students to define while you check homework, and then go over the list together as a class.
4. Put important terms and definitions on index cards and use them like flashcards.

5. Briefly summarize the material in your own words, or call on students to do the same.

Student Notebooks

You might require your students to take notes in a large spiral notebook. (This same notebook could be used for homework assignments.) Check occasionally to see that each student is taking notes carefully and that his notes are adequate for review.

Homework Assignments

You can teach your students the importance of faithfulness in completing daily assignments by consistently checking their homework each day. Decide beforehand what procedure you will follow for any students who have incomplete work. Many teachers find it helpful to keep a card file for extra work assigned for homework.

If you will consistently check homework and then follow through with your procedure for incomplete work, you will have few homework offenders. You will be able to teach not only more subject content, but also the important character traits of self-discipline and dependa-bility.

It is not necessary to grade homework assignments, but you may wish to do so occasionally. Encourage your students to keep their completed homework assignments in a folder for review.

Oral Reading Quizzes

"Pop" reading quizzes keep students accountable for their homework reading. For this reason, it is important that these quizzes be unannounced and unpredictable. Reading quizzes are provided in the Daily Pacing for each chapter. The following procedure may be used:

1. Have the students clear their desks and take out two clean sheets of paper, a pen, and a pencil. Students should write in pen on one sheet of paper and use the other as a cover sheet.
2. Read each quiz question twice. Remind your students to cover their answers.
3. After the last question, have the students exchange papers. Students should grade in pencil.
4. Read each answer twice.
5. Instruct the students to write the number missed at the top, sign their name as grader, and pass the quizzes forward to be collected.

Record the quiz grades later. "Pop" quizzes should take about 5 minutes to give, grade, and collect.

Laboratory Exercises

Chemistry labs are scheduled in the Daily Pacing of this Teacher Guide. Students should be assigned as many of the suggested labs as possible. Each lab exercise is thoroughly explained in the Lab Manual. Students should begin Lab Report Sheets during the lab and complete them for homework. These lab reports should be discussed and collected in the lesson following the lab.

After checking the lab reports, return them to the students; have the students place them in a Chemistry lab notebook. You may wish to check lab notebooks periodically throughout the year.

Video Labs

For your convenience, the labs in the Lab Manual have been videotaped. You may use these tapes to supplement your students' work if they are having difficulty with a particular lab, or use them instead of doing the lab if you do not have the necessary equipment or supplies. Use of the video labs will save you hours of preparation time.

Supplement for Advanced Studies

Chemistry: Precision and Design is intended to give the student a solid foundation in the fundamental concepts of chemistry. For more advanced studies, such as for students interested in pursuing college-level chemistry in the future, a Supplement for Advanced Studies is available. The supplement contains

- *advanced material* beyond the scope of a basic course, with special emphasis on the mathematical (quantitative) aspects of chemistry;
- *examples and exercises* for additional practice in both basic and advanced topics; and
- *additional labs* for hands-on practice in quantitative and analytical chemistry.

Science Project Explanation

An important part of the science course is the science project that each student will do. *Science in Action* guides students through the science project from start to finish. Step-by-step instructions, samples, and helpful tips make this work-text an invaluable resource. The project begins in lesson 6 and continues through lesson 106. The students each work individually on their own project outside class, though work is assigned and checked in class.

Through this project, the student learns library research techniques, scientific research methods, and graphic design principles. Involvement in a science project not only kindles a student's interest in science, but also instills the character qualities of diligence and persistence in solving problems. It helps the student learn to follow directions and to work carefully and independently. It is also your opportunity to awaken students to the exciting area of science experimentation.

A listing of each phase of the science project is given below with the lesson numbers where the parts are scheduled in the Daily Pacing. (See the Scope and Sequence in this Teacher Guide for an overview of project deadlines.) For more information, see "To the Teacher" in *Science in Action.*

Laboratory Exercises

The parts of the science project are described as follows. The lesson numbers refer to the lessons in the Daily Pacing in which each step is scheduled.

1. Introduction **Lesson**
- Science Project introduced 5
- Science Project Work Schedule completed 5
- topic introduced 5
- Science Project Notebook introduced 5
- Topic Selection Worksheet due 10

2. Background
- introduced 8
  - bibliography cards due 11
  - outline due 16
  - note cards due 21
- first draft due 26
- Background First Draft Check due 26
- rewritten first draft due 29
- final draft due 32

3. Investigation
- investigation introduced 32
- Problem Selection Worksheet due 36
  - investigation plan introduced 36
  - first draft due 41
  - Investigation Plan Evaluation 41
  - revised investigation plan due 46
  - final investigation plan due 51
- investigation begins 51
- journal introduced 51
  - journal check 1 61
  - journal check 2 66
  - journal check 3 71
  - journal check 4 76
  - journal check 5 81
- Getting Started Worksheet due 55
- investigation complete 91
- journal complete 91

4. Followup
- introduced 81
- followup first draft due 91
- final draft due 96

5. Exhibit and Presentation
- dates chosen for presentation 66
- exhibit introduced 76
- exhibit explained 86
- presentation explained in more detail 95
- Science Project Notebook explained for exhibit 95
- exhibit due 102–113
- presentations begin 102
- presentations end 113

Safety in Chemistry Class

As a lab class, chemistry involves working with substances that can be harmful or fatal if misused. Some form of clothing protection (such as a lab coat or lab apron) and appropriate eye protection (e.g., safety goggles) should be worn while performing labs, lecture demonstrations, etc. that require the use of chemicals; an appropriately rated fire extinguisher should also be close at hand. These precautions should be observed when preparing solutions prior to class time as well. Failure to do so may result in stains, damage to clothing, or serious injury (including burns and permanent blindness).

As the teacher, it is your responsibility to be familiar with the hazards posed by various chemicals, mixtures of chemicals, and laboratory equipment (whether purchased or improvised). Materials Safety Data Sheets are available from your administrators or from chemical suppliers. Also be aware of local, state, and Federal laws and regulations governing the use, storage, and disposal of chemicals.

Every effort has been made to alert the teacher and the student to possible hazards and to teach and emphasize safety rules. The publisher is not responsible for accidents or injury incurred while performing labs, lecture demonstrations, or other procedures outlined in the text, lab manual, or Teacher Guide, or for improper disposal of any substances involved.

Pacing, Notes, Answer Keys

(All page numbers refer to Chemistry: Precision and Design *unless otherwise noted.)*

Chapter 1 (pp. 2–33)

Chemistry: An Introduction

Suggested Daily Pacing

1 **Welcome** students and explain material and procedures.

Preview textbooks, *Chemistry: Precision and Design* and *Chemistry Laboratory Manual.*

Introduce ch. 1, Chemistry: An Introduction.

Teach pp. **3–7,** sec. **1.1** Chemistry: The Science of Matter—**1.2** Measurement in Chemistry, up to Measuring length and volume.

Review lesson.

Assign homework and explain homework procedures.

HW: Review pp. 3–7; read pp. 7–10, up to Scientific Notation. Know all chart information for bold type prefixes in Table 1.1.

2 **Give Quiz 1** (over p. 6, Table 1.1). (All written quizzes are located in *Chemistry* Quizzes book. Refer to the Teacher Key for answers and suggested quizzing/grading procedures.)

Review pp. 3–7.

Teach pp. **7–10,** sec. **1.2** (cont.), up to Scientific Notation.

Review lesson.

HW: Read *Lab Manual* Lab 1 in preparation for lecture lab. Read pp. 10–12, up to Precision and Accuracy in Measurement. Answer p. 19, questions 1–2.

3 **Check** and discuss homework.

Review pp. 7–10.

Teach pp. **10–12,** sec. **1.2** (cont.), up to Precision and Accuracy in Measurement.

Review lesson.

Teach Lab 1: Laboratory Regulations and Safety Rules: A Demonstration. Students should fill in Lab 1 Report Sheet during lecture.

HW: Complete and return signed Lab 1 Report Sheet. Read pp. 12–15, up to Significant figures in calculations. Review the lab procedures and safety prodedures taught in Lab 1.

Note: You may wish to adjust the homework on lab days to give students extra time to complete their lab reports. For example, if students have a large portion of Lab 1 Report Sheet to complete, you could assign them to read only pp. 12–13 for homework. Then have students read pp. 14–15 during homework check in les. 4.

4 **Give Quiz 2** (over Lab 1).

Check and discuss homework.

Collect signed lab statements (bottom of Lab 1 Report Sheet).

Review pp. 10–12.

Teach pp. **12–15,** sec. **1.2** (cont.), up to Significant figures in calculations.

Review lesson.

HW: Read pp. 15–16, up to Problem-solving strategies. Answer p. 19, questions 3 and 4. Bring *Science in Action* to class.

5 **Check** and discuss homework.

Review pp. 12–15.

Teach pp. **15–16,** sec. **1.2** (cont.), up to Problem-solving strategies.

Review lesson.

Science Project (SP): Before class, read the Science Project explanation at the front of this *Teacher Guide.* Notice the chart that lists each project part and the lesson in which each is due. Also preview *Science in Action.* Use your school calendar and the Project Overview on pp. viii and ix to determine dates for the Work Schedule on pp. 7–8. In class, introduce science project and the *Science in Action* text. Have students fill in dates on the Work Schedule. Briefly discuss choosing topics, using *Science in Action,* pp. 1–6, and explain the Science Project Notebook. Assign Topic Selection Worksheet, p. 9, to be completed for les. 10.

HW: Read *Lab Manual* Lab 2 and complete Prelab Assignment. Review *Science in Action* pp. 1–6. Topic Selection Worksheet due les. 10.

6 **Check** and discuss homework.

Conduct Lab 2: Laboratory Techniques I.

HW: Complete Lab 2 Report Sheet. Read pp. 16–19. Answer p. 19, question 5.

7 **Check** and discuss homework.

Review pp. 15–16.

Teach pp. **16–19,** sec. **1.2** (cont.).

Review lesson.

HW: Read pp. 20–25, up to sec. 1.4 Energy and Matter. Answer p. 19, question 6, and p. 25, questions 1–5. Bring *Science in Action.* Topic Selection Worksheet due lesson 10.

8 **Give** "pop" reading quiz over pp. 20–25:

1. List the four states of matter. *solid, liquid, gas, plasma*
2. Which state of matter is believed to be the most abundant in the universe? *plasma*
3. In which state of matter are particles close together, but free to move about? *liquid*
4. Which state of matter has no definite volume and is relatively easy to compress? *gas*
5. What substances cannot be broken down into simpler substances by ordinary chemical means? *elements*

Check and discuss homework.

Review pp. 16–19.

Teach pp. **20–25,** sec. **1.3** Matter.

Review lesson.

SP: Introduce **Investigation Background** and the **bibliography** for it, using *Science in Action* pp. 11–13. Assign six bibliography cards for les. 11 (ch. 2). First draft of Investigation Background will be due in les. 26 (ch. 4).

HW: Read *Lab Manual* Lab 3 and complete Prelab Assignment. Six bibliography cards due les. 11 (ch. 2). Investigation Background due les. 26 (ch. 4).

9 **Check** and discuss homework.

Conduct Lab 3: Laboratory Techniques II.

HW: Complete Lab 3 Report Sheet. Read pp. 25–29. Answer p. 29, questions 1–6. Complete Topic Selection Worksheet and bring *Science in Action.*

10 **SP:** Check Topic Selection Worksheet. (Have students read text pp. 30–31.) Make topic suggestions as needed. Answer any additional questions about the bibliography cards due next lesson.

Give "pop" reading quiz over pp. 25–29:

1. Give the term for the energy possessed by matter due to its motion. *kinetic energy*
2. Which type of reaction is always accompanied by some type of energy change? *chemical reaction*
3. State the law of conservation of energy. *Energy can be neither created nor destroyed.*
4. Give the term for the randomness of a substance or system. *entropy*
5. True or False: In an endothermic reaction, the products have a lower energy content than the reactants. *false*

Check and discuss homework.

Review pp. 20–25.

Teach pp. **25–31,** sec. **1.4** Energy and Matter—**1.5** Careers in Chemistry.

Review lesson.

HW: Read pp. 34–37, up to Separation of Mixtures. Complete six bibliography cards for next lesson. Bring *Science in Action.*

Teacher Notes

To the Teacher: This Teacher Guide contains a wide variety of information that you may find useful as you teach. These notes are intended primarily to provide you with

- *in-depth explanation* of principles and issues that are beyond the scope of student text, but which you may find useful in your teaching or personal study;
- *interesting facts* that you may wish to share with your class to enhance students' interest in chemistry;
- *background information* on various topics; and
- *annotated resource lists* for further study.

Many chapters also contain *chemical demonstrations* and *object lessons* that may be used to demonstrate principles of the text in a more dramatic or thought-provoking way.

Use of calculators in this course. Use of calculators is encouraged in this course so that students can focus as much as possible on the problem setup and the underlying chemical principles. (Do encourage students to check their answers, however.) Be prepared to provide guidance to the student who does not yet have a scientific calculator and is unsure what kind to purchase.

Chapter 1 Overview. Chapter 1 begins by demonstrating the relevance of chemistry in daily life, as well as presenting the Christian view of science in general. The SI (metric) system is briefly reviewed, followed by a few foundational problem-solving tools the students will need in this course: scientific notation, significant figures, and methods of unit conversions. Next is a foundational overview of matter and energy, followed by a brief discussion of a number of chemistry-related careers.

In this introductory chapter, be sure to be *positive* in your approach to chemistry, as this will set the tone for much of the year. Some students may come into your class with the idea that chemistry is dry, boring, and irrelevant; it is up to you to dispel this notion and whet the students' appetites to learn more. Some ways to do this as you go through this course are to

- highlight ways in which chemistry is applied in local industries, particularly "high-tech" fields;
- highlight ways in which chemistry is applied in the students' everyday lives;
- spend a minute or two the first day highlighting some of the interesting topics that will be studied throughout the year ("application" chapters such as 10–11 and 17–18 may generate particular interest);
- use object lessons and interesting chemical demonstrations wherever possible (see Chemical Demonstration ideas at end of teacher notes).

Importance of chemistry (1.1, p. 4). In industrialized nations, practical chemistry is even more important; without it, most of the modern technology we take for granted every day would not exist. There would be no steel, aluminum, brass, or glass, or concrete; houses and other buildings would have to be made of stone, wood, and dirt, with no lighting, no air conditioning, and a stone fireplace for heat. To get to school, you would have to walk, ride an animal, or drive a wooden cart. Such amenities as soap, toothpaste, makeup, and grooming aids would not exist. Most people would be subsistence farmers, subject to starvation if the crops failed.

Exactness of conversion factors (1.2, pp. 14–16). Note that metric to F.P.S. conversions can also be exact because many F.P.S. units are *defined* in terms of metric units; for example, a foot is defined as *exactly* 30.48 centimeters or 0.3048 meter. Any conversion using an exact relationship such as this does not limit the significant figures in the answer. Approximations such as 1 mile ≈ 1.609 km *do* limit significant figures, however, because 1.609 km is rounded; the exact, defined relationship is 1 mile = 1.609344 km. (See Appendix A of the text for other exact conversions.)

Equations involving physical constants are limited to the number of significant figures you use for the constant. For example, if you use the rough approximation $\pi \approx 3.14$, you are limited to 3 significant figures; if you use the more precise $\pi \approx 3.141592654$, you are limited to 10 significant figures.

Interestingly, according to Jonathan and Peter Borwein, it would take only 39 significant figures to express the circumference of a circle the size of the observable universe to within a billionth of a millimeter.[1]

[1]Neal Carothers, "A Common Book of Pi," <http://ernie.bgsu.edu/~carother/pi/Pi1.html> (9/30/98).

Limits of significant figures (1.2, pp. 14–16). Although significant figures are useful at the high-school level as a way to express uncertainty, they are not an end in themselves; they are merely a "crutch" to use until the student is exposed to more accurate methods of error analysis (error propagation, standard deviation, etc.) in college-level courses. The chief drawback of significant figures is that they introduce systemic error into calculations by skewing the error range up or down.

We can illustrate the limits of significant figures by converting 195 K to degrees Fahrenheit. Using "sig figs," we would solve the problem as follows:

Step 1

$T_{°C} = T_K - 273.15$

$T_{°C} = 195\text{ K} - 273.15$

$T_{°C} = -78.15\,°C \approx$ **$-78\,°C$** (rounded to ones' place)

Step 2

$°F = \frac{9}{5}(-78\,°C) + 32$

$°F = -108.4\,°F \approx$ **$110\,°F$** (rounded to 2 sig figs)

The answer is limited to 2 sig figs because of step 1.

Now let us contrast this approach with a slightly more sophisticated analysis. If we express the initial temperature as 195 K plus or minus 1 K and keep all our digits, we get an answer of **$-78.15\,°C \pm 1\,°C$** for step 1. Converting this to Fahrenheit in step 2, still keeping all digits, would give us a final answer of **$-108.67\,°F \pm 1.8\,°F$** (note that the error range is also converted since degrees F and C are different sizes). The latter method tells us that the true value lies within the range $-106.87\,°F$ to $-110.47\,°F$, whereas the significant figures method wrongly implies that the true value is between $-109\,°F$ and $-111\,°F$, a significant error.

When to round (1.2, pp. 15–16). When performing calculations with significant figures, it can be helpful to save rounding for the final answer; rounding intermediate answers can lead to increased error in the final answer (by further skewing the error range). However, if a problem combines different types of operations (addition and multiplication, for example), it is often easier to round the answer after the first operation before proceeding to the second. As a teacher, it is helpful to choose sample problems that give the same answer no matter when rounding is done, so that students do not have to worry about the issue.

Scientific notation and sig figs (1.2, pp. 15–16). The ambiguity of the zeros in a number such as 1000 may be eliminated by expressing it in scientific notation. By so doing we can express anything from one to four significant figures for the number 1000:

1×10^3	1.0×10^3	1.00×10^3	1.000×10^3
1 significant figure	2 significant figures	3 significant figures	4 significant figures

The form we use would depend upon how the number was obtained (rule 3) and how many figures are permitted.

Including units with measurements (1.2, p. 17). The importance of including units with measurements is illustrated by the 1999 loss of NASA's Mars Climate Observer spacecraft due to a units mixup. For some reason, the company that built the spacecraft gave certain force figures in pounds, but without units; the NASA technicians responsible for spacecraft navigation naturally assumed the figures were newtons (SI unit of force). As a result, erroneous navigational commands were sent that caused the $125 million spacecraft to burn up in the Martian atmosphere instead of going into orbit around Mars.

In 1983, a unit-conversion mixup caused an Air Canada jetliner to run out of fuel at cruising altitude. It seems that while refueling the Boeing 767 in Montreal, the ground crew erroneously used the conversion factor for lb/L (without units) while trying to convert liters to *kilograms*. They did this twice, leading them to add only 5000 L of fuel instead of the 20,000 L required for the plane to reach its destination. Fortunately, the pilot managed to crash-land the powerless airliner on a drag strip, saving the aircraft and its passengers.

Dimensional analysis (1.2, pp. 17–18). One way to test your students' understanding of dimensional analysis is to have them convert made-up units, as follows: 1 wot = 8 toon; 800 blem = 1 toon; 1 bor = 5 blem; convert 6 wots to bors.

$$6\text{ wot} \times \frac{8\text{ toon}}{1\text{ wot}} \times \frac{800\text{ blem}}{1\text{ toon}} \times \frac{1\text{ bor}}{5\text{ blem}} = \mathbf{7.68 \times 10^3\ bor}$$

or, convert 8 mbor to ctoon:

$$8\text{ mbor} \times \frac{10^{-3}\text{ toon}}{1\text{ mbor}} \times \frac{5\text{ blem}}{1\text{ bor}} \times \frac{1\text{ toon}}{800\text{ blem}} \times \frac{1\text{ ctoon}}{10^{-2}\text{ toon}} = \mathbf{5 \times 10^{-3}\ ctoon}$$

Although it is good for students to know how to do formal dimensional analysis (with conversion factors, etc.), you may wish to give students the alternative of using the step-by-step method throughout the rest of the year. Some students will find the formal dimensional analysis method more logical and less prone to error (particularly those who have trouble keeping units straight), while others will do better with the step-by-step method.

Gases and filling of containers (1.3, p. 21). Strictly speaking, a gas spreads immediately to fill its container only if the container is originally empty (i.e., contains a vacuum). If the container already contains a lightweight gas like helium, and a heavier gas like carbon dioxide or argon is poured into the container, then the heavier gas will puddle at the bottom of the container, temporarily displacing the lighter gas until the two gases mix by diffusion.

You can demonstrate this surprising principle by generating CO_2 in a beaker (such as by adding vinegar to baking soda). Because the room is already filled with air, the gas does not immediately fill the room, but (being heavier than air) collects in the bottom of the beaker and can be poured like an invisible liquid until it diffuses away (a process which takes many seconds). The presence of the invisible gas can be demonstrated by carefully pouring the CO_2 onto a lit candle (without spilling any of the liquid). If this is done properly, the candle will flicker and go out.

Classification of matter (1.3, pp. 21–23). You may wish to have vials of substances from several different categories (dry mixture, solution, element, compound, etc.) on hand to pass around the class while you are teaching; this can help to reinforce the different categories of matter.

Careers in Chemistry (1.5, pp. 30–31). You may wish to encourage students to research vocations of their interest and to use college catalogs to determine their course requirements, particularly as they relate to chemistry.

Lecture Demonstrations

Changing one substance into another (1.1, pp. 3–4). *Prior to class,* dissolve (1) several crystals of $KMnO_4$ in about 300 mL water in a 400-mL beaker; (2) 1 g $NaHSO_3$ (or Na_2SO_3) in very little water; and (3) 1 g $BaCl_2 \cdot 2\ H_2O$ in very little water. (**CAUTION:** $BaCl_2$ is toxic.) In class, add the $NaHSO_3$ solution to the "grape juice" ($KMnO_4$ solution), with stirring, to change it to "water"; then add the $BaCl_2$ solution, with stirring, to change it to "milk." Emphasize that an understanding and knowledge of chemistry enables one to change certain substances to other substances having different properties.

The reactions involved would have little meaning to the students at this point, but they are given below for your information:

(1) $H^+(aq) + 2\ MnO_4^-(aq) + 5\ HSO_3^-(aq) \longrightarrow 5\ SO_4^{2-}(aq) + 2\ Mn^{2+}(aq) + 3\ H_2O(l)$

(2) $Ba^{2+}(aq) + SO_4^{2-}(aq) \longrightarrow BaSO_4(s)$

States of matter (1.3, pp. 20–21). You may wish to heat one or more ice cubes in a flask or beaker to illustrate the terms in this section and the properties of the three common states of matter. Discuss the role of heat energy in determining the state (see also section 1.5).

Atoms, elements, and compounds (1.3, pp. 22–23). If you have a molecular model kit, you can use it to illustrate the concepts of atoms, elements, molecules, compounds, and mixtures:

- Hold up individual spheres of the same color; explain that these represent several atoms of the same element.
- Hold up individual spheres of different colors; these represent atoms of different elements.
- Hold up a model of H_2, O_2, or N_2; explain that this is a molecule of a diatomic element.
- Hold up models of H_2O, CO_2, etc.; explain that these are molecules of compounds such as water and carbon dioxide.
- On a desktop or table, place 3–4 models of an element (e.g., N_2) in one small group, and 3–4 models of a compound (e.g., H_2O) in another. Each group represents a pure substance. Then slide the two groups together to form a single randomly mixed group. This is a mixture.

If you do not have a molecular model set, a similar demonstration can be dome using toothpicks and small polystyrene foam balls (available from a craft store; the balls can be spray-painted if necessary).

Potential *vs.* kinetic energy (1.4, pp. 25–26). You can effectively illustrate the difference between potential energy (stored energy or energy due to an object's position) and kinetic energy by raising a book several feet above a desktop and then releasing it. Potential and kinetic chemical energy can be demonstrated by striking a large match (the potential energy in the chemical bonds is quickly and dramatically converted to heat energy).

Exothermic reaction (1.4, p. 29). Exothermic reaction: Pile about 5 g $KMnO_4$ in a crucible or evaporating dish and make a small depression in the pile with a spatula. Add about 1 mL glycerol to the depression and stand back; a purple flame is produced after several seconds. Placing the crucible or evaporating dish in a large beaker will help to contain the reactant particles during the reaction.

Endothermic reaction (1.4, p. 29). Measure about 50 g NH_4NO_3 (or NH_4Cl) into a capped bottle and add 100 mL H_2O; the solution becomes cold as the NH_4NO_3 dissolves. The bottle will remain cold for several minutes and may be capped and passed around the class.

Chapter 1 Bibliography

Shakhashiri, Bassam Z. *Chemical Demonstrations: A Handbook for Teachers of Chemistry.* 4 vol. Madison, WI: University of Wisconsin Press, 1983. A collection of several hundred interesting lecture demonstrations, ranging from very easy to quite involved. Organized topically; vol. 4 includes combined index. Some could also be used as extra class labs or could serve as ideas for student science projects. Potentially useful throughout the year, but mentioned here for your reference. Includes safety and disposal information and descriptions of the chemistry involved.

Answers to Text Questions

Section Review 1.1 (p. 5)

1. What branch of chemistry is said to be foundational to the other areas of chemistry? *physical chemistry*
2. What branch of chemistry concerns itself with the chemistry of living things? *biochemistry*
3. Name five areas in your everyday life where chemistry and chemical technology have had an impact. *clothing, transportation, agriculture, medicines, grooming aids, electronic devices, home furnishings, etc.*
4. What should be the Christian's view toward science? *Answers will vary. The Christian should realize that science deals only with the physical universe, not the spiritual, moral, or supernatural; that science cannot answer all our questions about the universe; but that it can help man to master or subdue nature for man's benefit. It can also help us to more clearly see God's wisdom and power as revealed in His Creation.*

Section Review 1.2 (p. 19)

1. Name the basic metric units of length, mass, and volume. *meter, gram or kilogram, liter*
2. From memory, state the meaning (value) of the following metric prefixes:
   - **a.** centi- *1/100 or* 10^{-2}
   - **b.** milli- *1/1000 or* 10^{-3}
   - **c.** micro- *1/1,000,000 (one millionth) or* 10^{-6}
   - **d.** mega- *1,000,000 (one million) or* 10^{6}
   - **e.** kilo- *1000 or* 10^{3}
   - **f.** nano- *1/1,000,000,000 (one billionth) or* 10^{-9}
3. Express the following numbers in scientific notation.
   - **a.** 0.0021 2.1×10^{-3}
   - **b.** 10,005 1.0005×10^{4}
   - **c.** 0.490 4.90×10^{-1}
   - **d.** 445,000 4.45×10^{5}
4. Tell how many significant figures are in the following:
   - **a.** 409 *3*
   - **b.** 0.0070 *2*
   - **c.** 15,000 *2*
   - **d.** 15,000. *5*
   - **e.** 800.00 *5*
   - **f.** 5.050 *4*
5. Express your answers to the following problems with the proper number of significant figures, rounding as necessary.
   - **a.** 201 + 3.55 + 97.391 =

     $$\begin{array}{r} 201 \\ 3.55 \\ \underline{+97.391} \\ 301.941 \end{array} \approx \mathbf{302} \text{ (to ones' place)}$$
   - **b.** 445.6 – 41 =

     $$\begin{array}{r} 445.6 \\ \underline{-41} \\ 404.6 \end{array} \approx \mathbf{405} \text{ (to ones' place)}$$
   - **c.** $\frac{6.24}{9.60} = \mathbf{0.650}$ *(3 sig figs)*
   - **d.** $(5000)(0.6411) = 3205.5 \approx \mathbf{3000}$ or 3×10^{3} *(1 sig fig)*
6. Perform the following conversions, observing rules for rounding and significant figures; express your answers in scientific notation where it is necessary.
   - **a.** 30.0 cm to m

     $$30.0 \text{ cm} \times \frac{10^{-2}\text{ m}}{1\text{ cm}} = \mathbf{0.300\ m} \text{ or } 3.00 \times 10^{-1}\text{ m}$$

     Note: *The conversion factor* $\frac{1\text{ m}}{100\text{ cm}}$ *could also be used, with equal results. Though exponential conversion factors will be used throughout this answer key, students who have grown up using the metric system may find non-exponential conversion factors such as this easier to remember.*
   - **b.** 1.45 da to s

     $$1.45\text{ da} \times \frac{24\text{ hr}}{1\text{ da}} \times \frac{60\text{ min}}{1\text{ hr}} \times \frac{60\text{ s}}{1\text{ min}} = 125{,}280\text{ s} \approx 125{,}000\text{ s or } 1.25 \times 10^{5}\text{ s}$$
   - **c.** 0.00590 g to mg

     $$0.00590\text{ g} \times \frac{1\text{ m}}{10^{-3}\text{ g}} = 5.90\text{ mg}$$
   - **d.** 5.0 cm/s to km/h

     $$5.0\frac{\text{cm}}{\text{s}} \times \frac{10^{-2}\text{ m}}{1\text{ cm}} \times \frac{1\text{ km}}{10^{3}\text{ m}} \times \frac{60\text{ s}}{1\text{ min}} \times \frac{60\text{ min}}{1\text{ hr}}$$

     $= \mathbf{0.18\ km/h}$ (or 1.8×10^{-1} km/h)

Section Review 1.3 (p. 25)

1. Differentiate between the three familiar states of matter in terms of shape, volume, and compressibility.
   - *A **solid** has a definite shape and volume and is extremely difficult to compress.*
   - *A **liquid** has a definite volume but no definite shape and is difficult to compress.*
   - *A **gas** has neither a definite shape nor a definite volume and is easily compressed.*

2. What is a plasma? *a hot gas in which atoms are partially broken down to form charged particles, or ions*

3. Differentiate between substance, element, compound, and mixture by defining them.
   - *A **substance** has unique properties which differentiate it from every other substance; included are both elements and compounds.*
   - *An **element** is a substance which cannot be broken down into simpler substances by ordinary chemical means, whereas a **compound** can be.*
   - *A **mixture** consists of a physical combination (rather than a chemical combination) of two or more substances, each retaining its own properties.*

4. State from memory four of Dalton's atomic theory postulates. *Any four of the following:*
   - *Every element consists of tiny, indivisible, indestructible particles called atoms.*
   - *All of the atoms of a particular element have the same size, mass, and chemical behavior.*
   - *Differences in properties of elements result from differences in the atoms of the elements.*
   - *The atoms of the elements combined in a compound are combined in a definite ratio.*
   - *A chemical reaction is the result of rearrangement, combination, or separation of atoms.*

5. Name the two laws which were derived from Dalton's atomic theory. *law of definite composition; law of multiple proportions*

Section Review 1.4 (p. 29)

1. Define *kinetic energy.* *energy possessed by matter due to its motion*
2. In which of the three common states of matter do molecules possess the greatest amount of kinetic energy? *gas*
3. What law states that matter and energy are neither created nor destroyed? *first law of thermodynamics (law of conservation of mass-energy)*
4. What name is given to the quantity describing the randomness of a system? *entropy*
5. State the second law of thermodynamics. *Every system left to itself will tend toward a condition of minimum potential energy and maximum entropy or disorder.*
6. What term describes a reaction, such as photosynthesis, in which the products contain more energy than the reactants? *endothermic*

Chapter 1 Review (p. 33)

1. What is chemistry? *the branch of science that deals with the study of the composition, structure, and properties of matter and the changes that matter undergoes*
2. Name five major branches of chemistry. *physical chemistry, organic chemistry, inorganic chemistry, biochemistry, and analytical chemistry*
3. Why can chemistry be considered the foundation of many other sciences? *Answers will vary. Because chemistry deals with the basic truths about matter, an understanding of chemistry is necessary for one to more fully understand any other branch of science. Chemical processes are involved in every area of scientific inquiry.*
4. How many milligrams are in a gram, a kilogram, and a metric ton?
   - *1,000 milligrams in a gram*
   - *1,000,000 milligrams in a kilogram*
   - *1,000,000,000 milligrams in a metric ton*
5. What is a system of measurement? *a collection of compatible, related units that can be used to measure such quantities as length, mass or weight, or volume.*
6. How do *mass* and *weight* differ? ***Mass** is a measure of the quantity of matter in an object; **weight** is a measure of the force of gravity upon an object.*
7. What is absolute zero? *Absolute zero is the coldest possible temperature, the temperature at which molecules cease to vibrate.*
8. How are the Celsius and Kelvin scales related? How are they different?
   - *The size of the degree used in both the Celsius and the Kelvin scales is equal.*
   - *The Celsius scale begins at the freezing point of water, whereas the Kelvin scale begins at absolute zero, the coldest possible temperature.*
9. Temperatures on the surface of the planet Venus can exceed 750. K even at night. What is this temperature on the following scales?

   a. Celsius

$$
\begin{aligned}
°C &= K - 273.15 \\
&= 750.\ K - 273.15 \\
&= 476.85\ °C \approx \mathbf{477\ °C}
\end{aligned}
$$

b. Fahrenheit

(method 1):

$$°F = [(°C + 40) \times \tfrac{9}{5}] - 40$$
$$= [(477\,°C + 40\,°C) \times \tfrac{9}{5}] - 40\,°F$$
$$= 890.6\,°F \approx \mathbf{891\,°F}$$

(method 2):

$$°F = \tfrac{9}{5}°C + 32$$
$$= \tfrac{9}{5} \times 477\,°C + 32$$
$$= 858.6 + 32 = 890.6\,°F \approx \mathbf{891\,°F}$$

Note: *Some error is introduced into the conversion in (b) because the Celsius temperature was rounded to 3 sig figs (477 °C instead of 476.85 °C) before beginning the calculation. If rounding is saved until the end of conversion (b), the correct answer will be 890.33 °F ≈* ***890 °F*** *instead. Both methods are acceptable, though the latter is slightly more accurate.*

10. Why is scientific notation useful? *Scientific notation provides a shorter, easier way to express extremely large or extremely small numbers.*

11. Express the following numbers in scientific notation.

a. 0.000 004 4.0×10^{-6}
b. 65,536 6.5536×10^{4}
c. 80 billion 8.0×10^{10}
d. 5 trillionths 5.0×10^{-12}

12. Are numbers obtained by counting considered exact numbers or approximate numbers? Why? *Numbers obtained by counting are considered exact numbers because there is no measurement involved.*

13. Distinguish between *accuracy* and *precision* in measurement. *Accuracy refers to how close the measurement is to the actual value, but precision concerns the reproducibility of results.*

14. Tell how many significant figures are in the following:

a. 10,240 *4*
b. 0.000 009 *1*
c. 520,200,000 *4*
d. 2.000 000 *7*
e. 200 *1*
f. 2.01 *3*

15. Perform the following calculations, using significant figures properly.

a. 2588 + 12.35 =

$$\begin{array}{r} 2588 \\ +12.35 \\ \hline 2600.35 \end{array} \approx \mathbf{2600.}$$

b. $2004 \times 0.071 =$ $142.284 \approx \mathbf{140}$ *or* $\mathbf{1.4 \times 10^2}$

c. $\frac{3.436}{1.28} = 2.684375 \approx \mathbf{268}$

16. In 1997, the British jet-powered car *Thrust SSC* set a land speed record of 1227.99 km/h.

a. What was the car's speed in miles per hour (1 mi ≈ 1.609 km)?

$$\frac{1227.99\ \cancel{km}}{h} \times \frac{1\ mi}{1.609\ \cancel{km}} = 763.20\ mi/h \approx \mathbf{763.2\ mi/h}$$

b. What was the car's speed in ft/s (1 mi = 5280 ft, exactly)?

$$\frac{1227.99\ \cancel{km}}{\cancel{h}} \times \frac{1\ \cancel{mi}}{1.609\ \cancel{km}} \times \frac{5280\ ft}{1\ \cancel{mi}} \times \frac{1\ \cancel{h}}{60\ \cancel{min}} \times \frac{1\ \cancel{min}}{60\ s} = 1119.361\ ft/s \approx \mathbf{1119\ ft/s}$$

Note: If exact conversions are used, the correct answers will be (a) ***763.038 mi/h*** *and (b)* ***1119.12 ft/s,*** *to proper significant figures. The discrepancy in (a) results from the slightly inaccurate conversion factor (1.609 km ≈ 1 mi) used above; the conversion factor also limits the answer to 4 sig figs instead of 6. (A mile is exactly 1.609344 km.)*

17. Name the three common states of matter. In which state do molecules possess the least amount of kinetic energy? *solid, liquid, and gas; solid*

18. In chemistry, what is meant by the term ***substance?*** *A substance is a form of matter that has its own unique properties which make it different from every other substance.*

19. Distinguish (a) between elements and compounds, (b) between atoms and molecules, and (c) between pure substances and mixtures.

a. A compound is a substance which can be broken down by chemical means into simpler substances, while an element is a substance which cannot be broken down into simpler substances by ordinary chemical means.

b. An atom is the smallest particle of an element that retains the characteristic of the element, while a molecule is two or more atoms linked together by chemical bonds. Molecules are the smallest particles that characterize a compound.

c. Pure substances are homogenous and of definite composition. Mixtures, on the other hand, are made up of two or more substances that are physically mixed, but not chemically combined.

20. What contribution did John Dalton make to the study of matter? *He was the first to propose an extensive model of the atom. Although his proposition was not entirely correct, his work laid the foundation for the law of definite composition and the law of multiple proportions.*

21. State the law of definite composition and the law of multiple proportions.

- *Law of definite composition: The ratios of the masses of each element in a given compound are always the same.*
- *Law of multiple proportions: When two elements can combine to form more than one compound, the masses of one element that combine with a fixed amount of the other element are in a ratio of small whole numbers.*

22. How does the relationship between carbon monoxide (CO) and carbon dioxide (CO_2) illustrate the law of multiple proportions? *The ratio of the weight of O in CO is **1** to **1$^1/_3$**; in CO_2, the ratio is **1** to **2$^2/_3$**. Therefore, the weights of O that will combine with 1 g C are in a ratio of **1$^1/_3$** to **2$^2/_3$** or **1:2.** The ratios are in multiples of small whole numbers.*

23. Does the gasoline in a car's gas tank represent kinetic or potential energy? Why? *The gasoline represents potential energy. Reasons given may vary; the energy is potential rather than kinetic because its energy is not yet being released (it is released in the car's engine when the gasoline is burned).*

24. What law states that every system left to itself will tend toward a condition of minimum potential energy and maximum entropy (disorder)? *second law of thermodynamics*

Chapter 2 (pp. 34–57)
Matter: The Substance of Chemistry

Suggested Daily Pacing

11 **SP:** Check **bibliography cards** for Investigation Background. (Have students read *Science in Action* p. 14.) Introduce the **outline** for the Investigation Background, using *Science in Action* p. 14. Assign Investigation Background tentative outline for les. 16.

Introduce ch. 2, Matter: The Substance of Chemistry.

Give "pop" reading quiz over pp. 35–37:

1. Give the term for a homogeneous part of a system that is in contact with, but physically distinct from, other parts of the system. *phase*
2. List three examples of physical properties. *Any three of the following: color, odor, density, hardness, solubility, taste, state*
3. True or False: Neither chemical nor physical changes affect the identity of a substance. *false*
4. True or False: The digestion of food is an example of a chemical change. *true*
5. List two of the four indications that a chemical change has occurred. *Any two of the following:*
   - *formation of a gas*
   - *formation of a precipitate*
   - *liberation or absorption of heat, light, or some other form of energy*
   - *a distinct change in color*

Teach pp. **35–37,** sec. **2.1** Properties and Changes of Matter, up to Separation of Mixtures.

Review lesson.

HW: Read pp. 37–41. Answer p. 39, questions 1 and 3–5 and p. 41, questions 1–3. Investigation Background tentative outline due les. 16.

12 **Check** and discuss homework.

Review pp. 35–37.

Teach pp. **37–39,** sec. **2.1** (cont.).

Demonstrate Lab 4: Paper Chromatography of Pigments and Dyes.

Note: You may want to ask the Prelab questions from the Lab 4 Report Sheet to stimulate student thinking as you demonstrate Lab 4. It is not necessary that students write down the answers to either the Prelab or Postlab questions.

Teach pp. **39–41,** sec. **2.2** Elements: Abundance and Names.

Review lesson.

HW: Read *Lab Manual* Lab 5 and complete Prelab Assignment. Memorize elements in bold type from Table 2.3, p. 40, and roots used in naming elements from Table 2.5 on p. 41 for quiz in les. 14.

13 **Check** and discuss homework.

Conduct Lab 5: Observation of Elements, Compounds, and Mixtures.

HW: Complete Lab 5 Report Sheet. Read pp. 42–47. Answer p. 47, questions 1–5. Study pp. 40–41, Tables 2.3 and 2.5. Investigation Background tentative outline due les. 16.

14 **Give Quiz 3** (over pp. 40–41, Tables 2.3 and 2.5).

Check and discuss homework.

Review pp. 37–41.

Teach pp. **42–47,** sec. **2.3** Subatomic Particles.

Review lesson.

HW: Read pp. 48–50. Answer pp. 50–51, questions 1–3.

15 **Check** and discuss homework.

Review pp. 42–47.

Teach pp. **48–50,** sec. **2.4** Atomic Number, Mass Number, Isotopes, and Ions.

Review lesson.

HW: Answer pp. 50–51, questions 4–6. Read pp. 51–55. Complete Investigation Background tentative outline and bring *Science in Action* to class.

16 **SP:** Check Investigation Background tentative outline. (Have students answer text p. 55, questions 1–3 and read *Science in Action* pp. 15–16.) Introduce **note cards** for Investigation Background, using *Science in Action* pp. 15–16. Explain proper procedures and remind students about plagiarism. Assign 30 note cards for les. 21 (ch. 3).

Check and discuss homework.

Review pp. 48–50.

Teach pp. **51–55,** sec. **2.5** Atomic Mass: Relative Masses of Atoms.

Review lesson.

HW: Answer text p. 55; questions 4 nd 5. Read *Lab Manual* Lab 6 and complete Prelab Assignment. Thirty note cards due les. 21 (ch. 3).

17 **Check** and discuss homework.

Conduct Lab 6: Physical and Chemical Changes I.

HW: Complete Lab 6 Report Sheet. Begin studying ch. 1–2 for Test 1 in les. 19.

18 **Check** and discuss homework.

Review ch. 1–2 for Test 1 in next lesson, using Chapter Reviews on pp. 32–33 and 56–57.

HW: Study ch. 1–2 for Test 1 in next lesson. Thirty note cards due les. 21 (ch. 3).

19 **Administer Test 1** over ch. 1–2. (All tests are located in *Chemistry* Tests Book. Refer to the Teacher Key for answers and suggested testing/grading procedures.)

HW: Read pp. 58–62. Memorize Table 3.1. Thirty note cards are due les. 21 (ch. 3).

Teacher Notes

Chapter 2 Overview. This chapter focuses on foundational concepts of the study of matter, expanding upon the brief introduction to matter in the previous chapter. The categories of matter are discussed, followed by an introduction to physical and chemical properties and changes. The elements and their symbols are introduced, followed by an introduction to subatomic particles. The chapter concludes with a discussion of element terminology: atomic number, mass number, ions, and atomic mass.

Particle accelerator photo (p. 34). The particle detector in the chapter opener photo is part of a huge particle accelerator near Geneva, Switzerland, operated by the European Laboratory for Particle Physics (CERN). The accelerator itself, over 50 miles in circumference and 16.8 miles in diameter, is located in the subwaylike underground tunnel shown on p. 397 of the text.

Chemical changes (2.1, p. 37). A photo illustrating the sodium/chlorine/sodium chloride relationship may be found on p. 58 of the text.

Fractional distillation (2.1, p. 38). Fractional distillation of petroleum will be discussed in section 18.2 (a diagram is found on p. 429).

Element names and symbols (2.2, p. 40). A detailed periodic table and index of chemical symbols are located inside the back cover of the textbook for quick reference.

It is important that students know the symbols of the most commonly discussed elements (those in bold print in Table 2.3), since they will be using this knowledge throughout the year. One written quiz over Table 2.3 is scheduled in the Suggested Daily Pacing; additional quizzes and/or verbal review in the days or weeks to come may also be helpful.

Subatomic particles (2.3, p. 42). Subatomic particles will be discussed further in chapters 7 and 17.

Cathode-ray tubes (2.3, p. 42). The display screens of most television sets and desktop computer monitors are advanced forms of cathode-ray tube. The stream of electrons ("cathode rays") is shaped into a narrow beam and rapidly scanned across the end of the tube to produce a picture. The inside face of the tube is coated with phosphorescent compounds of three different colors; by careful aiming of the beam(s), different colors are produced.

"Canal rays" (2.3, p. 43). Unlike "cathode rays," "canal rays" were found to vary in mass and charge. Protons were discovered by means of canal rays produced in a tube filled with hydrogen (the simplest element); "canal rays" of all other elements were found to have masses and charges that were multiples of the values for hydrogen.

Fundamental particles (2.3, p. 47). According to current theory, there are essentially four types of fundamental particles that can each appear in three "generations" or energy states (see chart below). The first-generation (ground state) versions of these particles are the up quark, the down quark, the electron, and the electron neutrino. All other particles (nucleons, mesons, etc.) are composites of two or more of these particles in various energy states.

Generation*	Charge $+2/3$	Charge $-1/3$	Charge −1	Uncharged
1st* (ground state)	up quark	down quark	electron	electron neutrino
2nd (higher energy)	charmed quark	strange quark	muon	muon neutrino
3rd (highest energy)	top quark	bottom quark	tau	tau neutrino

*The second and third generations can be thought of as high-energy forms of the first-generation particles (e.g., a muon has many of the properties of an electron but is more massive and contains more energy).

Neutrinos are difficult to study because they interact only weakly with other matter; for example, the sun shines brightly in neutrinos, which are produced in the nuclear reactions at the sun's core, but most of these neutrinos pass right through the earth without stopping. Quarks are difficult to study for different reasons; they bind together so tightly that they can be separated only at extreme energies (forming "quark-gluon plasma") and recombine almost instantly.

Isotope analogy (2.4, p. 48). One analogy that may be helpful in clarifying the concept of isotopes is to compare them to different varieties of apples (e.g., Jonathan, Winesap, Granny Smith, Red Delicious, etc.), which are slightly different but are all still the same fruit. Likewise, isotopes can be thought of as "varieties" of atoms of the same element (e.g., O-16, O-17, O-18; C-12, C-13, C-14).

Lecture Demonstrations

Phases (2.1, p. 36). The terms in figure 3.1 may be introduced and discussed using a multiphase system like that of Fig. 2.2; one possible combination is metal chunks + $CuSO_4(aq)$ + ice cube + vegetable oil + cork.

Density may also be reviewed and used to explain the layers or phases. For a simpler demonstration, "house" Italian salad dressing in a clear bottle is also a complex multiphase system.

Physical and chemical properties and changes (2.1, pp. 36–37). One simple object lesson is to use a piece of colored construction paper to introduce the idea of physical properties; ask the class to give as many as they can. Then ask them about its chemical properties; these cannot be determined apart from chemical reactions.

Physical change can then be demonstrated by tearing half of the sheet of construction paper into small pieces; which properties changed? (List the physical properties which changed.) Were chemical properties affected? (No.) Burn the other half of the paper over a sink to demonstrate a chemical change and a chemical property (combustible). Compare the properties of the ashes to those of the paper.

Four evidences of chemical change may be strikingly demonstrated as follows:

1. zinc strip + 6 *M* hydrochloric acid (H_2 gas and heat produced)
2. 0.1 *M* $Pb(NO_3)_2$ + 0.1 *M* KI (precipitate and color change to yellow)
3. burn a candle or redo the $KMnO_4$ + glycerol reaction from chapter 1 (heat and light)
4. heat 3 g $CuSO_4 \cdot 5\,H_2O$ in a test tube using a Bunsen burner (color change; endothermic process); add a few drops of water to the cooled product, $CuSO_4$ (color change; exothermic process)

Discovery of the electron and proton (2.3, pp. 42–43). If you have access to a cathode-ray tube and induction coil (available from science supply companies, but quite expensive), you can do a fascinating demonstration / reenactment of these early discoveries. Deflection of the beams may be seen by using a U-shaped magnet.

An inexpensive (but much less effective) demonstration is to hold a magnet in front of the screen of an old television set or computer monitor (which are cathode ray tubes, after all) and observe the changes in the screen pattern due to electron deflection as you move the magnet around.

Answers to Text Questions

Section Review 2.1 (p. 39)

1. Name four observations that suggest that a chemical change has occurred in a substance.

- *change in color*
- *formation of a gas*
- *liberation or absorption of energy (light, heat, etc.)*
- *formation of a precipitate*

2. In your own words, explain the process of simple distillation. *Answers may vary. Key concepts:*
- *Simple distillation is used to separate substances with widely varying boiling points in a mixture.*
- *The mixture is heated, and as the temperature rises, the more volatile component boils first.*
- *The vapor produced is collected, cooled, and condensed into a pure liquid.*
- *The less volatile component of the mixture is left behind in the original vessel (because it did not reach its boiling point).*

3. Identify the following as homogeneous mixtures (solutions), heterogeneous mixtures, elements, or compounds. You may need to use a dictionary to identify unfamiliar materials.

a. copper *element*
b. air *solution*
c. oxygen *element*
d. vinegar *solution*
e. water *compound*
f. table sugar *compound*
g. sweetened coffee *solution*
h. steel *solution or heterogeneous mixture*

4. Classify the following properties as chemical or physical. A dictionary may be helpful in identifying unfamiliar properties.

a. color *physical*
b. corrosive *chemical*
c. flammable *chemical*
d. easily oxidized *chemical*
e. ductile *physical*
f. very dense *physical*
g. explosive *chemical*

5. Classify each of the following as either a chemical change or a physical change.

a. burning of gasoline *chemical*
b. sawing of wood *physical*
c. melting of iron *physical*
d. evaporation of water *physical*
e. sugar dissolving in tea *physical*
f. cooking of meat *chemical*
g. fermentation of grape juice *chemical*

Section Review 2.2 (p. 41)

1. What is the most abundant element in the universe? In the earth's crust? In the earth as a whole? *hydrogen; oxygen; iron*

2. Give from memory the symbols for the following elements.

a. sulfur *S*
b. aluminum *Al*
c. calcium *Ca*
d. magnesium *Mg*
e. copper *Cu*
f. iron *Fe*
g. tin *Sn*
h. potassium *K*
i. mercury *Hg*
j. silver *Ag*
k. lead *Pb*
l. tungsten *W*
m. sodium *Na*
n. element 126 *Ubh*

3. Give from memory the names of the elements corresponding to the following symbols.

a. B *boron*
b. P *phosphorus*
c. He *helium*
d. Au *gold*
e. N *nitrogen*
f. F *fluorine*

Section Review 2.3 (p. 47)

1. What negatively charged particle was discovered through the study of cathode rays? *electron*

2. What positively charged particle was discovered through the study of canal rays? *proton*

3. What is the term for the dense central core of an atom? *nucleus*

4. What two types of subatomic particles are found in the dense central core of an atom? *protons and neutrons*

5. According to current theory, protons and neutrons are composed of what type of smaller particles? *quarks*

Section Review 2.4 (p. 50)

1. What characteristic of an atom determines its identity as a particular element? *the number of protons in the nucleus of the atom*

2. What is the name for atoms of the same element that differ in their mass numbers? *isotopes*

3. What is the term for an atom or molecule that has an unequal number of electrons and protons, resulting in a charge? *ion*

4. Complete the following table for the atoms or ions indicated. The first one is done for you.

Symbol	Z	A	N	Number of Electrons	Electrical Charge
${}^{3}_{2}He^{2+}$	2	3	1	0	2+
${}^{207}_{82}Pb$	82	207	125	82	0
${}^{10}_{5}B$	5	10	5	5	0
${}^{109}_{47}Ag^{+}$	47	109	62	46	1+

5. Complete the following table. The first one is done for you.

Symbol	Z	A	N	Number of Electrons	Electrical Charge
$^{191}_{79}Au^{3+}$	79	191	112	76	3+
$^{235}_{92}U$	92	235	143	92	0
$^{126}_{53}I^{-}$	53	126	73	54	1−
$^{36}_{16}S^{2-}$	16	36	20	18	2−

6. Write the symbol for the isotope of each of the following elements.
   a. silicon that has 15 neutrons in the nucleus. $^{29}_{14}Si$
   b. platinum that has a mass number of 190. $^{190}_{78}Pt$
   c. carbon that has 8 neutrons in the nucleus. $^{14}_{6}C$

Section Review 2.5 (p. 55)

1. Differentiate between the actual mass of an atom and the relative atomic mass. *The actual mass of an atom is given in grams, whereas the relative mass of an atom is the mass relative to carbon-12 and is given in atomic mass units, u.*
2. What laboratory instrument is used to measure relative masses of atoms? *mass spectrometer*
3. What unit is used to measure atomic mass? *atomic mass unit (u)*
4. Calculate the average atomic mass of magnesium in its naturally occurring form, given the following percent abundances and isotopic masses: 78.70% ^{24}Mg (23.98504 u), 10.13% ^{25}Mg (24.98584 u), and 11.17% ^{26}Mg (25.98259 u).
   Average atomic mass of Mg:
   $(0.7870)(23.98504\ u) + (0.1013)(24.98584\ u) + (0.1117)(25.98259\ u)$
   $= 18.88\ u + 2.531\ u + 2.902\ u$
   $= 24.313\ u \approx \mathbf{24.31\ u}$ *(2 decimal places allowed)*
5. Naturally occurring lithium consists of two isotopes having the following percentages and relative masses: 7.42% ^{6}Li (6.01512 u) and 92.58% ^{7}Li (7.01600 u). Calculate the average atomic mass of lithium.
   Average atomic mass of Li:
   $= (0.0742)(6.01512\ u) + (0.9258)(7.01600\ u)$
   $= 0.446\ u + 6.495\ u$
   $= \mathbf{6.941\ u}$ *(3 decimal places)*

Chapter 2 Review (p. 57)

1. Classify each of the following as a homogeneous mixture (solution), a heterogeneous mixture, an element, or a compound.
   a. iron *element*
   b. blood *heterogeneous mixture*
   c. brass *homogeneous mixture*
   d. distilled water *compound*
   e. soil *heterogeneous mixture*
   f. window cleaner *homogeneous mixture*
   g. uranium *element*
   h. shampoo *homogeneous mixture*
   i. soft drink *homogeneous mixture*
   j. Italian salad dressing *heterogeneous mixture*
   k. honey *homogeneous mixture*
   l. sea water *homogeneous mixture*
2. Which type of mixture contains multiple phases? Which type consists of only a single phase? *heterogeneous mixture; homogeneous mixture*
3. List four observations that may indicate a chemical change has occurred in a substance.
   - *the formation of a gas. the formation of a precipitate (an insoluble substance)*
   - *the liberation or absorption of heat, light, or some other form of energy*
   - *or a distinct change in color*
4. Indicate whether each of the following represents a physical property or a chemical property.
   a. boiling point *physical*
   b. texture *physical*
   c. heavy *physical*
   d. fireproof *chemical*
   e. brittle *physical*
   f. rust-resistant *chemical*
5. Does the consumption of food involve physical changes or chemical changes? Explain your answer. *Both physical and chemical changes are involved in the consumption of food. Physical changes to the food occur in the mouth as the teeth grind the food into smaller pieces. Chemical changes occur as the digestive process breaks down the food into usable nutrients.*
6. Classify the following changes as chemical or physical.
   a. cutting of meat *physical*
   b. leaves changing color in autumn *chemical*
   c. baking a cake *chemical*
   d. magnetizing a nail *physical*
   e. cutting the grass *physical*
   f. lighting a candle *physical*
7. Give from memory the symbols for the following elements.
   a. titanium *Ti*
   b. argon *Ar*
   c. silicon *Si*
   d. uranium *U*
   e. chlorine *Cl*
   f. iodine *I*
   g. manganese *Mn*
   h. platinum *Pt*
   i. plutonium *Pu*
   j. element 119 *Uue*

8. Give from memory the names of the elements corresponding to the following symbols.

a. Zn *zinc* **d.** O *oxygen* **g.** Ag *silver*
b. C *carbon* **e.** Ne *neon* **h.** Pb *lead*
c. H *hydrogen* **f.** U *uranium*

9. From what are the symbols for the elements potassium and sodium derived? *their Latin names*

10. Which of the three basic subatomic particles that compose an atom is the least massive? *the electron*

11. What type of smaller particles is thought to make up protons and neutrons? *quarks*

12. Distinguish between atomic number and mass number. ***Atomic number*** *(Z) refers to the number of protons in the nucleus, whereas* ***mass number*** *(A) refers to the sum of both protons and neutrons in the nucleus.*

13. What is an isotope? *Isotopes are atoms of the same element that differ in their mass numbers.*

14. Write the symbol for the isotope of each of the following elements.

a. hydrogen that has 1 neutron in the nucleus $^{2}_{1}H$
b. uranium that has a mass number of 235 $^{235}_{92}U$
c. carbon that has 6 neutrons in the nucleus $^{12}_{6}C$

15. What is an ion? What determines whether an ion is a cation or an anion?

- *An* ***ion*** *is an atom (or molecule) that is electrically charged because it has a different number of electrons than protons.*
- *If an atom has* more *electrons than protons, it will have an excess of negative charge, making it an* ***anion.***
- *If an atom has* fewer *electrons than protons, it will have an excess of positive charge, making it a* ***cation.***

16. How many protons, neutrons, and electrons does each of the following atoms and ions contain?

a. $^{2}H^{+}$ $p = 1, n = 1, e = 0$
b. ^{6}He $p = 2, n = 4, e = 2$
c. ^{223}Fr $p = 87, n = 136, e = 87$
d. $^{44}Ca^{2+}$ $p = 20, n = 24, e = 18$
e. $^{78}Se^{2-}$ $p = 34, n = 44, e = 36$
f. $^{59}Co^{2+}$ $p = 27, n = 32, e = 25$

17. What unit is used to measure atomic mass? Upon what standard is this unit based? *atomic mass unit (u); this measurement is based on $^{1}/_{12}$ the mass of an atom of the carbon-12 isotope ($^{12}_{6}C$).*

18. The element europium exists naturally as two stable isotopes having the following percent abundances and isotopic masses: 48.01% ^{151}Eu (150.9196 u) and 51.99% ^{153}Eu (152.9209 u). Calculate the average atomic mass of europium.

Average atomic mass of Eu:

$= (0.4801)(150.9196\ u) + (0.5199)(152.9209\ u)$

$= 72.46\ u + 79.50\ u$

$= \mathbf{151.96\ u}$

Chapter 2

Chapter 3 (pp. 58–73)

Stoichiometry: Elements and Compounds

3.1 Formulas and Names
3.2 Naming Ionic Compounds
3.3 The Mole

Suggested Daily Pacing

20 **Return** and go over graded Test 1.

Check homework.

Introduce ch. 3, Stoichiometry: Elements and Compounds.

Discuss homework.

Teach pp. **59–62,** sec. **3.1** Formulas and Names.

Review lesson.

Give Quiz 4 (over pp. 60–61, Table 3.1 and Naming Binary Molecular Compounds).

HW: Read pp. 62–64, up to Finding Empirical Formulas of Ionic Compounds. Answer p. 62, questions 1 and 2. Complete thirty note cards and bring *Science in Action.*

21 **SP:** Check number and form of note cards. (Have students answer text p. 67, question 1, and read *Science in Action* pp. 16–17.) Introduce **first draft** of Investigation Background, using *Science in Action* pp. 16–17. Assign first draft of Investigation Background for les. 26 (ch. 4). Background First Draft Check form (p. 19) will also be due in les. 26 (ch. 4).

Check and discuss p. 67, question 1.

Review pp. 59–62.

Teach pp. **62–64,** sec. **3.2** Naming Ionic Compounds, up to Finding Empirical Formulas of Ionic Compounds.

Review lesson.

HW: Read *Lab Manual* Lab 7. Study p. 23, Table 3.2, for a quiz in les. 23. Investigation Background first draft and Background First Draft Check form due les. 26 (ch. 4).

22 **Discuss** homework.

Conduct Lab 7: Physical and Chemical Changes II.

HW: Complete Lab 7 Report Sheet. Read pp. 64–67. Answer p. 67, question 2. Study p. 63, Table 3.2.

23 **Give Quiz 5** (over p. 63, Table 3.2).

Check and discuss homework.

Review pp. 62–64.

Teach pp. **64–67,** sec. **3.2** (cont.).

Review using Concept Review 1: Naming Compounds. (All Concept Reviews are located in *Chemistry* Tests Book.)

HW: Answer p. 67, questions 3–4. Read pp. 68–72. Answer pp. 72–73, questions 1, 3, and 4. Investigation Background first draft and Background First Draft Check form due les. 26 (ch. 4).

24 **Check** and discuss homework.

Review pp. 64–67.

Give Quiz 6 (over pp. 62–72).

Teach pp. **68–72,** sec. **3.3** The Mole.

Review lesson.

HW: Answer pp. 72–73, questions 2, 5, and 6. Read pp. 74–78.

Teacher Notes

Chapter 3 Overview. Much of this chapter discusses formulas and names of chemical compounds, which are the basic "language" of chemistry. Following this, the text discusses how relationships at the molecule or formula level can be carried over to the macroscopic or laboratory level by means of the unit of measurement known as the mole.

Salt mine photo (3.1, p. 59). The salt mine shown on p. 59 is located approximately 1000 feet beneath the surface of Avery Island, a dome-shaped island located in a marshy region of coastal Louisiana that has been mined for salt since the 1860s. A sense of scale is given by the miners with flashlights in the bucket at the end of the boom, as well as the miners in the receding passageway.

The salt is mined by drilling vertical holes in the salt, placing explosives in the holes, and blasting to create a loose mass of salt (as in the foreground) that can be carried away by front loaders and dump trucks. Striations from previous drilling and blasting can be seen on the wall in the foreground.

Naming compounds (3.1, p. 61). In order for students to be able to know when to use prefix-based names versus ion-based names, they must be able to identify an element as metal or nonmetal. (Compounds of two nonmetals tend to be molecular, whereas compounds of a metal and a nonmetal tend to be ionic; ionic names are studied in section 3.2.) If you wish, the metal-nonmetal classification may be reviewed using a large periodic table or the periodic table at the back of the student text. Note that hydrogen is classified as a nonmetal.

Names and formulas of ions (3.2, p. 63). It is important that students learn the names and charges of the ions in Table 3.2, since this terminology is basic to much of the course. Table 3.3 need not be memorized since it is primarily for historical reference.

Students may already be familiar with some of the ion names in Table 3.2 because they are associated with many well-known substances:

- sodium chloride (table salt)
- hydrogen peroxide (antiseptic solution)
- sodium bicarbonate (baking soda)
- ammonium nitrate and ammonium phosphate (fertilizers)
- sodium fluoride (toothpastes)
- sodium hydroxide (lye)
- hydrogen cyanide (poison)
- calcium carbonate (Tums®antacid tablets; limestone)

Pointing out familiar applications of the ions as you go through the list can help cement the names in the students' minds by associating them with familiar substances.

You may wish to briefly review or informally quiz over the ions in Table 3.2 until the students have mastered them. A written quiz over these ions is scheduled in lesson 23.

"Molecular mass" and ionic compounds (3.3, p. 68). Strictly speaking, it is proper to speak of molecular mass only for compounds actually composed of discrete (separate or distinct) molecules. For ionic compounds, in which molecules do not exist, the term is technically *formula mass*. However, for the sake of simplicity, we will not distinguish between the two in this text, but will use the term "molecular mass" to encompass both concepts.

Avogadro's number (3.3, p. 69). Avogadro's number is sometimes called the *Avogadro constant* and may be symbolized by either N or N_A.

Mole conversion factors (3.3, p. 70). From our definition of mole, we have the equality

$$1 \text{ mole} = 6.022 \times 10^{23} \text{ particles}$$

from which we can obtain two conversion factors:

$$\frac{1 \text{ mole}}{6.022 \times 10^{23} \text{ particles}} \quad \text{and} \quad \frac{6.022 \times 10^{23} \text{ particles}}{1 \text{ mole}}$$

The "particles" may be any object, though in most cases they will be atoms, molecules, ions, or electrons.

Molar mass (3.3, p. 70). Note that molecular mass is given in units of *u*, whereas molar mass is given in units of *g*.

Lecture Demonstrations

Avogadro's number and moles (4.2, pp. 68–70). Display one mole of several substances, such as in Fig. 3.4 (e.g., 32 g sulfur, 12 g carbon, 64 g copper, 180 g aspirin, 18 g water, 58 g table salt, 342 g table sugar, etc.). Also display one dozen of several types of balls (e.g., 7 tennis balls, table-tennis balls, baseballs, marbles, BB's, etc.). Tell the students that the same number of particles (molecules or atoms) is in each of the substances displayed (Avogadro's number), just as the same number of each type of balls is displayed; because of the size differences in the particles and in the balls, the same number occupies differing volumes and has differing masses.

Answers to Text Questions

Section Review 3.1 (p. 62)

1. Name the following binary molecular compounds.
   - **a.** BrO_2 *bromine dioxide*
   - **b.** Cl_2O_7 *dichlorine heptoxide*
   - **c.** ICl_3 *iodine trichloride*
   - **d.** SeF_6 *selenium hexafluoride*
   - **e.** AsF_3 *arsenic trifluoride*
   - **f.** N_2O_5 *dinitrogen pentoxide*
   - **g.** ICl *iodine monochloride*
   - **h.** OF_2 *oxygen difluoride*

i. XeF_4 *xenon tetrafluoride*
j. PI_3 *phosphorus triiodide*

2. Write formulas for the following compounds.
   a. diboron trioxide B_2O_3
   b. carbon diselenide CSe_2
   c. carbon monoxide CO
   d. tetrasulfur dinitride S_4N_2
   e. disulfur difluoride S_2F_2
   f. dibromine monoxide Br_2O
   g. dinitrogen tetroxide N_2O_4
   h. phosphorus trichloride PCl_3

Section Review 3.2 (p. 67)

1. From memory, give names to the following ions. Use the Stock system where appropriate.
   a. Ca^{2+} *calcium ion*
   b. PO_4^{3-} *phosphate ion*
   c. Fe^{3+} *iron(III) ion*
   d. $C_2H_3O_2^-$ *acetate ion*
   e. $H_2PO_4^-$ *dihydrogen phosphate ion*
   f. K^+ *potassium ion*
   g. $Cr_2O_7^{2-}$ *dichromate ion*
   h. N_3^- *nitride ion*
   i. S^{2-} *sulfide ion*
2. Name the following ionic compounds.
   a. $NaNO_2$ *sodium nitrite*
   b. $AgNO_3$ *silver nitrate*
   c. CuCl *copper chloride*
   d. $PbSO_4$ *lead(II) sulfate*
   e. $Zn_3(PO_4)_2$ *zinc phosphate*
   f. $NH_4C_2H_3O_2$ *ammonium acetate*
3. Write the formula for the ionic compound formed between the following pairs:
   a. sodium ions and sulfate ions Na_2SO_4
   b. Pb^{4+} and PO_4^{3-} $Pb_3(PO_4)_4$
   c. iron(III) ions and chloride ions $FeCl_3$
   d. K^+ and $Cr_2O_7^{2-}$ $K_2Cr_2O_7$
4. Write formulas for the following ionic compounds.
   a. calcium phosphide Ca_3P_2
   b. potassium sulfide K_2S
   c. lead(IV) chromate $Pb(CrO_4)_2$
   d. sodium hydrogen phosphate Na_2HPO_4

Section Review 3.3 (pp. 72–73)

1. What units are used to express molecular mass? *atomic mass units, u*
2. Calculate the molecular mass of each of the following.
   a. sucrose, $C_{12}H_{22}O_{11}$ $(12 \times 12.01\ u) + (22 \times 1.008\ u) + (11 \times 16.00\ u) \approx \mathbf{342.30\ u}$
   b. xenon hexafluoride, XeF_6
   $131.3\ u + (6 \times 19.00\ u) \approx \mathbf{245.3\ u}$
   c. methane, CH_4
   $12.01\ u + (4 \times 1.008\ u) \approx \mathbf{16.04\ u}$
3. How many molecules of hydrogen would there be in one mole of hydrogen? *6.022×10^{23} molecules of hydrogen in one mole H_2*
4. Define the term ***molar mass.*** *The molar mass of a substance is the mass in grams of one mole of that substance.*
5. Assume you are given 0.44 mol of a substance.
   a. How many atoms are present if the substance is lead metal, Pb?
   $0.44\ mol\ Pb \times \frac{6.022 \times 10^{23}\ atoms\ Pb}{1\ mol\ Pb}$
   $\approx \mathbf{2.6 \times 10^{23}\ atoms\ Pb}$
   b. How many molecules are present if the substance is sucrose, $C_{12}H_{22}O_{11}$? *0.44 mol*
   $C_{12}H_{22}O_{11} \times \frac{6.022 \times 10^{23}\ molecules\ C_{12}H_{22}O_{11}}{1\ mol\ C_{12}H_{22}O_{11}}$
   $\approx \mathbf{2.6 \times 10^{23}\ molecules\ C_{12}H_{22}O_{11}}$
   c. How many formula units are present if the substance is calcium carbonate, $CaCO_3$?
   $0.44\ mol\ CaCO_3 \times \frac{6.022 \times 10^{23}\ formula\ units\ CaCO_3}{1\ mol\ CaCO_3}$
   $\approx \mathbf{2.6 \times 10^{23}\ formula\ units\ CaCO_3}$
6. Give the molar mass of each of the following substances. (Hint: Remember that the molar mass in grams is the same as the molecular mass in *u*.)
   a. Zn ***65.38 g Zn/mol***
   b. AgCl $(1\ mol\ Ag \times 107.9\ g/mol\ Ag) + (1\ mol\ Cl \times 35.45\ g/mol\ Cl) = \mathbf{143.35\ g\ AgCl}$
   c. O_2 $2\ mol\ O \times 16.00 g/mol\ O = \mathbf{32.00\ g\ O}$
   d. Na_2SO_4
   $(2\ mol\ Na \times 22.99\ g/mol\ Na) + (1\ mol\ S \times 32.06\ g/mol\ S) + (4\ mol\ O \times 16.00\ g/mol\ O)$
   $= \mathbf{142.04\ g\ Na_2SO_4}$

Chapter 3 Review (p. 73)

1. Explain the difference between molecular compounds and ionic compounds. *(Wording may vary.) Molecular compounds consist of individual molecules, each containing a certain number of atoms. Ionic compounds consist of crystals containing an indefinite number of atoms that combine in a definite ratio.*

2. Distinguish between molecular formulas and empirical formulas. Which type is the same as a formula unit? *A molecular formula gives the actual number of each type of atom in the compound. An empirical formula, on the other hand, shows only the simplest ratio of atoms in a compound. An empirical formula is the same as a formula unit.*
3. Why are molecular formulas not practical for ionic compounds? *Ionic compounds do not consist of definite numbers of atoms; they combine only in a fixed ratio.*
4. From memory, give the names of the following ions:
   a. PO_4^{3-} *phosphate* **d.** OH^- *hydroxide*
   b. NH_4^+ *ammonium* **e.** Fe^{2+} *iron(II)*
   c. NO_3^- *nitrate* **f.** SO_4^{2-} *sulfate*
5. Name the following compounds.
   a. CuI *copper(I) iodide*
   b. FeO *iron(II) oxide*
   c. $Zn(ClO_3)_2$ *zinc chlorate*
   d. P_2Cl_5 *diphosphorus pentachloride*
   e. $Ca(HCO_3)_2$ *calcium bicarbonate* or *calcium hydrogen carbonate*
   f. CI_4 *carbon tetraiodide*
   g. PBr_3 *phosphorus tribromide*
   h. $Pb(NO_3)_2$ *lead(II) nitrate*
   i. NH_4NO_2 *ammonium nitrite*
   j. $K_2Cr_2O_7$ *potassium dichromate*
6. Write the correct name or formula:
   a. the name of N_2F_4 *dinitrogen tetrafluoride*
   b. the name of SiO_2 *silicon dioxide*
   c. the name of $NaHCO_3$ *sodium bicarbonate*
   d. the name of $(NH_4)_2SO_4$ *ammonium sulfate*
   e. the molecular formula of sulfur dioxide SO_2
   f. the molecular formula of uranium hexafluoride UF_6
   g. the empirical formula of benzene (C_6H_6) CH
   h. the empirical formula of $C_{12}H_{22}O_{11}$ *as written*
   i. the empirical formula of ammonium hydroxide NH_4OH
   j. the empirical formula of ammonium phosphate $(NH_4)_3PO_4$
7. Which is the proper name of SnO_2—tin(I) oxide, tin(II) oxide, or tin(IV) oxide? Why? *tin(IV) oxide; the two oxide ions each have a 2– charge, for a total of 4–. The tin must have an equal and opposite charge (4+) to balance it.*
8. Give the formulas for the following compounds.
   a. aluminum dihydrogen phosphate $Al(H_2PO_4)_3$
   b. sulfur difluoride SF_2
   c. potassium sulfate K_2SO_4
   d. magnesium acetate $Mg(C_2H_3O_2)_2$
   e. iron(III) chloride $FeCl_3$
   f. lead(II) sulfide PbS
   g. dinitrogen monoxide N_2O
   h. mercury(II) bromide $HgBr_2$
   i. silicon dioxide SiO_2
   j. ammonium carbonate $(NH_4)_2CO_3$
9. What is the relationship between the mole and Avogadro's number? *(Wording may vary.) Avogadro's number is simply a very large number, equal to* 6.022×10^{23}*; a mole is Avogadro's number of anything.*
10. How many water molecules may be found in 2.5 moles of water?

$$2.5 \text{ mol } H_2O \times \frac{6.022 \times 10^{23} \text{ molecules } H_2O}{1 \text{ mol } H_2O}$$
$$\approx \mathbf{1.5 \times 10^{24} \text{ molecules } H_2O}$$

11. What would be the mass in grams of 2.5 moles of water?

$$2 \text{ mol } H \times 1.008 \text{ g/mol } H = 2.016 \text{ g}$$
$$+\ 1 \text{ mol } O \times 16.00 \text{ g/mol } O = 16.00 \text{ g}$$
$$\text{molar mass of } H_2O = 18.016 \text{ g} \approx 18.02 \text{ g}$$
$$(2.5 \text{ mol } H_2O) \times \frac{18.02 \text{ g } H_2O}{1 \text{ mol } H_2O} \approx \mathbf{45 \text{ g } H_2O}$$

12. Calculate the molar mass of each of the following:
   a. iron(II) oxide, FeO
   $$1 \text{ mol Fe} \times 55.85 \text{ g/mol Fe} = 55.85 \text{ g}$$
   $$+\ 1 \text{ mol O} \times 16.00 \text{ g/mol O} = 16.00 \text{ g}$$
   $$\text{molar mass of FeO} = \mathbf{71.85 \text{ g}}$$
   b. hydrogen peroxide, H_2O_2
   $$2 \text{ mol H} \times 1.008 \text{ g/mol H} = 2.016 \text{ g}$$
   $$+\ 2 \text{ mol O} \times 16.00 \text{ g/mol O} = 32.00 \text{ g}$$
   $$\text{molar mass of } H_2O_2 = 34.016 \approx \mathbf{34.02 \text{ g}}$$
   c. uranium hexafluoride, UF_6
   $$1 \text{ mol U} \times 238 \text{ g/mol U} = 238 \text{ g}$$
   $$6 \text{ mol F} \times 19.00 \text{ g/mol F} = 114.00 \text{ g}$$
   $$\text{molar mass of } UF_6 = 352.00 \approx \mathbf{352 \text{ g}}$$
   d. calcium carbonate, $CaCO_3$
   $$1 \text{ mol Ca} \times 40.08 \text{ g/mol Ca} = 40.08 \text{ g}$$
   $$1 \text{ mol C} \times 12.01 \text{ g/mol C} = 12.01 \text{ g}$$
   $$+\ 3 \text{ mol O} \times 16.00 \text{ g/mol O} = 48.00 \text{ g}$$
   $$\text{molar mass of } CaCO_3 = \mathbf{100.09 \text{ g}}$$
13. What would be the mass (in grams) of 5.00 moles of gold?

$$5.00 \text{ mol Au} \times \frac{196.97 \text{ g Au}}{1 \text{ mol Au}}$$
$$= 984.84 \text{ g Au} \approx \mathbf{985 \text{ g Au}}$$

Chapter 3

Chapter 4 (pp. 74–91)

Stoichiometry: Chemical Reactions

4.1 Balancing Chemical Equations
4.2 Classification of Chemical Reactions
4.3 Quantitative Relationships from the Balanced Equation

Suggested Daily Pacing

25 **Check** homework.

Review pp. 68–72.

Introduce ch. 4, Stoichiometry: Chemical Reactions.

Discuss homework.

Teach pp. **75–78,** sec. **4.1** Balancing Chemical Equations.

Review lesson.

HW: Answer p. 79, question 1. Complete Investigation Background first draft. Bring Investigation Background first draft, Background First Draft Check form, and *Science in Action.*

26 **SP:** Check first draft of Investigation Background; check Background First Draft Check form. (Have students answer p. 79, question 2.) Make suggestions as needed. Explain how to rewrite first draft, using *Science in Action* p. 17. Assign rewritten first draft for les. 29.

Check and discuss homework.

Review pp. 75–78 using Concept Review 2: Balancing Chemical Equations.

HW: Finish Concept Review 2. Read pp. 79–82, up to Double Displacement Reactions. Rewritten first draft due les. 29.

27 **Check** and discuss homework.

Give Quiz 7 (over pp. 75–78).

Review pp. 75–78.

Teach pp. **79–82,** sec. **4.2** Classification of Chemical Reactions, up to Double Displacement Reactions.

Review lesson.

HW: Read *Lab Manual* Lab 8 and complete Prelab Assignment.

28 **Check** and discuss homework.

Conduct Lab 8: Stoichiometry of a Single Displacement Reaction.

HW: Complete Lab 8 Report Sheet. Complete rewritten first draft of Investigation Background. Bring *Science in Action.*

29 **Check** and discuss homework.

SP: Check rewritten first draft of Investigation Background. (Have students read text pp. 82–84 and answer p. 85, questions 1 and 2.) Using *Science in Action,* pp. 17–18, explain how to edit and do final copy of Investigation Background. Explain Background Final Check. Go over sample Background paper in *Science in Action,* pp. 25–34. Assign final copy of Investigation Background for les. 32.

Check and discuss p. 85, questions 1 and 2.

Review pp. 79–82.

Teach pp. **82–84,** sec. **4.2** (cont.).

Review lesson.

HW: Read pp. 85–89. Answer p. 89, questions 1–3. Final copy of Investigation Background due les. 32.

30 **Give Quiz 8** (over pp. 79–84).

Check and discuss homework.

Review pp. 82–84.

Teach pp. **85–89,** sec. **4.3** Quantitative Relationships from the Balanced Equation.

Review lesson. If time, have students answer p. 89, question 4; discuss.

HW: Read *Lab Manual* Lab 9 and complete Prelab assignment.

31 **Check** and discuss homework.

Conduct Lab 9 Stoichiometry of a Double Displacement Reaction.

Review lesson.

HW: Complete Lab 9 Report Sheet. Begin studying ch. 3–4 for Test 2 in les. 33. Answer p. 73, Review Exercises 4 and 12; also answer p. 91, Review Exercises 2, 4, and 10. Complete final copy of Investigation Background, using the Background Final Copy Check. Bring the Investigation Background report, the Background Grade Form, and *Science in Action.*

32 **SP:** Collect Investigation Background to be graded. (When grading, use the Background Grade Form; save grade to average with Investigation Plan grade.) Introduce investigation, using Science in Action, pp. 35–38. Emphasize safety concerns. Have students mark important points in their copy of *Science in Action.* Assign choosing a problem or question for investigation and completing the Problem Selection Worksheet for les. 36 (ch. 5).

Check and discuss homework.

Review ch. 3–4 for Test 2 in next lesson, using Chapter Reviews on pp. 72–73 and 90–91.

HW: Study ch. 3–4 for Test 2 in next lesson. Problem Selection Worksheet due les. 36 (ch. 5).

33 **Administer Test 2** over ch. 3–4.

HW: Read pp. 92–95. Answer p. 95, questions 1–3.

Teacher Notes

Chapter 4 Overview. After the mastery of chemical formulas in the previous chapter, students are now ready to tackle writing and balancing chemical equations—representations for chemical reactions. If chemical formulas (chapter 3) are thought of as the "words" of the language of chemistry, then chemical equations are the "sentences" we use to describe chemical reactions. Categories of reactions are then discussed, followed by how the chemical equation relates to our everyday macroscopic or molar level.

Balancing chemical equations (4.1, pp. 76–77). The text presents a systematic approach to balancing equations, but (as with any skill) *practice* is necessary for mastery; you may wish to balance several equations on the chalkboard using the procedures on pp. 76–77, guiding your students through the steps until they grasp the process.

Changing subscripts when balancing equations (4.1, pp. 76–77). The reason that subscripts cannot be changed while balancing an equation is that to do so would change what substance we are talking about. For example, we cannot balance the equation

$$H_2 + O_2 \longrightarrow H_2O$$

by changing it to

$$H_2 + O_2 \longrightarrow H_2O_2$$

because the first equation describes the formation of water (H_2O), but the second describes the formation of hydrogen peroxide (H_2O_2). If we want a balanced equation describing the formation of water, we must stick with H_2O.

Balanced net ionic equations (4.2, p. 84). In any chemical equation, the sum of the charges on the left side of the yields sign must equal the sum of the charges on the right. This fact can serve as an additional check to determine whether your net ionic equation is correct.

Lecture Demonstrations

Types of reactions (4.2, pp. 79–83). If time permits, demonstrating an example of each type of reaction in front of the students can help bring these abstract concepts down to a more concrete level. Some possibilities are as follows:

Combination: (1) Add about 20 mL of distilled water to about 50 g of CaO in a 150-ml beaker (reaction 5.11); after several seconds, heat and steam are produced and the volume of solid increases. (Product may be disposed of in trash can after it is cool.) (2) Open a reagent bottle of concentrated HCl (6-*M* or stronger) and a bottle of concentrated aqueous ammonia. Hold both bottles upright with the bottle openings next to each other. (**CAUTION:** Be careful not to spill either liquid; wear appropriate protective attire.) The vapors that diffuse out of the bottles react in the air above the bottles to form solid NH_4Cl, forming a white "smoke" above the bottles (see Fig. 15.3). This demonstration works best in relatively still air. The reaction is $NH_3(g) + HCl(g) \longrightarrow NH_4Cl(s)$

Decomposition: (1) Heat a small amount of table sugar (sucrose, $C_{12}H_{22}O_{11}$) in an old test tube over a burner flame. The sugar decomposes into carbon and water vapor (which may condense on the walls of the tube as droplets of water). (2) Use an electrolysis apparatus to decompose water into hydrogen and oxygen (see Fig. 10.2).

Single displacement: (1) React a piece of zinc or magnesium with dilute (6 *M*) HCl. (2) Alternatively, drop a *small* piece of sodium, about the size of a small pea, into a 250-mL beaker of water and cover with a wire gauze to prevent spattering. (**CAUTION:** Too large a piece may cause the hydrogen produced to explode; caustic sodium hydroxide [lye] is produced. Wear suitable protective attire, including eye protection.) (3) Another possibility is to place a clean piece of copper (use steel wool) in a petri dish of 0.1 *M* $AgNO_3$ placed on an overhead projector; observe crystal growth and appearance of blue color in the solution.

Double displacement: Mix equal volumes of 0.1 *M* K_2CrO_4 and 0.1 *M* $Pb(NO_3)_2$, 0.1 *M* $AgNO_3$ and 0.1 *M* NaCl, or 0.1 *M* $CuSO_4$ and 0.1 *M* NaOH in test tubes; these form yellow, blue, and white precipitates, respectively.

The above demonstrations also serve as an opportunity to review the evidences that a chemical reaction has occurred (p. 37) by having students observe which evidence(s) are present in each case.

Limiting reactant (4.3, p. 87). The concept of limiting reactant can also be illustrated by bringing in a 10-pack of hot dogs and an 8-pack of hot dog buns. If the "reactants" were used to make complete hot dog meals, the bread would be the "limiting reactant" and would limit the total number of complete hot dog meals produced to 8 rather than 10.

Answers to Text Questions

Section Review 4.1 (p. 79)

1. Balance the following equations, using the guidelines given in this section. (4.1)
   a. $Al(s) + O_2(g) \longrightarrow Al_2O_3(s)$
   $4\,Al(s) + 3\,O_2(g) \longrightarrow 2\,Al_2O_3(s)$
   b. $H_2SO_4(aq) + LiOH(aq) \longrightarrow Li_2SO_4(aq) + H_2O(l)$
   $H_2SO_4(aq) + 2\,LiOH(aq) \longrightarrow Li_2SO_4(aq) + 2\,H_2O(l)$
   c. $NH_3(g) + O_2(g) \xrightarrow{\Delta} N_2(g) + H_2O(g)$
   $4\,NH_3(g) + 3\,O_2(g) \longrightarrow 2\,N_2(g) + 6\,H_2O(g)$
   d. $Ca(ClO_3)_2(aq) \xrightarrow{\Delta} CaCl_2(aq) + O_2(g)$
   $Ca(ClO_3)_2(aq) \longrightarrow CaCl_2(aq) + 3O_2(g)$
2. Write the formulas for the reactants and products in each problem, as indicated, and balance the equations.
   a. Write the equation to show how solid iron(III) oxide is formed from its elements.
   $4\,Fe(s) + 3\,O_2(g) \longrightarrow 2\,Fe_2O_3(s)$
   b. When it is heated, magnesium hydroxide solid forms magnesium oxide solid and gaseous water.
   $Mg(OH)_2(s) \longrightarrow MgO(s) + H_2O(g)$
   c. Aluminum metal reacts with aqueous phosphoric acid (H_3PO_4) to produce hydrogen gas and a precipitate of aluminum phosphate.
   $2\,Al(s) + 2\,H_3PO_4(aq) \longrightarrow 3\,H_2(g) + 2\,AlPO_4(s)$
   d. Gaseous chlorine reacts with aqueous sodium iodide to form an aqueous solution of iodine and sodium chloride.
   $Cl_2(g) + 2\,NaI(aq) \longrightarrow I_2(aq) + 2\,NaCl(aq)$

Section Review 4.2 (p. 85)

1. Classify the reactions in Section Review 4.1, exercises 1 and 2 (p. 79) as combination, decomposition, single displacement, or double displacement reactions.

(Exercise 1)	*(Exercise 2)*
a. combination	*a. combination*
b. double displacement	*b. decomposition*
c. single displacement	*c. single displacement*
d. decomposition	*d. single displacement*

2. Explain the difference between an ionic equation and a net ionic equation. *An ionic equation includes both reacting and nonreacting ions in the equation while a net ionic equation includes only those ions that react.*

Section Review 4.3 (p. 89)

1. According to the following reaction, how many moles of hydrogen are needed in order to produce 4 moles of ammonia?
   $$3\,H_2(g) + N_2(g) \longrightarrow 2\,NH_3(g)$$
   6 moles of hydrogen are needed.
2. How many moles of CO_2 will be produced by the combustion of 0.6 mol pentane (C_5H_{12}) according to the following equation?
   $$C_5H_{12}(l) + 8\,O_2(g) \longrightarrow 5\,CO_2(g) + 6\,H_2O(g)$$
   $$0.6\ mol\ C_5H_{12} \times \frac{5\ mol\ CO_2}{1\ mol\ C_5H_{12}} = \mathbf{3\ mol\ CO_2}$$
3. Water can be produced from hydrogen and oxygen according to the following reaction:
   $$2\,H_2(g) + O_2(g) \longrightarrow 2\,H_2O(g)$$
   a. If a chemist has 1 mole hydrogen and 1 mole oxygen to react, which one is the limiting reactant? *hydrogen*
   b. How much H_2O (in moles) could be produced from 1 mole hydrogen and 1 mole oxygen?
   1 mole H_2O

4. The exhaled carbon dioxide produced as a normal waste product of metabolism must be removed from the cabins of space vehicles. On the space shuttle, CO_2 is removed from the cabin air by lithium hydroxidel, which reacts as follows:
$$2\ LiOH(s) + CO_2(g) \longrightarrow Li_2CO_3(s) + H_2O(l)$$
What mass of CO_2 can be removed from the atmosphere by 1.00 lb (454 g) of LiOH?
$$454\ g\ LiOH \times \frac{1\ mol\ LiOH}{23.95\ g\ LiOH} \times \frac{1\ mol\ CO_2}{2\ mol\ LiOH} \times \frac{44.01\ g\ CO_2}{1\ mol\ CO_2} = \mathbf{417\ g\ CO_2}$$

Chapter 4 Review (p. 91)

1. State the law of conservation of mass as it applies to chemical equations. *Either of the following is acceptable:*
   - *The sum of the masses of the products is always equal to the sum of the masses of the reactants.*
   - *Atoms are not created or destroyed in chemical reactions, only rearranged.*
2. Balance the following chemical equations:
   a. $FeCl_3(aq) + NaOH(aq) \longrightarrow Fe(OH)_3(s) + NaCl(aq)$
   $FeCl_3(aq) + 3NaOH(aq) \longrightarrow Fe(OH)_3(aq) + 3\ NaCl(aq)$
   b. $P_4(s) + Cl_2(g) \longrightarrow PCl_5(s)$
   $P_4(s) + 10\ Cl_2(g) \longrightarrow 4\ PCl_5(s)$
   c. $KClO_3(s) \longrightarrow KCl(s) + O_2(g)$
   $2\ KClO_3(s) \longrightarrow 2\ KCl(s) + 3\ O_2(g)$
3. Write the formulas for reactants and products in each, as indicated, and balance the equations.
   a. When aqueous solutions of barium chloride and ammonium carbonate are mixed, solid barium carbonate precipitates; aqueous ammonium chloride is also formed.
   $BaCl_2(aq) + (NH_4)_2CO_3(aq) \longrightarrow BaCO_3(s) + 2\ NH_4Cl(aq)$
   b. Aqueous potassium cyanide reacts with aqueous hydrochloric acid (HCl) to form gaseous hydrogen cyanide (HCN, a deadly poison) and aqueous potassium chloride.
   $KCN(aq) + HCl(aq) \longrightarrow HCN(g) + KCl(aq)$
   c. Aqueous solutions of iron(III) sulfate and barium hydroxide form precipitates of barium sulfate and iron(III) hydroxide when they are mixed.
   $Fe_2(SO_4)_3 + 3\ Ba(OH)_2(aq) \longrightarrow 3\ BaSO_4(s) + 2\ Fe(OH)_3(s)$
   d. Hexane (C_6H_{14}), a liquid, burns in air (O_2) to form gaseous carbon dioxide and water.
   $2\ C_6H_{14}(l) + 19\ O_2(g) \longrightarrow 12\ CO_2 + 14\ H_2O(l)$
4. Classify the following reactions as combination, decomposition, single displacement, or double displacement.
   a. $SO_3(g) + H_2O(l) \longrightarrow H_2SO_4(l)$ *combination*
   b. $CaC_2(s) + 2\ H_2O(l) \longrightarrow C_2H_2(g) + Ca(OH)_2(s)$ *double displacement*
   c. $N_2H_4(l) + O_2(g) \longrightarrow N_2(g) + 2\ H_2O(g)$ *single displacement*
   d. $NH_4NO_3(l) \longrightarrow N_2O(g) + 2\ H_2O(g)$ *decomposition*
5. What is a net ionic equation? *a chemical equation which shows only those ions that react and ignores ions which do not react*
6. What is meant by the term ***spectator ion?*** *ions in an equation which do not react*
7. Write net ionic equations for the following reactions:
   a. $Ba(s) + 2\ HCl(aq) \longrightarrow BaCl_2(aq) + H_2(g)$
   $Ba(s) + 2\ H^+(aq) \longrightarrow Ba^{2+}(aq) + H_2(g)$
   b. $2\ HCl(aq) + Cu(OH)_2(s) \longrightarrow 2\ H_2O(l) + CuCl_2(aq)$
   $2\ H^+(aq) + Cu(OH)_2(s) \longrightarrow 2\ H_2O(l) + Cu^{2+}(aq)$
8. To what does the term ***limiting reactant*** refer in a chemical reaction? *the reactant that determines the amount of product that can be formed*
9. How many moles of oxygen are needed to produce 3.17 mol carbon monoxide from its elements by a synthesis reaction?
   reaction: $2\ C(s) + O_2(g) \longrightarrow 2\ CO(g)$
   $$3.17\ mol\ CO \times \frac{1\ mol\ O_2}{2\ mol\ CO} = \mathbf{1.59\ mol\ O_2}$$
10. Tarnishing of silver is due to the presence of small amounts of hydrogen sulfide occurring naturally in the atmosphere due to decaying organic material and volcanic activity. Its reaction with silver and atmospheric oxygen is as follows:
$$4\ Ag(s) + 2\ H_2S(g) + O_2(g) \longrightarrow \underset{\text{(tarnish)}}{2\ Ag_2S(s)} + 2\ H_2O(l)$$
How many grams of Ag_2S could be produced from 1.70 g H_2S if sufficient amounts of the other reactants were present?
$Ag_2S = 2 \times 107.87\ g + 1 \times 32.06\ g = 247.8\ g/mol$
$H_2S = 2 \times 1.01\ g + 1 \times 32.06\ g = 34.08\ g/mol$
$$1.70\ g\ H_2S \times \frac{1\ mol\ H_2S}{34.08\ g\ H_2S} \times \frac{2\ mol\ Ag_2S}{2\ mol\ H_2S} \times \frac{247.8\ g\ Ag_2S}{1\ mol\ Ag_2S} = \mathbf{12.4\ g\ Ag_2S}$$

Chapter 4

Chapter 5 (pp. 92–117)
Gases

5.1 Kinetic-Molecular Theory
5.2 Gas Pressure
5.3 The Gas Laws
5.4 Diffusion, Partial Pressures, and Stoichiometry

Suggested Daily Pacing

34 **Check** homework.

Return and go over graded Test 2.

Introduce ch. 5, Gases.

Discuss homework.

Teach pp. **93–95,** sec. **5.1** Kinetic-Molecular Theory.

Review lesson.

HW: Read pp. 95–99, up to 5.3 The Gas Laws. Answer p. 99, questions 1–4. Problem Selection Worksheet due les. 36.

35 **Give** "pop" reading quiz over pp. 95–99:

1. True or False: The higher the temperature of a gas, the greater the average kinetic energy of the molecules in the gas. *true*
2. What is defined as "force per unit area"? *pressure*
3. Name three of the five units which are used to measure pressure. *Any three of the following: mmHg, Pascal, bar, atm, torr*
4. What does the abbreviation "atm" stand for? *standard atmosphere*
5. What instrument is used to measure atmospheric pressure? *barometer*

Check and discuss homework.

Review pp. 93–95.

Teach pp. **95–99,** sec. **5.2** Gas Pressure.

Review lesson.

HW: Answer p. 99, question 5. Read pp. 99–104, up to Combined Gas Law: Volume, Pressure, and Temperature. Complete Problem Selection Worksheet. Review *Science in Action* pp. 35–38. Bring *Science in Action* to class.

36 **SP:** Check Problem Selection Worksheet and make suggestions as needed. (Have students answer text p. 99, questions 5–6.) Make sure selections chosen follow guidelines in *Science in Action,* especially safety concerns on pp. 37–38. Consider availability of materials. Tell students to place worksheet in the Science Project Notebook. Introduce the **Investigation Plan,** using *Science in Action,* pp. 45–47. Assign first draft of Investigation Plan for les. 41.

Check and discuss p. 99, questions 5–6.

Review pp. 95–99.

Teach pp. **99–104,** sec. **5.3** The Gas Laws, up to Combined Gas Law: Volume, Pressure, and Temperature.

Review lesson.

HW: Read pp. 104–108. Answer p. 109, questions 1–5. First draft of Investigation Plan due les. 41.

37 **Check** and discuss homework.

Review pp. 99–104.

Teach pp. **104–108,** sec. **5.3** (cont.).

Review lesson.

HW: Answer p. 109, questions 6–8. Read *Lab Manual* Lab 10 and complete Prelab Assignment.

38 **Check** and discuss homework.

Conduct Lab 10: Charles's Law.

HW: Complete Lab 10 Report Sheet. Read pp. 109–112, up to Gases in Chemical Reactions. Answer p. 115, questions 1, 3, and 4. First draft of Investigation Plan due in les. 41.

39 **Give Quiz 9** (over pp. 99–108.

Check and discuss homework.

Review pp. 104–108.

Teach pp. **109–112,** sec. **5.4** Diffusion, Partial Pressures, and Stoichiometry, up to Gases in Chemical Reactions.

Review lesson.

HW: Read pp. 112 –115. Answer p. 115, questions 2, 5, and 6.

40 **Check** and discuss homework.

Review pp. 109–112.

Teach pp. **112–115,** sec. **5.4** (cont.).

Review lesson.

HW: Answer p. 115, questions 7 and 8. Begin studying ch. 1–5 for Test 3 (Nine-Weeks Exam) in les. 43. Answer p. 33, Review Exercises 9–16. Complete first draft of Investigation Plan. Bring Investigation Plan, Investigation Evaluation form, and *Science in Action.*

41 **SP:** Check Investigation Plan and make suggestions on Investigation Plan Evaluation. (Have students answer text p. 57, Review Exercises 1, 6–7, and 14–16.) Give general hints on **revising Investigation Plan first draft,** using *Science in Action* p. 47. Assign revised Investigation Plan for les. 46 (ch. 6).

Check and discuss p. 57, Review Exercises 1, 6–7, and 14–16.

Review ch. 1–2 for Test 3 (Nine-Weeks Exam), using important concepts from Chapter Reviews 1–2.

HW: Continue studying ch. 1–5 for Test 3 (Nine-Weeks Exam). Have parents sign First Draft Evaluation form. Revised Investigation Plan is due les. 46 (ch. 6).

Note: Assign 10–15 questions from Chapter Reviews 3–5.

42 **Check** and discuss homework.

Review ch. 1–5 for Test 3 (Nine-Weeks Exam), using important concepts from Chapter Reviews 1–5.

HW: Study ch. 1–5 for Test 3 (Nine-Weeks Exam) in next lesson.

43 **Administer Test 3** (Nine-Weeks Exam) over ch. 1–5.

HW: Read *Lab Manual* Lab 11 and complete Prelab Assignment.

Teacher Notes

Chapter 5 Overview. This chapter explores the nature and properties of gases, laying the foundation for the study of reactions involving gases in later chapters. After an introduction to the kinetic-molecular theory, which is basic to an understanding of gases, the chapter explains the concept of pressure and how it may be measured. The various gas laws are introduced, culminating in the ideal gas equation, which can be thought of as all of the other gas laws rolled into one. The chapter concludes with a discussion of diffusion, partial pressures, and the stoichiometry of gases in chemical reactions.

Kinetic-molecular theory (5.1, p. 94). Though we know that molecules are not really solid spheres, visualizing gases as perfectly elastic balls (something like Superballs™) bouncing around the room at high speeds may help in the discussion of the kinetic-molecular theory.

Temperature and kinetic energy (5.2, p. 95). Since the temperature of a gas is a measure of the average kinetic energy of its molecules, *any* two gases at the same temperature have the same average KE. This is true regardless of the relative masses of the gases concerned; in a sample of He and a sample of $C_2H_2F_4$ (R-134a) at the same temperature, the average kinetic energy of an He atom is precisely the same as the kinetic energy of a $C_2H_2F_4$ molecule. The lighter atoms make up for their lack of mass by moving at greater velocity.

Pressure unit comparisons (5.2 p. 96). The following comparisons may help students relate the units of pressure to real-world situations:

Mt. Everest, peak	5.0 psi	0.34 atm	260 torr	35 kPa
sea level	14.7 psi	1.0 atm	760 torr	101 kPa
bottom of 8-ft swimming pool	18 psi	1.2 atm	939 torr	125 kPa
car tire @35 psi above atmospheric	50 psi	3.4 atm	2570 torr	343 kPa
surface of Venus	1330 psi	91 atm	69,000 torr	9.2 MPa
medical oxygen cylinder (p. 216)	2000 psi	136 atm	103,400 torr	13.8 MPa
deepest spot in ocean (~36,000 ft)	16,000 psi	1090 atm	830,000 torr	110 MPa
center of Earth	52.8 Mpsi	3.6 Matm	2.73 Gtorr	364 GPa

Standard pressure (5.2, p. 96). The students will be greatly helped if they memorize the value for standard pressure (760 torr). This figure will be commonly used in solving gas-law problems.

Solving gas-law problems (5.3, p. 101). Although the text uses a "common-sense" ratio correction factor approach to solving gas law problems (Boyle's, Charles's, and the combined gas law), they can also be solved by "plugging" values into the correct equation. You may find that the approach used in the text allows some students to better reason out the solution and helps avoid forgetting equations on the test; it also allows all the gas law problems to be solved by virtually the same method. Either approach is perfectly acceptable, however; learning equations may be helpful for students who will go on to physics or who plan to study chemistry in college. Regardless of the method used, students will find it helpful to check their answers to make sure they are reasonable.

Combined gas law (5.3, pp. 104–105). The use of the table for data is important here. Note that the volume dependence on pressure is unrelated to the volume dependence on temperature; each has its own effect, the pressure not "knowing" what the temperature is doing and the temperature not "knowing" what the pressure is doing.

Avogadro's law (5.3, pp. 106–107). One might wonder why the gas pressure is proportional to the average *kinetic energy* of the particles, regardless of their mass and momentum, since heavier molecules would exert more force against the container when they collide with the walls. It would seem more logical at first glance that pressure would be more correlated with momentum, since it is their inertia, not their energy, that presses the walls of the container outward. Actually, the correlation with energy is almost a coincidence; the force exerted by each collision *does* increase in direct proportion to the momentum (not the energy), but the *number* of collisions decreases by the same proportion at any given temperature.

As an illustration of this fact, consider two imaginary gases, one with a molecular mass of 10 u and a second with a molecular mass of 40 u, at the same temperature (same average kinetic energy). The laws of physics tell us that the molecules of the 10-u gas will be moving twice as fast, on average, as the molecules of the 40-u gas ($KE = \frac{1}{2}mv^2$; see text p. 25). Even at half the speed, each molecule of the 40-u gas has twice the momentum of a 10-u molecule because of its greater mass. As a result, each collision between a 40-u molecule and the container exerts twice as much force against the container wall as a 10-u molecule. *However,* the 10-u molecules collide with the walls twice as often because they are moving faster; *although they exert only half as much force with each collision, they have twice as many collisions.* As a result, the same pressure is exerted by both gases.

Molar volume (5.3, p. 107). It is recommended that students memorize the value of the molar volume (22.4 L), as they will need this information when solving any ideal gas problem. They should also keep in mind that it has that value *only* at STP.

Partial pressures (5.4, p. 110). Note that Dalton's law applies *only* to pressure and *not* to volume. This is true because all components in a mixture of gases occupy the entire volume of the container (and would still do so even if all the other components were removed).

Air bag safety (5.4, p. 115). By 1999, air bags had deployed in roughly 3.5 million crashes and may have saved nearly 5000 lives; an estimated 50% of those saved were unbelted drunk drivers. Officially, air bags had also killed close to 150 people in low-speed crashes who would otherwise have definitely survived; an estimated 15% of deaths in high-severity frontal crashes are also air bag related.[1] Using just the low-speed crash statistics, current air bags kill 1 child or small adult for every 15–20 sober adults theoretically saved. Passenger-side air bags rate the worst, killing 1 child per 10 adults saved and 2 children per child saved.[2] As a result, experts now warn that ***children under 13 should never sit in the front seat of an air-bag-equipped vehicle,*** and that petite or elderly adults sit as far away from the air-bag module as possible, unless the air bag can be switched off.

The problem is not with air-bag technology, but with misguided government standards. For many years, Federal regulations (FMVSS 208) insisted that all air bags be calibrated primarily for *large, unbelted males* in the *worst 1% of crashes,* even though air bags are extremely dangerous when used without belts. Unfortunately, optimizing air bags for large men who refuse to wear seat belts can lead to *increased* risk of death or injury for children, small adults (particularly women), and the elderly in the vast majority of crashes. Since over 70% of Americans faithfully wear seat belts, it would seem more logical to calibrate air bags primarily for *belted* individuals, which would provide superior protection while minimizing risk.

As a result of public pressure, manufacturers and regulators are developing more complex systems to provide responsible seat belt users with an acceptable level of safety while retaining the unbelted-male mandate. FMVSS 208 is being revised (effective 2006) to require cars to sense occupant size, position, and seat belt status and adjust air-bag power and inflation threshold accordingly.

[1]Cammisa MX, Ferguson SA, Lund AK, Reed RT, "Driver Fatalities in Frontal Crashes of Airbag-Equipped Vehicles: A Review of 1989–96 NASS Cases." *Airbag Technology 2000* (SP-1493), SAE 2000 World Congress, Detroit, MI, reprinted in <http://www.hwysafety.org/fed/nhtsa_ds_akl_123099.pdf> pp. 10–18.

[2]Braver ER, Ferguson SA, Greene MA, Lund AK, "Reductions in deaths in frontal crashes among right front passengers in vehicles equipped with passenger air bags." *Journal of the American Medical Association* **278**(17) (5 November 1997) 1437–9; Graham JD, Thompson KM, Goldie SJ, Segui-Gomez M, Weinstein MC. "The cost-effectiveness of air bags by seating position." *Ibid.* 1418-25.

Lecture Demonstrations

Kinetic-molecular theory (5.1, p. 94). The kinetic-molecular theory can be illustrated using a transparent plastic box or storage container (a box with squared-off floor-wall junctions works best). Put several BBs, ball bearings, or marbles in the bottom of the box, place the box on the overhead projector, and shake it back and forth; the "molecules" will collide vigorously with each other and with the walls of the container. (You may wish to place a transparency sheet on the overhead to prevent it from being scratched). The faster you shake the box, the faster the "molecules" move and the more collisions occur; this corresponds to increased temperature. Slowing the shaking corresponds to decreased temperature; ceasing the shaking altogether corresponds to absolute zero (ignoring quantum effects, of course). Adding more "molecules" to the box increases the number of collisions.

This same box can be used to demonstrate several other principles throughout this chapter:

- Boyle's law (5.3, pp. 100–101). Block off half of box with cardboard divider and shake with "molecules" confined to half the box; then remove divider and allow same number of "molecules" to vibrate throughout box; fewer collisions (less "pressure") occur in the larger volume.
- Diffusion (5.4, pp. 109–110). Use a cardboard divider as above, but cut a small opening in the center to allow some of the "molecules" to pass through.
- Partial pressures (5.4, pp. 110–111). Place a mixture of BBs and larger ball bearings in the box and shake. Point out that the "pressure" (collisions with the walls) produced by each type is proportional to the number of balls of each type in the box.

Atmospheric pressure (5.2, p. 96). If you have access to a barometer that reads in millibars or mmHg, you may wish to note the barometer reading as you teach the lesson, pointing out to the students that this figure represents the pressure upon their bodies at this very moment. Using this figure to calculate the total pressure upon your desktop (by converting pressure to lb/in^2 and multiplying by desktop area in in^2) can be an eye-opening experience; the total force pressing down on even a 36×48-inch desktop amounts to nearly 13 *tons.* (The desktop does not collapse only because it is being pressed upon by the same force from beneath.)

Air pressure can be dramatically demonstrated as follows. Obtain an *empty,* flat-sided one-gallon steel can and seal the mouth with an appropriately sized one-hole stopper (make sure it forms a tight seal). Insert a *short* piece of glass tubing into the mouth of the stopper, attaching the hose of a vacuum pump to the exposed end. Begin pumping the air out of the can with the vacuum pump; the can's walls will bulge inward at first, then finally buckle under the weight of the air. An empty 3-liter soda bottle can also be used. Note that a can that has contained gasoline, petroleum distillates, etc. should not be used as residual vapors (a) are noxious and flammable and (b) could conceivably damage some vacuum pumps. Relatively inexpensive hand vacuum pumps with integral gauges and included tubing are available at many auto parts stores; make sure the tubing diameter is compatible with any glassware you intend to use it with. Much more expensive pumps can be purchased from scientific supply companies.

In a slightly more dramatic version of this demonstration, pour 10–20 mL of water into the bottom of the can and heat the can (with the cap OFF) on a laboratory hot plate. (**CAUTION:** Do *not* use a can that has ever contained a flammable liquid such as gasoline or petroleum distillates, as an explosion could result.) Explain that as the water boils, the steam formed will flush the air out of the can. When the water is boiling and a good flow of steam is coming from the spout, quickly remove the can from the hot plate (using oven mitts) and screw the cap on tightly. As the water inside condenses, the pressure inside the can will drop dramatically, allowing the external pressure to crush the can. (Note: This works only with airtight cans having tight-sealing, non-vented lids.)

The second version above can also be performed with an empty soda can. Add 2–3 mL of water to the can and heat the can over a Bunsen burner (using a ring stand and wire gauze) until steam is rushing out of the opening. *Quickly* pick up the can with beaker tongs and invert it into a large bowl of cold water so that the mouth of the can is at least 1" below the surface. The external air pressure should crush the can quite dramatically.

Manometers (5.2, p. 97). Demonstrating the operation of a real manometer (if you have access to one) can make the manometer portion of this lesson more rewarding. Keep in mind, however, that the main point of this section is the concept of pressure itself rather than the equipment used to measure it.

Boyle's law (5.3, p. 100). Several demonstrations may be used to teach or illustrate Boyle's law:

a. Plug the end of the air hose of a bicycle hand pump, place the pump on a bathroom scale (digital works best), and press down on the pump handle. Relate the force you are exerting (shown by the scale) to the volume of the air trapped in the pump, referring to Fig. 5.8 of the text as you do so. The volume of air you are compressing can be estimated by marking the shaft of the pump at regular intervals with a permanent marker beforehand, or by standing a meter stick in front of the pump.

b. Place a round, partially inflated balloon into a large filter flask (or vacuum jar, if you have one); stopper the flask with a rubber stopper (or seal the jar); and connect the suction fitting to a vacuum pump or water aspirator using an appropriate length of vacuum tubing. Begin pumping or turn on the aspirator and note how the balloon's volume increases as the pressure inside the flask is reduced, and how it decreases when the pressure is allowed to return to normal.

c. Obtain a plastic oral syringe (*not* an injection syringe) and cap from a local pharmacy; the larger sizes (6-mL or larger) tend to work better than the smaller ones. These can be used in two ways:

- Pull back the plunger to fill the syringe with air, seal the end with your finger or an airtight syringe cap, and press down on the plunger with your other hand. If the cap is airtight and the plunger slides easily, results will match Boyle's law. If you wish, hold the syringe upside down by the barrel and press the plunger upon a scale to read force; the volume of trapped air can be read directly from the barrel. Syringes are often inexpensive enough that you can buy several and perform the demonstration as a class activity.
- Gently suspend the syringe in a vertical position (nozzle down) from a ring stand using a flat-topped test-tube clamp or buret clamp (be sure that the syringe rests on the finger flange and that the clamp does not compress the barrel; otherwise the plunger will stick). After filling the cylinder with air and plugging it with an airtight cap (glued in place if necessary), begin adding identical hardcover books or other weights one at a time to the top of the plunger (balance the stack with your hand if necessary) and observe the volume decrease that occurs with each added weight. Have students plot $1/V$ *vs.* number of books on graph paper; results should approximate Fig. 5.8. Some authorities recommend that this demonstration be done with a 30-mL glass syringe instead, but these are more expensive and can be difficult to obtain.

Charles's law (5.3, pp. 102–103). A few minutes ahead of time, begin heating an empty 250-mL (or larger) Florence or Erlenmeyer flask in a shallow hot water bath (*not* over a flame or on a hot plate; an empty flask will quickly overheat and break). When the flask is hot and you are ready to perform the demonstration, quickly stretch the mouth of a deflated balloon over the mouth of the flask and remove it from the water. Cool the flask under running water, followed by an ice bath; the balloon should contract into the flask. (Do not transfer any glassware immediately from heat to an ice bath to minimize the risk of shattering.) Returning the flask to the hot bath will again force the balloon out of the flask.

If the flask is left in the hot and cold baths long enough for the temperatures to stabilize at both extremes, we can calculate the volume decrease that should occur. By plugging the initial and final temperatures (in kelvins) into equation 5.9, we can calculate that the air in the flask should contract to about 73% of its former value when transferred from a near-boiling bath to an ice-water bath, assuming the pressure remains constant. (The actual volume decrease may be slightly less due to stiffness of the balloon.) If you wish to have students do the calculation, have a couple of Celsius thermometers on hand to take the temperature of the hot- and cold-water baths.

A faster variant of this demonstration is to use two or three identical balloon-covered flasks (or empty carbonated beverage bottles) instead of just one. Leave the first one in the hot-water bath, transfer the second to the ice-water bath, and allow the third (if present) to cool to room temperature. During the lesson, explain what you did and point out that all three started out just like the one in the hot-water bath, but as they cooled the air inside them shrunk.

Molar volume object lesson (5.3, p. 107). The 22.4-L molar volume of an ideal gas can be demonstrated by finding a beach ball with a diameter of about 13.8 inches (or a circumference of 43.3 inches). The inflated volume of such a ball will be approximately 22.4 liters, so that when inflated it would contain about 1 mole of air molecules (assuming its pressure is within 1 psi or so of atmospheric pressure).

Graham's law of diffusion (5.4, p. 110). Obtain about a 1-m length of glass tubing (8 mm o.d.) and two rubber eyedropper bulbs. Clamp the tubing securely in the horizontal position to a support stand. Label one end "NH_3" and the other "HCl." Using separate eyedroppers, place 3–4 drops of 15 *M* NH_3 ("concentrated") and 3–4 drops of 12 *M* HCl ("concentrated") into the tips of separate eyedropper bulbs. Carefully and simultaneously place the bulbs onto the proper ends of the tube, being careful not to squeeze the bulbs as you fit them over the ends. (Only 2–3 mm of the tube needs to be inside each rubber bulb.) Within approximately 5–10 minutes, a ring of white NH_4Cl should be visible nearer the HCl end of the tube. On a qualitative basis, it shows that NH_3—the lighter gas—travels farther than the heavier gas. If you wish to quantify this, measure the distance d from each tube end to the center of the white ring. A value of approximately 1.5 should be obtained for the ratio d_{NH_3}/d_{HCl}.

Answers to Text Questions

Section Review 5.1 (p. 95)

1. List five properties of gases.
   Any five of the following:
   - *completely miscible*
   - *mix or diffuse rapidly*
   - *flow easily*
   - *have mass*
   - *readily compressed*
   - *expand and contract with temperature changes*
   - *completely fill any vessel of any shape into which they are placed*
2. State the postulates of the kinetic-molecular theory.
   1. Gas molecules are in constant, rapid motion.
   2. Gas molecules undergo elastic collisions.
   3. The KE of gas molecules is directly related to temperature.
   4. Gas molecules are very far apart and have negligible volume compared to the volume of the gas.
   5. Gas molecules have negligible attractive forces between them.
3. Tell whether the following are direct or inverse proportions; k is a constant and the other letters are variables.
   a. $C = kd$ *direct*
   b. $a = \frac{k}{b}$ *inverse*
   c. $PV = k$ *inverse*
   d. $\frac{V}{T} = k$ *direct*
   e. $E = mk^2$ *direct*
   f. $g = \frac{\sqrt{k}}{r}$ *inverse*

Section Review 5.2 (p. 99)

1. How are mmHg, torr, and atm related?
   760 mmHg = 760 torr = 1 atm
2. What is a manometer? *a common laboratory device used to measure gas pressure*
3. A pressure of 56 mmHg is equal to how many torr? *56 torr (1 mmHg = 1 torr)*
4. What is standard pressure in torr? *760 torr*
5. A sample of gas is connected to an open-end manometer. Tell whether the gas sample or the atmosphere has the greater pressure in each of the following.
   a. The mercury level is 12 mm higher in the side open to the atmosphere. *gas sample pressure is greater*
   b. The mercury level is 37 mm higher in the side open to the gas. *atmospheric pressure is greater*
   c. The mercury level is 115 mm lower in the arm open to the gas. *gas sample pressure is greater*
6. A gas sample is connected to a closed-end manometer. The difference in mercury levels in the two arms is 115 mm. What is the gas pressure in torr if the atmospheric pressure is 750. torr? (See Example 5.2) *The gas pressure is 115 mm, the difference in mercury levels. (Remember that the closed-end manometer is not open to atmospheric pressure, but instead has a vacuum in one end of the tube, resulting in an absolute reading.)*

Section Review 5.3 (pp. 108–109)

1. State Boyle's law. *At constant temperature for a given mass of gas, volume varies inversely with pressure (PV = k).*

Chapter 5

2. If the pressure on a balloon were doubled, what would happen to the balloon's volume? If the pressure were quadrupled? *If the pressure on a balloon were doubled, the balloon's volume would be halved; if the pressure were quadrupled, the balloon's volume would be reduced to one fourth of its original volume.*
3. Sperm whales are the deepest-diving whales known. When a sperm whale dives from the surface to great depths, the air in its lungs progressively shrinks until the lungs are completely collapsed. When the whale ascends, its lungs return to their former size. Use Boyle's law to explain this phenomenon. *The further the whale descends from the surface, the greater the water pressure that surrounds it. Therefore, as the pressure increases, the volume must decrease ($PV = k$); conversely, as the water pressure decreases as the whole ascends, the volume will increase to its original size.*
4. State Charles's law. *The volume of a given mass of a gas at constant pressure is directly proportional to the absolute temperature.*
5. What temperature scale must be used when working with Charles's law? *Kelvin*
6. Suppose the absolute temperature inside a tank of compressed air doubles. What will happen to the pressure inside the tank, if the volume remains constant? (Relate temperature to the kinetic energy of molecules.) *The pressure inside the tank doubles. (Since the absolute temperature doubles, the kinetic energy doubles, resulting in double the number of collisions per unit area and double the pressure.)*
7. In chemistry, what is meant by the term STP? *standard temperature and pressure (0 °C or 273.[15] K and 1 atm)*
8. Calculate the number of moles of oxygen in 1.00 L at 25 °C and 1.00 atm, assuming the gas behaves ideally.

P	V	n	T
1.00 atm	1.00 L	?	298 K

$$n = \frac{PV}{RT}$$

$$= \frac{(1.00\ \text{atm})(1.00\ \text{L})}{(0.0821\ \text{L·atm/K·mol})(298\ \text{K})}$$

$$= \mathbf{4.09 \times 10^{-2}\ mol\ O_2}$$

Section Review 5.4 (p. 115)

1. What is diffusion? *the process of mixing molecules of one substance through another by random molecular motion*
2. Consider three gases: chlorine (Cl_2), Freon-12 (CCl_2F_2), and radon (Rn). According to Graham's law of diffusion, which gas would you expect to diffuse fastest through a room? Which would diffuse slowest? *Chlorine, the lightest (70.90 u), would be expected to diffuse the fastest; radon, the heaviest 222 u), would be expected to diffuse the slowest.*
3. Tell which gas of each pair below would diffuse more rapidly at the same temperature and pressure.
   a. He *vs.* Ar *helium (He)*
   b. UF_6 *vs.* Cl_2 *chlorine (Cl_2)*
   c. H_2 *vs.* O_2 *hydrogen (H_2)*
4. State Dalton's law of partial pressures. *The total pressure of a mixture of gases is equal to the sum of the partial pressures of each gas.*
5. What is the partial pressure of N_2 in a mixture of N_2 and O_2 having a total pressure of 1075 torr if the partial pressure of O_2 is 720. torr?

$$P_{total} = p_{N_2} + p_{O_2}$$

$$1075\ \text{torr} = p_{N_2} + 720.\ \text{torr}$$

$$p_{N_2} = \mathbf{355\ torr}$$

6. Why is it necessary to correct the pressure of a gas that is collected over water? *A gas collected over water is saturated with water vapor. The actual pressure of the gas is equal to the total pressure minus the partial pressure of the water vapor.*
7. When calculating stoichiometric relationships in gas reactions using the combined gas law, why is it important to convert the volumes and pressures to STP? *(Answers will vary.) The ideal gas law (as presented in the text) is valid only at STP.*
8. The reaction for the burning of one type of match tip is as follows:
   $$P_4S_3(s) + 8\,O_2(g) \xrightarrow{\Delta} P_4O_{10}(g) + 3\,SO_2(g)$$
   What volume in L of SO_2 at STP can be produced by the burning of 1.00 g P_4S_3 in excess O_2?

$$1.00\ \text{g}\ P_4SO_3 \times \frac{1\ \text{mol}\ P_4S_3}{220.1\ \text{g}\ P_4S_3} \times \frac{3\ \text{mol}\ SO_2}{1\ \text{mol}\ P_4S_3} \times \frac{22.4\ \text{L}\ SO_2}{1\ \text{mol}\ SO_2} = \mathbf{0.305\ L\ SO_2}$$

Chapter 5 Review (p. 117)

1. Name three properties of gases that distinguish them from liquids and solids. *easily compressible, molecules far apart, completely fill their container, negligible attractive forces between them*
2. Distinguish between the units *atm, mmHg,* and *torr.*
   1 atm = 760 mmHg = 760 torr
3. What is standard pressure in torr? In atm?
   760 torr; 1 atm
4. A sample of gas in a flask is connected to an open-end manometer.
   a. The mercury level is 12 mm higher in the side open to the atmosphere. What is the pressure of the sample gas if P_{atm} = 772 torr?
   P_{gas} = 772 torr + 12 torr = ***784 torr***
   b. What is the pressure of the gas if the level of mercury is 37 mm higher in the side open to the gas and P_{atm} = 765 torr?
   P_{gas} = 765 torr − 37 torr = ***728 torr***
   c. What must be the gas pressure if P_{atm} = 757 torr and the mercury level is 115 mm lower in the arm open to the gas?
   P_{gas} = 757 torr + 115 torr = ***872 torr***
5. In your own words, state Boyle's law. *(Wording will vary.) At constant temperature for a given mass of gas, volume varies inversely with pressure.*
6. Tell what change in pressure would accompany the following changes in volume.
   a. 5.0 L to 2.5 L *pressure doubles*
   b. 155 mL to 620 mL *pressure decreases to $\frac{1}{4}$ original value.*
   c. 30.0 mL to 10.0 mL *pressure triples*
   d. 65 mL to 130 mL *pressure halved*
7. A tank of helium gas at 25.0 °C has a pressure of 100. atm and a volume of 50.0 L. How many 10-liter helium balloons could be filled from the tank, assuming no change in temperature and a pressure in the balloons of 1.05 atm?

	initial	final
P	100. atm	1.05 atm
V	50.0 L	?

P↓, V↑

$V_f = 50.0\ L \times \frac{100.\ atm}{1.05\ atm} = 4760\ L$

4760 L ÷ 10 L per balloon = ***476 balloons***

8. Suggest what could be done to a balloon full of nitrogen to accomplish the following changes:
   a. increase its volume *increase the temperature of the gas inside the balloon; decrease the pressure upon the balloon*
   b. decrease the speed of the molecules *decrease the temperature of the gas inside the balloon (by placing it in the freezer, etc.)*
9. In your own words, state Charles's law. *(Wording will vary.) The volume of a given mass of a gas at constant pressure is directly proportional to the absolute temperature.*
10. What would happen to the volume of a balloon that was placed in boiling water? In the freezer? *According to Charles's law, temperature and volume are directly related. Therefore, the volume of the balloon would increase in direct proportion to the increase of temperature and would likely explode in the boiling water. A balloon in the freezer would decrease in volume as the temperature decreased, shrinking the balloon.*
11. A gas occupying 24.5 L at 38 °C is cooled to −8 °C at constant pressure. What will be the final volume of the gas?

	initial	final
V	24.5 L	?
T	311 K	265 K

T↓, V↓

$V_f = 24.5\ L \times \frac{265\ K}{311\ K} = \mathbf{20.9\ L}$

12. What will be the volume of ammonia at 30.0 °C and 805 torr if its volume is 21.0 L at 752 torr and 5.0 °C?

	initial	final
P	752 torr	805 torr
V	21.0 L	?
T	278.2 K	303.2 K

P↑, V↓
T↑, V↑

$V_f = 21.0\ L \times \frac{752\ torr}{805\ torr} \times \frac{303.2\ K}{278.2\ K} = \mathbf{21.4\ L}$

13. A sample of hydrogen is collected over water at 30.°C and a pressure of 0.960 atm.
    a. What is the partial pressure of the hydrogen in the sample?
    $p_{H_2} = P_{atm} - p_{H_2O}$
    $= 0.960\ atm - 0.0419\ atm$
    $= 0.9181\ atm \approx \mathbf{0.918\ atm}$
    b. If the total volume of gas collected is 27.1 L, how many moles H_2 were collected?
    Use p_{H_2} (0.918 atm) as the pressure:

Chapter 5

P	V	n	T
0.918 atm	27.1L	?	30. °C

$N = \frac{PV}{RT} = \frac{(0.918\ atm)(27.1 L)}{(0.0821\ L \cdot atm/K \cdot mol)(303\ K)}$

$\approx$ ***1.00 mol H_2***

14. In each pair, determine the substance that would diffuse more rapidly at the same temperature and pressure.

a. CO *vs.* CO_2 *CO*

b. HCN *vs.* Cl_2 *HCN*

c. SO_3 *vs.* O_2 O_2

15. Octane, one of the major components of gasoline, burns in air according to the following equation:

$$C_8H_{18}(l) + O_2(g) \longrightarrow CO_2(g) + H_2O(g)$$

a. Write a balanced equation for this reaction:

$2\ C_8H_{18}\ (l) + 25\ O_2\ (g) \longrightarrow 16\ CO_2(g) + 18\ H_2O(g)$

b. What volume in L of O_2 at STP is needed to burn 1.00 L (702 g) of octane?

$702\ g\ C_8H_{18} \times \frac{1\ mol\ C_8H_{18}}{114.26\ g\ C_8H_{18}} \times \frac{25\ mol\ O_2}{2\ mol\ C_8H_{18}} \times \frac{22.4\ L\ O_2}{1\ mol\ O_2} = \mathbf{1.72 \times 10^3\ L\ O_2}$ *(at STP)*

c. What volume of O_2 at 18.0 °C and 0.975 atm is needed?

	initial	final	
P	1.00 atm	0.975 atm	P↓, V↑
V	1.72 x 10, L	?	
T	273.15 K	291.2 K	T↓, V↑

$V_f = 1.72 \times 10^3\ L\ O_2 \times \frac{1.00\ atm}{0.975\ atm} \times \frac{291.2\ K}{273.15\ K}$

$= \mathbf{1.88 \times 10^3\ L\ O_2}$

16. The average resting teenager has a respiration rate of about 20 breaths/min. Assume that each breath is 300. mL at 20.0 °C and 750. torr.

a. What volume in L of air at STP is breathed per minute?

$\frac{300\ mL}{1\ breath} \times \frac{20\ breaths}{1\ minute} \times \frac{0.001\ L}{1\ mL} = \mathbf{6.00\ L/min}$

	initial	final	
P	750. torr	760 torr	P↑, V↓
V	6 L	?	
T	293 K	273 K	T↓, V↓

$V_f = 300\ mL \times \frac{6.00\ L}{1\ min} \times \frac{750.\ torr}{760\ torr} \times \frac{273.15\ K}{293.2\ K} = \mathbf{5.52\ L/min}$

b. What volume of air at STP is used per day?

$V_f = \frac{5.52\ L}{1\ min} \times \frac{60\ min}{1\ hour} \times \frac{24\ hours}{1\ day}$

$= \mathbf{7.95 \times 10^3\ L/day}$

17. What volume will 445 mL of H_2S at STP occupy at 730. torr and 27 °C?

	initial	final	
P	760 torr	730. torr	P↓, V↑
V	445 mL	?	
T	273.15 K	300. K	T↑, V↑

$V_f = 445\ mL\ H_2S \times \frac{760\ torr}{730.\ torr} \times \frac{300.\ K}{273.15\ K}$

$= \mathbf{509\ mL\ H_2S\ or\ 5.09 \times 10^{-1}\ L\ H_2S}$

Chapter 6 (pp. 118–137)

Chemical Thermodynamics

Suggested Daily Pacing

44 **Return** and go over graded Test 3.

Check and discuss homework.

Introduce ch. 6, Chemical Thermodynamics.

Conduct Lab 11, Parts I–II: Analysis of Household Chemicals.

HW: Complete Lab 11 Report Sheet (Parts I–II). Revised Investigation Plan due les. 46.

45 **Check** and discuss homework.

Conduct Lab 11, Parts III–V: Analysis of Household Chemicals.

HW: Complete Lab 11 Report Sheet (Parts III–V). Read pp. 118–121. Answer p. 122, questions 1–3. Complete revised Investigation Plan and bring *Science in Action.*

46 **Check** and discuss Lab 11 Report Sheet.

SP: Check revised Investigation Plan. (Have students answer text p. 122, questions 4–5.) Make suggestions as needed. Use *Science in Action* pp. 47–52 to explain how to prepare the final Investigation Plan. Go over sample Investigation Plan on pp. 53–59. Assign final Investigation Plan for les. 51.

Check and discuss p. 122, questions 1–7.

Teach pp. **119–121,** sec. **6.1** Energy.

Review lesson.

HW: Read pp. 122–123. Answer p. 129, questions 1–3. Final Investigation Plan due les. 51.

47 **Check** and discuss homework.

Review pp. 119–121.

Teach pp. **122–123,** sec. **6.2** Heat in Chemical Reactions, up to Calorimetry: Measurement of Heat.

Review lesson.

HW: Read pp. 124–126, up to Heats of Reaction. Answer p. 129, questions 4 and 5.

48 **Check** and discuss homework.

Review pp. 122–123.

Teach pp. **124–126,** sec. **6.2** (cont.), up to Heats of Reaction.

Review lesson.

HW: Answer p. 129, questions 6 and 7. Read pp. 126–129. Final Investigation Plan due les. 51.

49 **Check** and discuss homework.

Give Quiz 10 (over pp. 119–126).

Review pp. 124–126.

Teach pp. **126–129,** sec. **6.2** (cont.)

Review lesson.

HW: Answer p. 129, questions 8 and 9. Read *Lab Manual* Lab 12 and complete Prelab Assignment.

50 **Check** and discuss homework.

Conduct Lab 12: Calorimetry: Specific Heat of a Metal.

HW: Complete Lab 12 Report Sheet. Read pp. 130–132. Answer p. 132–133, questions 1–4. Complete final Investigation Plan, using Investigation Plan Final Check. Bring Investigation Plan Grade Form and *Science in Action.*

51 **SP:** Collect final Investigation Plan to be graded. Use Investigation Plan Grade Form. See instructions on grading sheets (Appendix A of *Science in Action*). Students should now **begin investigations.** Introduce Getting Started Worksheet, p. 63, due les. 55 (ch. 7). Introduce the **journal,** using *Science in Action* pp. 65–67, and assign first journal check of 4 entries for les. 61 (ch. 7).

Check and discuss homework.

Review pp. 126–129.

Teach pp. **130–132,** sec. **6.3** Heat and Changes of State.

Review lesson.

HW: Answer p. 133, question 5. Read pp. 133–135. Answer p. 135, questions 1–4. Getting Started Worksheet due les. 55 (ch. 7). First journal check (four entries minimum) is in les. 61 (ch. 7).

52 **Give** "pop" reading quiz over pp. 133–135:

1. The term *entropy* refers to the measure of what aspect of a system? *disorder or randomness of a system*
2. What symbol is used for entropy? *S*
3. What scientific law does entropy illustrate? *second law of thermodynamics*
4. Considering only the system, would the evaporation of water result in a positive or negative change in entropy? *positive (increased entropy)*
5. True or False: Reactions that decrease the entropy of a system are almost always spontaneous. *false*

Check and discuss homework.

Review pp. 130–132.

Teach pp. **133–135,** sec. **6.4** Entropy.

Review lesson.

HW: Answer p. 135, questions 5 and 6. Begin studying ch. 6 for Test 4 in les. 54. Answer p. 137, Review Exercises 6–11, 14, and 17. Getting Started Worksheet due les. 55 (ch. 7). First journal check (4 entries minimum) is in les. 61 (ch. 7).

53 **Check** and discuss homework.

Review ch. 6 for Test 4 in next lesson, using Chapter Review on pp. 136–137.

HW: Study ch. 6 for Test 4 in next lesson.

54 **Administer Test 4** over ch. 6.

HW: Read pp. 138–143. Complete Getting Started Worksheet.

Teacher Notes

Chapter 6 Overview. Although thermodynamic principles can be abstract and difficult, they are a basic fact of chemistry and allow us to understand *why* many processes occur the way they do.

The chapter begins by introducing and defining some basic thermodynamics terms. The concept of enthalpy and how it relates to endothermic and exothermic reactions are discussed, followed by a discussion of how energy changes in chemical reactions are measured (calorimetry). Changes of state are also shown to involve the absorption or release of heat energy. The chapter concludes with a brief discussion of entropy and the second law of thermodynamics.

Note that this chapter presents an *introduction* to chemical thermodynamics rather than a comprehensive study. For more advanced thermodynamic concepts such as Gibbs free energy (ΔG) and how it governs chemical spontaneity, see the *Supplement for Advanced Studies.*

Chapter opener photo (p. 118). The missile in the photograph is a Boeing RGM-84 Harpoon, a sea-skimming anti-ship cruise missile. The rocket motor serves to accelerate the missile to cruise speed; a small turbofan engine then takes over for cruise flight.

Joules *vs.* calories (6.1, p. 12). An older unit of heat sometimes encountered in thermodynamics is the *calorie,* most familiar from food labels. Unfortunately, at least four different definitions of the calorie exist:

- the ***thermodynamic calorie,*** defined as exactly 4.184 J. This is "the" calorie of chemistry and physics and is the one used in the text.
- the ***conventional calorie*** or *15 °C calorie,* equal to 4.1855 ±0.0005 J; defined as the amount of heat required to raise the temperature of a gram of water from 14.5 °C to 15.5 °C.
- the ***International Table calorie,*** defined as exactly 4.1868 J, but commonly rounded to 4.187 J. This calorie is commonly encountered in mid-20th-century scientific and technical works.
- the ***food calorie*** or *kilocalorie,* defined as exactly 1000 thermodynamic calories (4184 J). It is sometimes designated *Calorie* (capital *C*) to distinguish it from the other calories. This is the calorie used on food labels.

This confusion is one reason that most scientists prefer joules to calories.

Calorimetry: measurement of heat (6.2, p. 124). Some students may need to be reminded that *heat* and *temperature* are not the same. Heat is a form of kinetic energy ("thermal energy"), whereas temperature can be thought of as a measure of heat intensity (average amount of heat or kinetic energy *per molecule*). For example, a thimble of boiling water contains less heat energy than a swimming pool full of lukewarm water, even though the temperature (average KE) of the boiling water is higher; the much larger number of water molecules in the pool more than makes up for the lower average KE of each molecule.

Specific heat (6.2, p. 124). Students may find it helpful to memorize the value for the specific heat of water. Be sure students understand this material before performing Lab 12.

Heats of reaction (6.2, p. 126). ΔH must be considered from the standpoint of the system: if the system *lost* heat energy to the surroundings, ΔH is *negative;* if it *gained* heat energy from the surroundings, ΔH is *positive.*

An analogy of "Δ$" in a checking account may help students keep the sign of ΔH straight. If you pay out money by writing a check (analogous to an exothermic reaction in which heat is "paid out"), you *decrease* the amount of money left in your account; Δ$ from your perspective is thus negative because you have "lost" money to your surroundings. On the other hand, if someone writes *you* a check (analogous to an endothermic reaction in which heat is "taken in"), the amount in your account *increases,* and Δ$ is positive, because you have "gained" money from your surroundings.

Heat and changes of state (6.3, p. 130). Depending on your focus, you may wish to have students memorize ΔH_{vap} and ΔH_{fus} for water.

Entropy (6.4, pp. 133–135). Equating the words *entropy* and *disorder* may help students understand the concept. Examples of the normal tendency toward disorder are all around us. Students have undoubtedly noticed, for example, that their rooms at home naturally tend to become disorderly rather than orderly unless work is exerted. Likewise, new cars, clothing, etc. tend to become old-looking (rusted, tattered) unless regularly maintained.

Lecture Demonstrations

Enthalpy changes (6.2, pp. 126–128). One or more of several demonstrations may be performed to illustrate negative or positive enthalpy changes.

a. Using a spatula, carefully mix 3 g $KClO_3$ (potassium chlorate) and 1 g table sugar (sucrose) and place it in an evaporating dish or in the middle of the base of a support stand. Make a small depression in the middle of the pile and add one drop of concentrated sulfuric acid (H_2SO_4); stand back. Smoke and flame will be produced after a couple of seconds. *Do not store the mixture of sugar and $KClO_3$.* Residue from the reaction may be flushed down the drain with water.

b. Pile about 5 g $KMnO_4$ in a crucible or evaporating dish and make a small depression in the pile with a spatula. Add about 1 mL glycerol to the depression and stand back; a purple flame is produced after several seconds. Placing the crucible or evaporating dish in a large beaker will help to contain the reactant particles during the reaction. **CAUTION:** Highly exothermic. Wear eye protection.

Entropy (6.4, p. 133). The dye-diffusion demonstration pictured in Fig. 6.10a of the text can be done in class for added effect. Fill an appropriately sized beaker with hot water and add several drops of food coloring from a dropper. The food coloring will gradually spread until the water is of uniform color. (The demonstration can also be performed with room-temperature water, but the diffusion rate is slower.)

If you used a transparent box and ball bearings to illustrate the kinetic-molecular theory (Chapter 5 Lecture Demonstrations), you can reuse those materials here to illustrate entropy. Place a couple of dozen BBs at one end of the box and a dozen large ball bearings or marbles at the other end. Place this on the overhead, showing the orderly arrangement, and then shake the box for 3–4 seconds to thoroughly mix the spheres. Point out that it would take considerably more time and effort to restore the spheres to their previous orderly arrangement than it took to mix them up.

Answers to Text Questions

Section Review 6.1 (p. 122)

Concept Review

1. What is *energy?* *the ability to do work*
2. Distinguish between *potential energy* and *kinetic energy.* *Potential energy is energy associated with the position of an object relative to a force upon it. Kinetic energy is energy associated with motion; it depends on mass and velocity.*
3. What does "ΔE" mean? *change in the internal energy of a system*
4. What sign would the internal energy change have if work was done *by* a system? *negative*
5. What is a state function? *a property with a value determined only by the state of the system, not the path taken to arrive at that state.*

Application

6. In a certain process, 245 J of work was done by a system on its surroundings and 45 J of heat was lost to the surroundings. What was ΔE for the system?
   $\Delta E = q + w = -45\ J + (-245\ J) = \mathbf{-290\ J}$
7. What is ΔE for a system if 300 J of heat is added to the system and no work is done? $w = 0\ J$, $q = +300\ J$; $\Delta E = q + w = \mathbf{+300\ J}$

Section Review 6.2 (p. 129)

Concept Review

1. In your own words, explain the meaning of the term *enthalpy.* *(Answers will vary.) Enthalpy refers to the heat content of a system. Though very similar to internal energy, enthalpy also takes into account the pressure and volume of the system.*
2. Distinguish between an endothermic process and an exothermic process. *In an endothermic process, heat energy is* absorbed, *with the resulting products gaining energy and becoming cooler. In an exothermic process, heat energy is* released; *the resulting products have less internal energy and are warmer.*
3. What is meant by the symbol ΔH? *change in the enthalpy or "heat content" of a system*
4. Define *specific heat.* *Specific heat is the amount of heat required to raise the temperature of one gram of a certain substance by one Celsius degree.*
5. What laboratory instrument is used to measure heat energy changes? *calorimeter*

Application

6. Calculate the amount of heat energy needed to raise the temperature of the water in a 40-gal (151-kg) home water heater from 19.0 °C (66.2 °F) to 60.0 °C (140. °F). (Example 6.2)
   $q = mc_{sp}\Delta t$
   $\Delta t = t_f - t_i = 60.0°C - 19.0°C = \mathbf{41.0\ °C}$
   $m = 151\ kg \times \frac{1000\ g}{1\ kg} = 151{,}000\ g$
   $q = (151{,}000\ g)\ (4.18\ J/g \cdot °C)\ (41°C)$
   $q \approx \mathbf{25{,}8000{,}000\ J\ or\ 258 \times 10^7\ J}$
7. What quantity of heat energy is needed to raise the temperature of 1 pound (454 g) of aluminum from 25.0 °C to its melting point, 660. °C? [$c_{sp}(Al) = 0.900\ J/g \cdot °C$] (Example 6.2)
   $q = mc_{sp}\Delta t$
   $= (454\ g)(0.900\ J/g \cdot °C)(635°C)$
   $= \mathbf{2.59 \times 10^5\ J}$
8. Sodium metal reacts violently with water to produce aqueous sodium hydroxide and hydrogen gas. Calculate the enthalpy change for this reaction. (Example 6.3)
   $\Delta H° = \Delta H°_{f(products)} - \Delta H°_{f(reactants)} =$
   $\Delta H° = [(2\ mol \times \frac{-469.60\ kJ}{mol}) + (1\ mol \times \frac{0\ kJ}{mol})] -$
   $[(2\ mol \times \frac{0\ kJ}{1\ mol}) + (2\ mol \times \frac{-285.8\ kJ}{mol})]$
   $\Delta H° = \mathbf{-367.6\ kJ}$ (or -183.8 kJ per mole Na)
9. Propane (C_3H_8), the major component of LP gas, is often used as a heating and cooking fuel in homes, RV's, and camping equipment, and can also be used as a motor fuel. When propane is burned (reacted with oxygen), $CO_2(g)$ and $H_2O(g)$ are produced.
   a. Write an equation for the reaction and calculate the enthalpy change for the combustion of propane. (Example 6.3)
   $C_3H_8(g) + 5\ O_2(g) \longrightarrow 3\ CO_2 + 4\ H_2O(g)$
   $\Delta H° = [3\ mol \times \frac{-393.5\ kJ}{1\ mol} + 4\ mol \times \frac{-241.8\ kJ}{1\ mol}] -$
   $[1\ mol \times \frac{-103.8\ kJ}{1\ mol} + 5\ mol \times \frac{0\ kJ}{1\ mol}]$
   $= \mathbf{-2{,}043.9\ kJ}$
   b. How much heat can be produced by the combustion of 50.0 g propane? (Example 6.4)
   $50.0\ g\ C_3H_8 \times \frac{1\ mol\ C_3H_8}{44.11\ g\ C_3H_8} \times \frac{-2043.9\ kJ}{1\ mol\ C_3H_8}$
   $= \mathbf{-2.32 \times 10^3\ kJ}$

Section Review 6.3 (p. 132–133)

Concept Review

1. What is heat of fusion? Heat of vaporization? ***Heat of fusion*** *is the amount of heat required to melt one gram of a substance at its normal melting point.* ***Heat of vaporization*** *is the amount of heat required to vaporize one gram of a substance at its normal boiling point.*
2. What is the difference between heat of vaporization and heat of condensation? ***Heat of vaporization*** *refers to the heat absorbed in converting liquid water to steam, whereas* ***heat of condensation*** *refers to the heat released when converting steam to liquid water.*

Application

3. A pot of water on the stove is boiling at a slow boil. What will happen to the temperature of the water if the stove burner is turned up higher, causing the water to boil more rapidly? *The temperature of the water will remain the same.*
4. Why can a given mass of steam at 100 °C burn your skin more severely than the same mass of liquid water at 100 °C? *Steam contains 2260 J/g more heat energy than liquid water at the same temperature.*
5. How many joules of heat energy are needed to accomplish each of the following:
   a. to melt 60.5 g ice at 0.0 °C? $q_{fus} = m\Delta H_{fus} = 60.5\ g \times 334\ J/g = \mathbf{2.02 \times 10^4\ J}$
   b. to vaporize 50.0 g water at 100.0 °C? $q_{vap} = m\Delta H_{vap} = 50.0\ g \times 2260.\ J/g = \mathbf{1.13 \times 10^5\ J}$
   c. to heat 900.0 g water from 18.0 °C to 98.0 °C?
   $q_{H_2O} = mc_{sp}\Delta t$
   $= 900.0\ g \times 4.18\ J/g{\cdot}°C \times 80.0\ °C$
   $= \mathbf{3.01 \times 10^5\ J}$
   d. to heat 20.0 g ice at –35.0 °C to 0.0 °C? (See Table 6.1 for c_{sp} of ice.) $q_{ice} = mc_{sp}\Delta t = 20.0\ g \times 2.06\ J/g{\cdot}°C \times 35.0\ °C = \mathbf{1.44 \times 10^3\ J}$

Section Review 6.4 (p. 135)

Concept Review

1. What is meant by the term *entropy?* *a measure of the disorder of a system*
2. What law states that the entropy of the universe is always increasing? *second law of thermodynamics*
3. What is meant by the symbol "ΔS"? *change in entropy*
4. When ΔS is positive, does this mean that disorder has increased or decreased? Explain. *When ΔS is positive, the entropy has increased; therefore, the disorder has increased.*

Application

5. Arrange the following systems in order of increasing randomness or disorder. (Begin with the ***most ordered*** system.)
   1 mol liquid ammonia
   1 mol gaseous ammonia
   1 mol solid ammonia
   least random → most random:
   solid NH_3 → liquid NH_3 → gaseous NH_3
6. Predict whether ΔS would be positive or negative for each of the following; give a reason for your answer.
   a. $CO_2(s) \longrightarrow CO_2(g)$ *positive; gas is more disordered than solid*
   b. $H_2O(l) \longrightarrow H_2O(s)$ *negative; solid is less disordered than liquid*
   c. $S(s) + 3\ F_2(g) \longrightarrow SF_6(g)$ *negative; fewer moles of gas (1) on product side than reactant side (3)*
   d. $NaHSO_4(s) + NaCl(s) \longrightarrow HCl(g) + Na_2SO_4(s)$ *positive; more moles of gas (1) on product side than reactant side (0)*
   e. $2\ NaHCO_3(s) \longrightarrow Na_2CO_3(s) + H_2O(g) + CO_2(g)$ *positive; more moles of gas (2) on product side than reactant side (0)*
   f. $CuSO_4(s)$ separates from $CuSO_4(aq)$ *negative; solid is less disordered than aqueous solution*

Chapter 6 Review (p. 137)

1. What definition is commonly used for the word *energy?* *the ability to do work*
2. When speaking of thermodynamic concepts, what is the *system?* The *surroundings?* *The system is the portion of the universe or sample of matter being studied. "Surroundings" refers to the remainder of the universe excluding the system being studied.*
3. What is a *state function?* How does this concept relate to internal energy? *(Wording may vary.) A state function is a property whose value is determined only by the state of the system. Internal energy cannot be measured, but its changes can be. Since E is a state function and therefore determined only by the state of the system, we do not need to take into account the "path" taken to reach E, but can instead simply subtract to calculate change in E.*

4. In what direction does heat always naturally flow in a system? *from higher to lower temperature*
5. Name the SI unit of energy, work, and heat. *joule (J)*
6. How does internal energy (E) relate to the concept of potential energy? Why is enthalpy (H) a better measure of potential energy in chemical systems than E?
   E *is the sum of the energies in the system, while potential energy is the energy resulting from a force in the surroundings acting upon the system.* H *is a better measure of potential energy in chemical systems because* H *takes pressure and volume into account, while* E *does not.*
7. For each of the following, determine whether the characteristic suggests an exothermic or an endothermic process.
   a. reaction absorbs heat energy *endothermic*
   b. product is cold to the touch *endothermic*
   c. heat can be regarded as a product *exothermic*
   d. releases heat energy *exothermic*
8. What is the *specific heat* of a substance? How is this quantity symbolized? *The specific heat of a substance, symbolized* C_{sp}, *is the amount of heat required to raise the temperature of 1 g of that substance by 1 Celsius degree.*
9. What is the purpose of a calorimeter? *to measure changes in heat energy*
10. A 92.2-g sample of gold at 100.0 °C is placed in 100.0 g water at 21.0 °C; the final temperature of the gold and water is 23.2 °C. What is the specific heat of gold?

$$c_{sp} = \frac{(100.0\ g)(4.18\ J/g{\cdot}°C)(2.2\ °C)}{-(92.2\ g)(76.8\ °C)}$$

$$= \frac{(919.6\ J)}{7080.96\ g{\cdot}°C} = \mathbf{0.13\ J/g{\cdot}°C}$$

11. Molten iron solidifies at 1530 °C, and its ΔH_{fus} = 267 J/g. Its specific heat as a liquid is 0.45 J/g·°C and 0.44 J/g·°C as a solid. Calculate the quantity of heat lost when 28 kg of iron does each of the following:
    a. cools as a liquid from blast furnace temperature, 1840 °C, to its melting point;
    $q_{Fe(l)} = mc_{sp}\Delta t$
    $= (28{,}000\ g)\ (0.45\ J/g\ °C)(-310\ °C)$
    $= \mathbf{-3.9 \times 10^6\ J}$
    b. solidifies at its melting point; $q_{fus} = m\Delta H$
    $= (28{,}000\ g)(-267\ J/g) = \mathbf{-7.5 \times 10^6\ J}$
    c. cools as a solid from its melting point to room temperature, 25 °C.
    $q_{Fe(s)} = mc_{sp}\Delta t$
    $= (28.000\ g)\ (0.44\ J/g{\cdot}°C)\ (-1505\ °C)$
    $= \mathbf{-1.9 \times 10^7\ J}$
12. What is *heat of reaction?* Why might this quantity be important in such fields as power plant engineering? *Heat of reaction is the total amount of heat liberated or absorbed between the start of a reaction and its end, when all the products are at the original temperature of the reaction. Engineers at a coal- or gas-fired power plant must know the heat of reaction of the fuel they are using so that they know how much fuel is required to generate a given amount of energy, for example.*
13. What is *enthalpy of formation?* How does this quantity allow us to predict whether a given reaction will be endothermic or exothermic? *Enthalpy of formation is the change in enthalpy that occurs when one mole of a compound is formed from free elements in their standard states.*
    The enthalpy of the products must equal the sum of the enthalpies of reactants and the change in enthalpy of the reactants. If we know the enthalpy of formation for each of the reactants and products, we can calculate the overall enthalpy of the reaction and predict if the reaction will be exothermic or endothermic.
14. The reaction between aluminum and iron(III) oxide (the thermite reaction) is as follows:
    $Al(s) + \frac{1}{2}\ Fe_2O_3(s) \rightarrow \frac{1}{2}\ Al_2O_3(s) + Fe(s)$
    a. Calculate $\Delta H°$ for the reaction using Table 6.2.

$$\left[\tfrac{1}{2}\ mol\ Al_2O_3 \times \frac{-1669.8\ kJ}{1\ mol\ Al_2O_3} + 1\ mole\ \frac{0\ kJ}{1\ mol}\right] - \left[1\ mol \times \frac{0\ kJ}{1\ mol} + \tfrac{1}{2}\ mol\ Fe_2O_3 \times \frac{-822.2\ kJ}{1\ mol}\right]$$

$$= \mathbf{-\ 423.8\ kJ}$$

    b. Is the reaction endothermic or exothermic? *exothermic (heat given off as a product)*
15. Distinguish between *heat of fusion* and *heat of vaporization.* *Heat of fusion is the quantity of heat required to melt 1 g of a substance at its melting point; heat of vaporization is the amount of heat required to vaporize 1 g of a substance at its normal boiling point.*

16. What is *entropy?* How does this concept relate to the second law of thermodynamics? *Entropy is a measure of the disorder or randomness in a system. The second law of thermodynamics states that a system left to itself will tend toward a state of minimum state of potential energy, or maximum disorder.*

17. Tell whether each of the following represents an increase or a decrease in entropy (from the standpoint of the object, not the system as a whole):

a. evaporation of a puddle *increase*
b. detonation of TNT *increase*
c. combustion of gasoline *increase*
d. separation of air into its component gases *decrease*
e. construction of a building *decrease*
f. demolition of a building *increase*
g. digestion of food *increase*
h. freezing of a lake *decrease*

Chapter 6

Chapter 7 (pp. 138–161)

Light, Electrons, and Atomic Structure

Suggested Daily Pacing

55 **Return** and go over graded Test 4.

SP: Check Getting Started Worksheet and make suggestions as needed. (Have students answer text p. 143, questions 1–4.) Remind students of first journal check in les. 61.

Introduce ch. 7, Light, Electrons, and Atomic Structure.

Check and discuss p. 143, questions 1–4.

Teach pp. **139–143,** sec. **7.1** The Nature of Light.

Review lesson.

HW: Read pp. 144–149, up to the Concepts in Chemistry box. Answer p. 152, questions 1 and 3–6. First journal check (4 entries minimum) will be in les. 61.

56 **Give Quiz 11** (over pp. 139–143).

Check and discuss homework.

Review pp. 139–143.

Teach pp. **144–149,** sec. **7.2** Electrons and the Structure of the Atom, up to the Concepts in Chemistry box.

Review lesson.

HW: Read pp. 149–151. Answer p. 152, questions 2, 7–8.

57 **Check** and discuss homework.

Review pp. 144–149.

Teach pp. **149–151,** sec. **7.2** (cont.).

Review lesson.

HW: Read *Lab Manual* Lab 13 and complete Prelab Assignment. First journal check (4 entries minimum) is in les. 61.

58 **Check** and discuss homework.

Demonstrate Lab 13: Flame Tests. Have students complete Lab 13 Report Sheet in class.

Collect Lab 13 Report Sheet.

HW: Read pp. 152–155. Answer p. 159, questions 1–3.

59 **Check** and discuss homework.

Review pp. 149–151.

Teach pp. **152–155,** sec. **7.3** Electron Configuration and Quantum Numbers, up to Electron Configurations.

Review lesson.

HW: Read pp. 156–159. Answer p. 159, questions 4–9.

60 **Check** and discuss homework.

Review pp. 152–155.

Teach pp. **156–159,** sec. **7.3** (cont.).

Review lesson. Begin working on Concept Review 3: Electron Configuration and Quantum Numbers.

HW: Complete Concept Review 3: Electron Configuration and Quantum Numbers. Complete 4 journal entries (minimum) and bring Journal Check Report.

61 **SP:** Carefully check journal to note progress and mark appropriate comments on Journal Check Report. (Have students answer p. 159, questions 10 and 11.) The next journal check (minimum of 6 entries total) is in les. 66 (ch. 8). Explain that the required number of entries for journal check is cumulative. The six entries due in les. 66 include the four entries checked in this lesson plus two new entries.

Check and discuss p. 159, questions 10 and 11.

Give Quiz 12 (over pp. 150–159).

Check and discuss homework.

HW: Read pp. 162–165. Answer p. 166, questions 1–3. Next journal check (minimum of 6 entries total) will be in les. 66 (ch. 8).

Teacher Notes

Chapter 7 Overview. The focal point of this chapter is the way electrons are arranged about an atom. The chapter begins by using the study of light to introduce basic principles of the quantum theory. The hydrogen spectrum is introduced, and students are shown how it eventually led to the Bohr model, the first quantum model of the atom. Further refinements by de Broglie, Schrödinger, Heisenberg, and Born are discussed, leading to our present understanding of atomic structure. The chapter then discusses precisely how electrons are arranged in atoms, and how the gradual filling of orbitals results in different valence electron configurations for different elements.

Frequency of light (7.1, p. 141). Some texts use the Greek letter υ (*nu*) to refer to frequency instead of f; either is acceptable, though f may be less confusing.

Measuring light wavelength (7.1, p. 141). Very short wavelengths of electromagnetic radiation were once commonly measured in units called *angstroms,* named after the Swedish physicist Anders Jonas Ångstrom; one angstrom (Å) is equal to $\frac{1}{10}$ nanometer, or 10^{-10} m. In recent years, the angstrom has been almost completely replaced by nanometers in most scientific usage.

Visible light (7.1, pp. 141–142). Electromagnetic waves that can be detected by the human eye ("visible light") have frequencies ranging from 4×10^{14} Hz to 8×10^{14} Hz and wavelengths from 770 to 390 nm.

Planck's constant (7.1, p. 143). The true value of Planck's constant is closer to $6.626\,068\,76 \times 10^{-34}$ J·s, although this is still an approximation. Planck's constant and the speed of light in a vacuum are presently thought to be two of the most fundamental constants of the universe.

The hydrogen spectrum (7.2, p. 147). The most important thing to remember about line spectrums is that each band of color is emitted by a specific electron transition between energy levels (Fig. 7.11b).

De Broglie and matter waves (7.2, p. 148). Louis-Victor de Broglie (1892–1987) was a graduate student at the University of Paris (the Sorbonne) when he formulated his matter-wave hypothesis, which he presented as part of his doctoral thesis *Recherches sur la Théorie des Quanta (Researches on the Quantum Theory).* Reportedly, his advisers initially rejected the thesis; it was not until Albert Einstein himself endorsed the hypothesis that the university reversed itself and granted De Broglie his doctorate degree. De Broglie was later awarded the 1929 Nobel Prize in physics for this discovery.

Schrödinger's equations (7.2, p. 148). The Schrödinger equations are extremely complex, making them difficult to solve except for the simplest atoms. For example, one form of Schrödinger's equation is

$$\frac{\partial^2\psi}{\partial x^2} + \frac{\partial^2\psi}{\partial y^2} + \frac{\partial^2\psi}{\partial z^2} + \frac{8\pi^2 m_e}{h^2} \times [E - V(x,y,z)] \times \psi(x,y,z) = 0$$

$$|\psi^2| = \text{electron charge density at point } (x,y,z)$$

where E = the energy of the atom, h = Planck's constant, and m_e is the mass of the electron. The variable ψ (Greek *psi*) is known as the *wavefunction;* calculating the charge density $|\psi^2|$ at a given point is sometimes referred to as "collapsing the wavefunction." In practice, approximations must usually be used to make the equations solvable, although increasingly powerful supercomputers have made solutions possible that were once out of reach.

Quantum mechanics and reality (7.2, pp. 149–150). It is important to distinguish between quantum mechanics as a mathematical description of reality and the various *interpretations* of quantum mechanics that have been proposed. The dominant interpretation among quantum physicists today, known as the "Copenhagen Interpretation" of quantum mechanics, holds that an electron has no real existence until someone measures it, at which time the not-really-real wavefunction "collapses" into a real particle. In essence, the CI interpretation of QM states that there is absolutely no reality beyond what is consciously observed. Not only does this interpretation have philosophical problems from a Biblical standpoint, *it is also contradicted by scientific aspects of quantum nonlocality in relativistic reference frames* (because it creates irresolvable conflicts between the principle of invariance and the principle of causality).[1]

Not many people are aware of these conflicts inherent in the Copenhagen Interpretation, nor are they aware that other standard interpretations of standard quantum mechanics exist that resolve these contradictions and also seem more compatible with a Biblical worldview.[2,3] However, many physicists seem to prefer the Copenhagen Interpretation for purely philosophical reasons.

[1]John G. Cramer, "The Transactional Interpretation of Quantum Mechanics," <http://www.npl.washington.edu/npl/int_rep/tiqm/TI_24.html>. These conflicts are described in non-mathematical terms in sections 2.4.3–2.4.4.

[2]Ibid., <http://www.npl.washington.edu/npl/int_rep/tiqm/TI_toc.html>.

[3]Sheldon Goldstein, "Quantum Theory without Observers," *Physics Today* March 1998, pp. 42–46 (Part 1), April 1998 pp. 38–42 (Part 2), February 1999 pp. 11+ (additional comments). At press time, archived at <http://www.math.rutgers.edu/~oldstein/papers/qts/qts.html> (paper) and <http://www.math.rutgers.edu/~oldstein/papers/qtwoe/qtwoe.html> (additional comments). These articles are quite technical and mathematical, but also include a great deal of qualitative description that may be understood apart from the math.

The uncertainty principle (7.2, p. 150). The uncertainty principle may be stated mathematically as follows:

$$m \times \Delta v \times \Delta x \geq \frac{h}{2\pi}$$

$$\text{mass of particle} \times \text{uncertainty in velocity} \times \text{uncertainty in position} \geq \frac{\text{Planck's constant}}{2\pi}$$

The equation may also be written

$$\Delta\rho\Delta x \geq \frac{h}{2\pi}$$

where $\Delta\rho$ (Greek *rho*) is uncertainty in momentum, because mass times velocity equals momentum.

Circumventing the uncertainty principle (7.2, p. 150). Interestingly, the uncertainty principle seems to stand as one of the most fundamental laws of the universe. Although many clever experiments have been designed to circumvent the uncertainty principle, particles always manage to respond in such a way as to defy measurement. The harder scientists try, the more abruptly particles react to evade the scientists' measurements.

The most startling of these effects, sometimes called *quantum nonlocality* or the *Einstein-Podolsky-Rosen paradox,* occurs when two particles are "entangled" into a single quantum state and then moved to widely separated locations. Measuring the properties of one of the "entangled" particles instantly affects the wavefunction of the other particle, *no matter how far apart they are,* because scientists would otherwise be able to calculate the initial states of both particles to a precision greater than the uncertainty principle allows.[4] This odd behavior is considered one of the most puzzling aspects of quantum physics.

[4]John Blanton *et al.*, "The EPR Paradox and Bell's Inequality Principle" (1996), <http://www.math.ucr.edu/home/baez/physics/bells_inequality.html>.

Orbits *vs.* orbitals (7.2, p. 151). Note the difference between the terms *orbit* (Bohr model) and *orbital* (quantum-mechanical model).

Electron-cloud model (7.2, p. 151). Born's electron-cloud model does *not* imply that the movement of electrons is entirely erratic. Despite their complexity, electron orbitals precisely obey the mathematical rules described by Schrödinger's equations.

One way to interpret the electron-cloud model is that the electron is moving so fast around the nucleus (on the order of 100 quadrillion times per second) that it appears as a "cloud" of charge instead of a moving point; hence the analogy to the blades of the desk fan. The same effect may be seen in an aircraft propeller or automotive cooling fan.

The only difference between the Schrödinger view of the electron and Max Born's view is that the former initially interpreted the wavefunction given by the Schrödinger equations $|\psi^2|$ as the *charge density of a wave,* whereas Born interpreted $|\psi^2|$ as the *probability* of finding a genuine, pointlike *particle.* Either interpretation works, although Born's model can occasionally lead to some bizarre conclusions (for example, it is difficult to picture a pointlike electron being in two places at once, or traveling along two paths simultaneously, but electrons occasionally do these things). It is interesting to note that Albert Einstein rejected Born's interpretation of the Schrödinger equations because it reduced the electron to a collection of probabilities rather than a mathematically describable entity.

Electron shell designations (7.3, p. 153). The letter designations for electron shells (K, L, M, etc.) are a holdover from pre-quantum-theory days, when they designated specific lines in the spectrograms of various elements. When the Bohr model was first introduced, the electron shell associated with a particular spectral line was often referred to by the letter designation of that line. In recent years, the use of the letter designations has diminished.

"Spin" quantum number (7.3, p. 155). The "spin" of an electron actually refers to the magnetic moment, which is described as either "parallel" or "antiparallel." Electrons with "parallel" spin are often referred to as having spin "up," whereas "antiparallel" electrons may be described as having spin "down." Our present understanding of "spin" is that it has more to do with the geometric properties of the electron than any sort of rotation, but this is far beyond the scope of this text.

The first three quantum numbers arise directly from solving the Schrödinger equation; the fourth quantum number arose in 1928 when Paul Dirac [dĭ·răk′] reformulated quantum mechanics as it applied to electrons to account for the effects of relativity.

Electron configurations (7.3, p. 156). Electron configurations will be studied in more detail in the following chapter.

Invention of the laser (7.3, p. 158). Maiman's laser was not the first device to take advantage of stimulated emission, but rather was the first to do so at short wavelengths. Microwave devices called *masers* (microwave amplification by stimulated emission of radiation) were invented toward the end of the 1950s, but did not offer many practical uses. It was the invention of the shorter-wavelength "optical maser," or laser, that opened the door to a revolution in science.

At the time of his invention, Maiman was a researcher at Hughes Electronics.

High-power lasers (7.3, p. 158). The reason that a 30-watt laser can cut metal while a 30-watt lamp cannot is simple: the energy from the light bulb is spread out over several square inches even if the target is in direct contact with the bulb, but the energy from the laser can be concentrated on a microscopic point. Thus, although the total energy output is the same, the laser can deliver millions of times more energy *per unit of area.*

At present, megawatt-class chemical lasers are the most powerful lasers in the world in terms of beam output energy. Although some pulsed research lasers can deliver far greater peak power ($>10^{15}$ watts), the pulse may last only a few femtoseconds for a total energy delivery of only a few dozen to a few hundred joules. A megawatt-class chemical laser, by contrast, can deliver millions of joules per second and can sustain this rate as long as the fuel lasts (as much as several minutes).

A prototype U.S. Army deuterium fluoride laser called MIRACL (Mid-Infrared Advanced Chemical Laser) has a steady-state power output of 2.2 megawatts (2.2 million watts) at a wavelength of 3800 nm.[1] Coupled with the Hughes SEALITE beam director (which looks like a cross between a telescope and a gun turret), MIRACL has successfully destroyed aircraft, supersonic missiles, and even a satellite in tests.

The COIL-equipped 747s mentioned in the text are being acquired under the USAF Airborne Laser program.[2] This aircraft class may eventually be designated AL-1A.

[1] "Mid-Infrared Advanced Chemical Laser (MIRACL)," <http://www.fas.org/spp/military/program/asat/miracl.htm>.
[2] See "Airborne Laser," <http://www.airbornelaser.com>.

Laser safety (7.3, p. 158). Even lasers of low power levels must be treated with respect. In the U.S. most laser pointers are classified as Class IIIa lasers, which means that they have the potential to cause eye damage if misused. Even a 5-milliwatt laser pointer could conceivably cause permanent eye damage if you stared into the beam at close range. (If the lens of your eye focuses the beam into a spot $^{1}/_{25}$ mm in diameter on the retina, the power density at that spot will be nearly a megawatt per square meter—potentially enough to burn the retina and scar your visual field for life.)

Gamma-ray lasers (7.3, p. 158). Recently, scientists have discovered that stimulated emission can also occur in excited atomic *nuclei,* making gamma-ray lasers feasible. The lasing medium would be a solid rod of a "nuclear isomer" such as Hf-178* (a nucleus in a long-lived excited state, denoted by the asterisk). The energy of the excited nuclei would be released by sending a very short pulse of X-rays through the rod, which would trigger an avalanche of intense, coherent gamma rays in its wake. Because of the high energy of gamma rays and the very short pulse length, beam energies in the exawatt range (10^{18} watts) are feasible from a very compact device.

Lecture Demonstrations

Line spectra (7.2, pp. 144–145). The discussion of light and the vocabulary in this section may be introduced by demonstrating how a spectroscope (available from Fisher, Carolina, Frey, Sargent-Welch) produces a line spectrum from one or more gas discharge (spectrum) tubes (e.g., hydrogen, mercury, neon); a Tesla coil or a spectrum tube power supply may be used to power the tubes. *Be cautious of overusing a Tesla coil* (more than 2 minutes continuously), to guard against burn-out. You may omit the spectroscope if you wish only to demonstrate the different colors obtained by exciting different elements.

Line spectra can also be seen by viewing the discharge of a sodium vapor lamp through a spectroscope or by separating the light from the lamp with a prism. Unfortunately, this is difficult to do in the daytime or in a classroom setting.

A continuous spectrum may be obtained by cutting a narrow slit (1–3 mm wide) in a piece of construction paper or aluminum foil, using a single-edged razor blade. In a darkened room, place the paper on an overhead projector and lay a prism over the slit. Vary the angle of the prism as necessary to project the spectrum onto a light-colored surface.

Standing waves (7.2, pp. 148–149). You may illustrate a standing wave by tying a length of rope or rubber tubing to a doorknob and moving it in such a way as to induce a standing wave—one containing nodes.

The uncertainty principle (7.2, p. 150). The Heisenberg uncertainty principle can be demonstrated by an analogy using a desk fan and a strobe light as follows. First, turn the fan on a high setting with the room lights on; you "see" the velocity of the fan blades, but their position is uncertain (the blades are blurred into what appears to be a disk-shaped mist). Then, leaving the fan on a high setting, turn off the classroom lights and direct the light from a repetitive strobe light onto the fan (for best results, adjust the frequency of the strobe so that the blades appear to be stationary from one flash to the next). With each flash, you can see the exact position of the blades (they appear "frozen" in place), but you no longer see the velocity. Adjusting the frequency of the strobe and/or the intensity of the classroom lighting can be used to illustrate the tradeoffs between knowing the position and knowing the velocity. (**Note:** If you have any students with epilepsy, check with them before performing this demonstration.)

Electron cloud model (7.2, p. 151). The electron cloud model may be illustrated in several ways:

- Run a desk fan or box fan on high and point out how the rapidly moving blades appear to form a disk-shaped cloud.

- Make a black dot on a piece of filter paper some distance from its center; attach the paper at its center to a variable speed drill or mixer. Show that the faster the speed the less able one is to determine the position of the dot. At high speed, the dot appears to occupy a circular region of space.

Answers to Text Questions

Section Review 7.1 (p. 143)

Concept Review

1. Sketch a wave and label the amplitude, wavelength, and frequency; then define these terms in words.

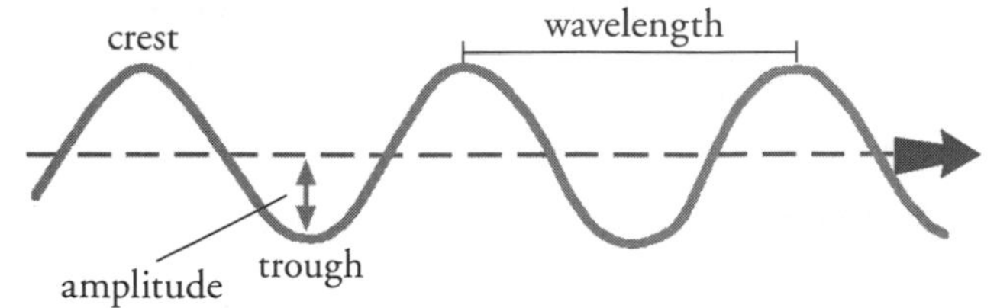

amplitude: half the distance between the crest and the trough of a wave

wavelength: distance between any two corresponding points on a wave

frequency: the number of crests or troughs passing a given fixed point per unit time

2. What is a photon? *a quantum of light; a "packet" or quantum of radiant energy*

Application

3. Refer to Fig. 7.4 and arrange photons of green, ultraviolet, red, and blue light in the following order:
   a. increasing wavelength
   ultraviolet, blue, green, red
   b. increasing frequency *red, green, blue, ultraviolet*
   c. increasing energy *red, green, blue, ultraviolet*
4. Some gamma rays originating in deep space have wavelengths on the order of 1×10^{-18} m, whereas an average radio wave has a wavelength on the order of 500 m. The energy associated with each of these radiations is as follows:
   gamma ray = 2×10^{-7} J; radio wave = 4×10^{-28} J
   By what factor are these gamma rays more energetic than an average radio wave?
   5×10^{20} times more energetic

Section Review 7.2 (p. 152)

Concept Review

1. What is meant by the term *continuous spectrum?* *a complete spectrum consisting of a smooth array of color rather than a set of discrete lines*
2. Tell what contribution each of the following scientists made to the theory of electron structure:
   a. Bohr *proposed a quantized model for the hydrogen atom*
   b. De Broglie *proposed that particles in motion have properties of waves*
   c. Schrödinger *proposed that the electron in an atom behaves as a wave as described by a mathematical equation*
   d. Heisenberg *stated that an electron's position and momentum cannot be measured simultaneously with precision*
3. Differentiate between the *ground state* and an *excited state* of an electron in a hydrogen atom. *The ground state of an electron is the lowest energy state for the electron, whereas any higher state for the electron is an excited state.*

4. How did the line spectrum of hydrogen support Bohr's model of the atom? *Only specific wavelengths or energies of light appear in the hydrogen spectrum, corresponding to specific transitions between fixed energy levels or orbits. If fixed energy levels did not exist, energies associated with electron transitions could assume any value, giving a continuous spectrum.*
5. What was the major failure of the Bohr model of the atom? *It could account only for the spectrum of the hydrogen atom; it failed when applied to more complex atoms.*
6. Explain what is meant by the phrase *wave-particle duality.* *Light can at times act like a particle and at other times act like a wave.*
7. What is the importance of the uncertainty principle as it relates to the arrangement of electrons in atoms? *Answers will vary. It led to a view of the atom that emphasized the probability finding the electron in a particular place rather than trying to describe an electron's behavior precisely.*
8. Differentiate between *orbit* and *orbital.* *An* ***orbit*** *is a definite path in which an electron can be found (in the Bohr model), whereas an* ***orbital*** *is a region in space in which there is a high probability of finding the electron.*

Section Review 7.3 (p. 159)

Concept Review

1. Give the name of each of the four quantum numbers, and tell what property of orbitals or electrons each describes.
   - ***principal quantum number*** *(n): main energy level of electron*
   - ***subshell quantum number*** *(l): type and shape of orbital*
   - ***orbital quantum number:*** *orientation of orbital in space*
   - ***spin quantum number:*** *direction of electron "spin"*
2. What is the shape of each of the following orbitals?
   a. the 2*s* orbital *spherical*
   b. the 4*p* orbital *dumbbell*
   c. the 6*s* orbital *spherical*
3. State the Pauli exclusion principle. How does this principle limit the number of electrons in the same orbital? *No two electrons in an atom may have the same four quantum numbers. If two electrons already share the same shell, subshell, and orientation, then they cannot also share the same spin quantum number. Since an electron can have only two possible spin values, there are only two electrons allowed in each orbital.*
4. How does Hund's rule affect the order in which the sublevels of an orbital are filled? *In a shell such as 'p,' which has three different subshells, each of those subshells must contain a single electron before they begin pairing.*
5. What are valence electrons? *electrons in the outermost shell of an atom; the electrons that generally take part in chemical bonding*
6. What is a Lewis symbol? Why are Lewis symbols useful? *A Lewis symbol is simply an electron dot formula of only the valence electrons. By showing how the electrons are paired in the atom, the Lewis symbol indicates how that atom will react with other atoms.*

Application

7. What is the maximum number of electrons that can occupy the following?
   a. the $n = 1$ energy level $2n^2 = 2(1)^2 = 2$
   b. the $n = 3$ energy level $2n^2 = 2(3)^2 = 18$
8. Give the number and types of sublevels that are possible for each of the following.
   a. $n = 2$ *2 subshells, s and p*
   b. $n = 4$ *4 subshells, s, p, d, f*
   c. $n = 3$ *3 subshells, s, p, d*
9. How many electrons, maximum, can a *d* sublevel contain? An *f* sublevel?
   A 'd' sublevel can contain 10 electrons. An 'f' sublevel can contain 14 electrons.
10. Write Lewis symbols for the following elements.
    a. carbon ·C:
    b. hydrogen H·
    c. selenium ·Se:
    d. xenon :Xe:
11. Write Lewis symbols for an element having seven outer (valence) electrons. :X:

Chapter 7 Review (p. 161)

1. As a wave's frequency increases, what happens to its wavelength? *wavelength will decrease*
2. Of what type of wave does light consist? *electromagnetic waves*
3. Give the speed of light in a vacuum (in m/s) to three significant figures. 3.00×10^8 *m/s*

Chapter 7

4. What is the electromagnetic spectrum? Into what seven broad categories is it commonly divided? *The electromagnetic spectrum is the complete range of wavelengths or frequencies of electromagnetic radiation. The seven broad categories are as follows: radio waves, microwaves, infrared waves, visible light, ultraviolet waves, X-rays, and gamma rays.*
5. The active ingredient in a particular sunscreen lotion absorbs light of wavelength 265 nm most efficiently. In what region of the spectrum is this wavelength? *ultraviolet*
6. Use of microwaves in cooking food has recently increased dramatically. Are microwaves longer or shorter than X-rays? *longer*
7. What is a ***photon?*** *a quantum of light or radiant energy*
8. State the quantum theory of light. *Light consists of tiny bundles or "packets" of energy called photons; the amount of energy a photon contains depends on its frequency.*
9. Distinguish between a continuous spectrum and a line spectrum. *A continuous spectrum is a complete array of all the visible colors or wavelengths of light; a line spectrum contains only certain colors or wavelengths, appearing as bright lines in the spectrum.*
10. What is the primary difference between the Bohr model of the atom and its predecessor, the Rutherford model? *Rutherford had explained only that electrons traveled around the nucleus; Bohr proposed that the electrons could travel only in certain orbits. As long as the electrons stayed in these orbits, they did not emit energy.*
11. What is the ***ground state*** of an electron in a hydrogen atom? *the lowest possible energy state (1s)*
12. In your own words, state the uncertainty principle. *It is impossible to simultaneously determine the momentum and the position of an electron with precision. One or the other can be measured, but not both.*
13. Distinguish between an ***orbital*** in the electron cloud model and an ***orbit*** in the Bohr model. *An orbital is a region in space in which there is a high probability of finding the electron; an orbit is a definite path along which the electron must be found.*
14. What is the ***electron configuration*** of an atom? Why is it important to the study of chemistry? *The electron configuration is the complete arrangement of electrons in an atom. The electron configuration determines how the atom will chemically bond and influences both shape and properties of molecules formed.*
15. What is a ***quantum number?*** What four qualities of an electron do the four quantum numbers describe? *A quantum number describes any electron in an atom. The four quantum numbers describe the electron's shell or energy level, the shape of its orbital, the orientation of its orbital in space, and its "spin."*
16. State the Pauli exclusion principle. Why does this principle limit the number of electrons that can occupy a particular orbital? *No two electrons in an atom may have the same set of four quantum numbers. If two electrons occupy the same orbital, they already share the same* n, l, *and orbital quantum numbers; therefore, their spin numbers must be different. Only two spin numbers are available; only two electrons are allowed per orbital.*
17. What are valence electrons? What is the maximum number of valence electrons that an atom can have? *Valence electrons are the outermost electrons; the maximum number of valence electrons is eight.*
18. Give the Lewis symbol of nitrogen (see Fig. 7.26). What do the dots represent? ·N̈:

    The dots represent the valence electrons of the nitrogen atom.
19. Give the Lewis symbols for the following elements.
    - **a.** $Z = 32$ Ge:
    - **b.** $Z = 18$:Är:
    - **c.** $Z = 5$ B:
    - **d.** $Z = 19$ K·
20. How many valence electrons are in each of the following atoms?
    - **a.** hydrogen *1*
    - **b.** iron *2*
    - **c.** beryllium *2*
    - **d.** chlorine *7*
    - **e.** aluminum *3*
    - **f.** neon *8*

Chapter 8 (pp. 162–183)
The Periodic Table

Suggested Daily Pacing

62 **Check** homework.

Review pp. 156–159.

Introduce ch. 8, The Periodic Table.

Discuss homework.

Teach pp. **163–165,** sec. **8.1** Historical Development of the Periodic Table.

Review lesson.

HW: Read pp. 166–169. Answer p. 169, question 1.

63 **Give** "pop" reading quiz over pp. 166–169:

1. Give the term for a vertical column of elements. *group*
2. Give the term for a horizontal row of elements. *period*
3. On which side of the periodic table are the metals found? *left*
4. What are the elements called that lie along the zig-zag line? *semimetals* or *metalloids*
5. What are the elements of Group VIIIA called? *noble gases*

Check and discuss homework.

Review pp. 163–165.

Teach pp. **166–169,** sec. **8.2** Classification of the Elements.

Review lesson.

HW: Answer p. 169, question 2. Read pp. 169–172. Next journal check (6 entries minimum) is in les. 66.

64 **Check** and discuss homework.

Review pp. 166–169.

Teach pp. **169–172,** sec. **8.3** Periodicity of Chemical Properties.

Review lesson.

HW: Answer p. 173, questions 1–3. Read pp. 173–175.

65 **Check** and discuss homework.

Review pp. 169–172.

Teach pp. **173–175,** sec. **8.4** Electron Configurations and the Periodic Table.

Review lesson.

HW: Answer p. 175, questions 1 and 2. Read pp. 175–178 up to Metallic Character. Complete 6 journal entries (minimum) and bring Journal Check Report.

66 **SP:** Carefully check journal to note progress; mark appropriate comments on Journal Check Report. Next journal check (10 entries minimum) is in les. 71. Have students sign up for science project oral presentations to be given in les. 102 through les. 113. (Give specific dates to your students. See pp. 101–102.) These *Teacher Guide* lessons plan 2–3 presentations per day; adjust number to fit size of your class. Students only pick a date for their presentations at this time.

Check and discuss homework.

Review pp. 173–175.

Teach pp. **175–178,** sec. **8.5** Periodic Properties of the Elements, up to Metallic Character.

Review lesson.

HW: Read pp. 179–181. Answer p. 181, questions 1, 4, and 6.

67 **Check** and discuss homework.

Review pp. 175–178.

Teach pp. **179–181,** sec. **8.5** (cont.).

Review lesson.

HW: Answer p. 181, questions 2, 3, and 5. Read *Lab Manual* Lab 14 and complete Prelab Assignment.

68 **Conduct Lab 14:** The Periodic Law.

Collect Lab 14 Report Sheet.

HW: Begin studying ch. 7–8 for Test 5 in les. 71. Answer p. 161, Review Exercises 8–10 and 16–20. Next journal check (10 entries minimum) is in les. 71.

69 **Check** and discuss homework.

Review pp. 175–181, using Concept Review 4: Trends in the Periodic Table.

HW: Answer p. 183, Review Exercises 1, 4, and 11–15. Study pp. 175–181 for quiz next lesson. Continue studying ch. 7–8 for Test 5 in les. 71.

70 **Check** and discuss homework.

Give Quiz 13 (over pp. 175–181).

Review ch. 7–8 for Test 5, using Chapter Reviews on pp. 160–161 and 182–183.

HW: Study ch. 7–8 for Test 5 in next lesson. Complete 10 journal entries (minimum) and bring Journal Check Report.

71 **SP:** Have each student pass forward his journal and a Journal Check Report Form.

Administer Test 5 over ch. 7–8.

SP: Carefully check journals and mark appropriate comments on Journal Check Reports. Return journals and report forms. Next journal check (12 entries minimum) is in les. 76.

HW: Read pp. 184–188, up to Covalent Bonding: Sharing Electrons. Answer p. 194, questions 1–3. Next journal check (12 entries minimum) is in les. 76.

Teacher Notes

Chapter 8 Overview. Although students have seen the periodic table in previous chapters, this chapter focuses on the periodic table as a means of classifying elements with similar properties together. The chapter begins with the history of the modern periodic table, followed by an overview of the broad groups of elements found within it. The alkali and alkaline earth metals are then used to illustrate periodic properties. The chapter then relates the table to electron configurations (chapter 7), showing how elements in the same vertical column have the same electron configuration (accounting for their similar properties). Finally, the chapter concludes with a look at general trends of element properties that occur in the table.

Mendeleev or Mendeleyev? (8.1, p. 164). Because the Russian (Cyrillic) alphabet is quite different from the Roman alphabet, it is often difficult to transliterate Russian names into English. Most older chemistry texts use the spelling *Mendeleev* for the famous Russian chemist, but this spelling often leads to severe mispronunciation (i.e., "mĕn′de·lēv" instead of the correct mĕn′de·lā′yef). Most modern sources transliterate the name as *Mendeleyev,* which more accurately reflects the Russian pronunciation. For this text, we have retained the *-eev* spelling for historical reasons, but be careful to pronounce it properly. (Actually, even the pronunciation mĕn′de·lā′yef is somewhat anglicized, but the correct Russian pronunciation myĭn·dyĭl·yā′yĕf is difficult for many native English speakers to pronounce.)

Classification of the elements (8.2, p. 166). A large wall chart of the periodic table (available from scientific supply companies) can be a great help as you teach the rest of this chapter. You may find it helpful to leave it up the rest of the year for quick reference.

Classifying elements (8.2, pp. 166–167). A goal of this section is to enable students to classify any element by identifying the group to which it belongs on the periodic table. This will give them insight into the properties of a given element even if the element itself is unfamiliar (e.g., the ability to classify rubidium as an alkali metal by looking at the periodic table gives you a good idea of the general properties of rubidium).

Hydrogen and the periodic table (8.2, p. 166). Note that hydrogen is classified as a nonmetal in Fig. 8.2 even though it is in group IA. This situation arises because its electronic configuration (one outer-shell electron) puts it in group IA, but its properties are more like those of the nonmetals at ordinary pressures. Hence it is *not* classified as an alkali metal. (We will revisit this subject in chapter 10.)

Alkali and alkaline earth metals (8.3, pp. 169–171). Alkali and alkaline earth metals are so named because they react with water to form basic (alkaline) solutions, such as in the reaction

$$Na + H_2O \longrightarrow NaOH + H_2$$

The pink color of the water in Fig. 8.9 is due to a small amount of the acid-base indicator *phenolphthalein* (chapter 16), which was added to visibly reveal the presence of hydroxide ions (phenolphthalein changes from colorless to a pink color in basic solutions).

Valence electrons and group number (8.4, p. 174). Students may be surprised by the ease with which the number of valence electrons and the Lewis symbol for any group "A" element (IA–VIIIA) may be determined simply by noting its group number (e.g., the halogens, group VIIA, have 7 valence electrons).

Electron affinity (8.5, p. 179). Another way to explain electron affinity is to compare it with ionization energy. Whereas ionization energy reflects an atom's tendency to *lose* an electron, electron affinity reflects an atom's tendency to *gain* an electron.

Lecture Demonstrations

Metals *vs.* nonmetals (8.2, p. 167). To contrast the properties of metals and nonmetals, have on hand samples of several metals (Cu, Pb, or Al [foil is fine]) and one or more nonmetals (carbon [charcoal], roll sulfur). Demonstrate that the metals are shiny and malleable, whereas the nonmetals are dull, brittle and crumbly.

Alkali metals (8.3, pp. 169–171). The similarity in chemical properties of sodium and potassium (or lithium) metal may be demonstrated by adding a pea-sized piece of each to separate 600-mL beakers each containing about 200 mL water plus a few drops of phenolphthalein indicator. **CAUTION: WEAR EYE PROTECTION and avoid contact with skin;** ensure that all students are well out of spatter distance. **Cover each beaker with a wire gauze** immediately after adding the Na or K to prevent its expulsion from the beaker. The beakers may be placed on the overhead projector for greater effect.

Size of ion *vs.* neutral atom (8.5, p. 176). One simple object lesson illustrating why an anion is larger than the neutral atom is to have six students stand in a circle with an equal distance between them (represents the valence electrons of a group VIA atom); in order to form the 2-ion, two more students ("electrons") must join the circle. If the space between the students is to remain the same the circle must become larger. You can also illustrate this principle using a circle of coins on an overhead projector.

Answers to Text Questions

Section Review 8.1 (p. 166)

1. Tell the contribution of each of the following to the development of the periodic table.
   - **a.** Moseley *showed that the periodicity of the elements was related to atomic number rather than to atomic mass*
   - **b.** Newlands *demonstrated the periodicity of elements for groups of eight elements (octaves)*
   - **c.** Döbereiner *one of the earliest chemists to show similarity of properties for groups of elements by arranging them in groups of three, or triads*
   - **d.** Mendeleev *arranged elements according to atomic mass with varying sizes of periods and with elements having similar properties in the same group; led to the modern periodic table*
2. Suggest some reasons why Mendeleev's periodic table was accepted by scientists. *(Answers will vary) It was useful for predicting properties of undiscovered elements. It continued to prove itself surprisingly accurate when new elements were discovered. It was arranged in a concise, orderly fashion.*
3. State the modern periodic law. *The properties of the elements are periodic functions of their atomic numbers.*

Section Review 8.2 (p. 169)

1. What is a period? A group? *In the periodic table, a period is a horizontal row of elements; a group is a vertical column of elements.*
2. Using the periodic table at the back of this book, **(1)** classify each of the following elements as a representative element, a transition metal, or an inner transition metal. **(2)** If it is classified as a representative element, tell whether it is a metal, a semimetal, or a nonmetal, and, if applicable, **(3)** give the group name. *(See also Fig. 8.5.)*
   - **a.** beryllium *representative element, metal, alkaline earth metal*

b. tin *representative element, metal*
c. silicon *representative element, semimetal*
d. tungsten *transition metal*
e. iodine *representative element, nonmetal, halogen*
f. chromium *transition metal*
g. sodium *representative element, metal, alkali metal*
h. aluminum *representative element, metal*
i. neon *representative element, nonmetal, noble gas*
j. sulfur *representative element, nonmetal, (chalcogen)*
k. cerium *inner transition metal*
l. americium *inner transition metal*
m. arsenic *representative element, semimetal*

Section Review 8.3 (p. 173)

1. Molten lithium is one of the most reactive substances known, reacting with almost every other element except the noble gases. Predict the reaction of molten lithium with each of the following elements if it forms Li_2O with oxygen.
   a. fluorine $2\,Li(l) + F_2(g) \longrightarrow 2\,LiF(s)$
   b. sulfur $2\,Li(l) + S(s) \longrightarrow Li_2S(s)$
2. It took 7 tons of the mineral pitchblende to isolate 1 g of the radioactive element radium, discovered by the Curies. Predict the reactions of radium with each of the following. (Be sure to balance the equations.)
   a. oxygen $2\,Ra(s) + O_2(g) \longrightarrow 2\,RaO(s)$
   b. liquid bromine $Ra(s) + Br_2(l) \longrightarrow RaBr_2(s)$
   c. water $Ra(s) + 2\,H_2O(l) \rightarrow Ra(OH)_2 + H_2(g)$
   d. hydrogen $Ra(s) + H_2(g) \longrightarrow RaH_2(s)$
3. Predict the formulas of the compounds of fluorine and each of the following.
   a. rubidium RbF
   b. selenium SeF_2
   c. tin SnF_4
   d. barium BaF_2
   e. phosphorus PF_3
   f. carbon CF_4

Section Review 8.4 (p. 175)

1. Why are valence electrons important? *The valence electrons are those electrons that are normally involved in chemical bonding and that determine chemical properties.*
2. Give Lewis symbols for each of the following elements.

a. I	:I:	g. Se	·Se:
b. Co	Co:	h. Sb	·Sb:
c. Be	Be:	i. K	K·
d. Fe	Fe:	j. O	·O:
e. Ra	Ra:	k. Si	·Si:
f. V	V:		

Section Review 8.5 (p. 181)

Example 8.3

1. Which atom in each of the following pairs has the *lower* first ionization energy?
   a. O, C *C*
   b. Ne, Na *Na*
   c. P, N *P*
   d. B, N *B*
2. Which atom in each of the following pairs has the *larger* electronegativity?
   a. O, F *F*
   b. Na, Cl *Cl*
   c. As, Bi *As*
3. Which is the *more* metallic element in each of the following pairs of elements?
   a. Al or B *Al*
   b. Na or Al *Na*
   c. Li or C *Li*

Example 8.4

4. Which is the *smaller* member of each pair?
   a. Mg, Mg^{2+} Mg^{2+}
   b. Si, Al *Si*
   c. O, O^{2-} *O*
   d. Xe, Ne *Ne*

Example 8.5

5. Using only the periodic table, list the following elements according to **(a)** *increasing* atomic radii, and **(b)** *increasing* electronegativities: Ca, Cs, F, Si, S.
   a. F, S, Si, Ca, Cs
   b. Cs, Ca, Si, S, F
6. Using only the periodic table, list the following elements according to *increasing* first ionization energy: Cs, Ga, Br, Sr, As, Ne.
   Cs, Sr, Ga, As, Br, Ne

Chapter 8 Review (p. 183)

1. Using Fig. 8.2 and 8.5, **(1)** classify each of the following elements as a representative element, a transition metal, or an inner transition metal. **(2)** If it is a representative element, tell whether it is a metal, nonmetal, or semimetal, and **(3)** give the group name if there is one.
   a. curium *(1) inner transition metal*
   b. lead *(1) representative element (2) metal*
   c. rutherfordium *(1) transition metal*
   d. francium *(1) representative element (2) metal (3) alkali metal*
   e. radon *(1) representative element (2) nonmetal (3) noble gas*
   f. gold *(1) transition metal*
   g. radium *(1) representative element (2) metal (3) alkaline earth metal*
   h. selenium *(1) representative element (2) nonmetal (3) chalcogen*
   i. bromine *(1) representative element (2) nonmetal (3) halogen*
   j. hydrogen *(1) representative element (2) nonmetal*

2. From memory, give **(a)** two properties of alkali metals and **(b)** two properties of alkaline earth metals. **(c)** Write balanced equations showing an alkali metal and an alkaline earth metal reacting with fluorine.
   a. two of the following: tend to have low densities; very chemically reactive; never found naturally in their free state; react with water to produce hydrogen gas and metal hydroxide; react with oxygen and water vapor in the air
   b. two of the following: silvery-white; malleable; ductile; less soft and have higher densities and melting points than alkali metals; less reactive than alkalis; but still too reactive to be found naturally as free elements
   c. $2\,M(s) + F_2(g) \rightarrow 2\,MF(s)$
   (M = any alkali metal)
   $M(s) + F_2(g) \rightarrow MF_2(s)$ *(M = any alkaline earth metal)*

3. Predict **(1)** the combining capacity (Section 8.3) of each of the following elements and **(2)** the chemical formulas of these elements combined with chlorine.
   a. radium *2;* $RaCl_2$
   b. iodine *1;* ICl
   c. thallium *3;* $TlCl_3$
   d. tellurium *2;* $TeCl_2$

4. Give the Lewis symbol for each of the following elements.
   a. Mg Mg:
   b. Os Os:
   c. Fr Fr·
   d. V V:
   e. P ·Ṗ: (with a dot below)
   f. Ge ·Ge: (with a dot below)
   g. Zn Zn:

5. Give the number of valence electrons found in atoms of the following elements.
   a. K *1*
   b. Ba *2*
   c. H *1*
   d. Cl *7*
   e. S *6*
   f. C *4*
   g. Al *-3*

6. On the basis of electron structure of the atom, explain the observed trends in each of the following.
   a. atomic radii *Atomic radii decrease across a period due to increasing nuclear charge and thus increased attraction between valence electrons and the nucleus. Radii increase down a group because each successive period has an additional energy level;* ***n*** *increases and size depends on* ***n****.*
   b. first ionization energies *First ionization energies increase across a period because increased nuclear charge attracts outer-shell electrons more strongly, making them more difficult to remove; more energy is needed. Ionization energies decrease down a group because the electrons being removed are in larger* ***n*** *levels which are further from the nucleus and its attractive force, therefore requiring less energy for their removal.*

7. Explain why group IIIA and group VIA elements have lower first ionization energies than group IIA and group VA elements, respectively.
   Group IIIA elements have a single ***p*** *electron in the highest energy level which is more easily removed than an electron from the more stable filled* ***s*** *sublevel found in group IIA elements. Group VIA elements have a paired electron in a* ***p*** *sublevel which requires less energy to remove (due to repulsion between paired electrons) than is required to remove an electron from the more stable half-filled* ***p*** *sublevel found in group VA elements.*

8. Using only your periodic table, arrange the following sets of elements according to **(1)** *increasing* first ionization energy and **(2)** *increasing* metallic character.

Chapter 8

a. S, Sr, Se, O Ba, Ca
   (1) Ba, Sr, Ca, Se, S, O
   (2) O, S, Se, Ca, Sr, Ba
b. Ar, Na, S, Al, K
   (1) K, Na, Al, S, Ar
   (2) Ar, S, Al, Na, K

9. How do electron affinity and first ionization energy differ? *Electron affinity is the energy involved in adding an electron to a neutral gaseous atom, whereas the first ionization energy is the energy needed to remove an electron from a neutral gaseous atom.*

10. Define what is meant by *electronegativity.* *Electronegativity refers to the ability of an atom to attract electrons to itself when it is chemically combined with another atom.*

11. Arrange the following sets of elements according to *increasing* electronegativity; use only your periodic table.
   a. Zn, As, F, P, O *Zn, As, P, O, F*
   b. Sn, I, Sr, Cs *Cs, Sr, Sn, I*
   c. C, Li, F, N *Li, C, N, F*

12. Tell which member of each of the following pairs is the *larger* and give a reason for your choice.
   a. Al, Ar *Al; further toward the left*
   b. F, Kr *Kr; more shells*
   c. H^-, H *H^-; more electrons with same nuclear charge*
   d. H^-, Be^{2+} *H^-; smaller nuclear charge for same number of electrons*
   e. Ca, As *Ca; further toward the left*
   f. Cu^+, Au^+ *Au^+; more shells*
   g. Sr^{2+}, Rb^+ *Rb^+; smaller nuclear charge for same number of electrons*
   h. Fe^{3+}, Fe^{2+} *Fe^{2+}; more electrons with same nuclear charge*
   i. N, F *N; further toward the left*
   j. Br, I *I; more shells*

13. Which of the following would you expect to have the *most negative* electron affinity?
   a. S
   b. Si
   c. Mg
   d. Cl
   e. Ar
   f. Na

   d. Chlorine would be expected to have the most negative electron affinity.

14. Which one of the following ions would you expect to have the *largest* radius?
   a. Ti^{4+}
   b. Mn^{7+}
   c. Sc^{3+}
   d. S^{2-}
   e. Cr^{6+}
   f. P^{3-}
   g. K^+

   g. The potassium ion would be expected to have the largest radius.

Chapter 9 (pp. 184–209)
The Chemical Bond and Intermolecular Forces

Suggested Daily Pacing

72 **Check** homework.

Return and go over graded Test 5.

Introduce ch. 9, The Chemical Bond and Intermolecular Forces.

Discuss homework.

Teach pp. **185–188,** ch. 9 introduction and sec. **9.1** Types of Chemical Bonds, up to Covalent Bonding: Sharing Electrons.

Review lesson.

HW: Read pp. 188–192, up to Bond Character. Answer pp. 194–195, questions 4–7.

73 **Check** and discuss homework.

Review pp. 185–188.

Teach pp. **188–192,** sec **9.1** (cont.), up to Bond Character.

Review lesson.

HW: Read pp. 192–194. Answer p. 195, questions 8–10. Next journal check (12 entries minimum) is in les. 76.

74 **Check** and discuss homework.

Review pp. 188–192.

Teach pp. **192–194,** sec. **9.1** (cont.).

Review lesson.

HW: Answer p. 195, questions 11 and 12. Read pp. 195–197, up to Molecular Shape.

75 **Give Quiz 14** (over pp. 186–194).

Review pp. 192–194.

Teach pp. **195–197,** sec. **9.2** Shapes and Properties of Molecules, up to Molecular Shape.

Review lesson.

HW: Answer p. 200, questions 1 and 2. Complete 12 journal entries (minimum). Bring Journal Check Report and *Science in Action.*

76 **SP:** Carefully check journal and mark appropriate comments on Journal Check Report. (Have students read text pp. 197–199.) Next journal check (minimum of 14 entries total) is in les. 81. Introduce **science project exhibit,** using *Science in Action* ch. 4, pp. 91–100. Explain that the exhibit is due on the same day as the oral presentation that the students have already signed up for in les. 66 (ch. 8). (Plan to answer additional questions in les. 86 [ch. 10].)

Check and discuss homework.

HW: Answer p. 200, question 3. Next journal check (14 entries minimum) is in les. 81.

77 **Check** and discuss homework.

Review pp. 195–197.

Teach pp. **197–199,** sec. **9.2** (cont.).

Review lesson.

HW: Answer p. 200, questions 4–6. Read pp. 200–203. Answer p. 204, questions 1 and 2.

78 **Give Quiz 15** (over pp. 195–199).

Check and discuss homework.

Review pp. 197–199.

Teach pp. **200–203,** sec. **9.3** Intermolecular Forces: Forces between Molecules.

Review lesson.

HW: Answer p. 204, questions 3–5. Read *Lab Manual* Lab 15 and complete Prelab Assignment. Next journal check (14 entries minimum) is in les. 81.

79 **Discuss** homework.

Conduct Lab 15: Molecular Models and Polarity.

HW: Complete Lab 15 Report Sheet. Read pp. 204–207. Answer p. 207, questions 1–4.

80 **Give** "pop" reading quiz over pp. 204–207:

1. What kind of solids have no ordered arrangement or pattern for the particles which compose them? *amorphous solids*
2. Give the term for the simplest repeating unit in a crystal. *unit cell*
3. Which type of solids have definite melting points? *crystalline solids*
4. What is another name for the face-centered cubic arrangement? *cubic close packing*
5. What do the letters LCD stand for? *liquid crystal display*

Check and discuss homework.

Review pp. 200–203.

Teach pp. **204–207,** sec. **9.4** Crystals.

Review lesson.

HW: Answer p. 209, Review Exercises 3–7. Read *Lab Manual* Lab 16 and complete Prelab Assignment. Complete 14 journal entries (minimum). Bring Journal Check Report and *Science in Action.*

81 **SP:** Carefully check journal and mark appropriate comments on Journal Check Report. (Have students read *Science in Action* pp. 75–79.) Describe how to **complete the investigation.** Introduce the **Investigation Followup,** using *Science in Action* pp. 75–79. Assign the investigation to be completed, the journal to be completed, and the first draft of the Investigation Followup to be written for les. 91 (ch. 10).

Check and discuss homework.

Conduct Lab 16: Crystal Structures.

HW: Complete Lab 16 Report Sheet. Begin studying ch. 1–9 for Test 6 (Semester Exam) in les. 85. Investigation, Journal, and first draft of Investigation Followup due les. 91 (ch. 10).

Note: Assign 10–15 items from Chapter Reviews 1–3.

82 **Check** and discuss homework.

Review ch. 1–3 for Test 6 (Semester Exam) in les. 85, using important concepts from Chapter Reviews 1–3.

HW: Continue studying ch. 1–9 for Test 6 (Semester Exam) in lesson 85.

Note: Assign 10–15 items from Chapter Reviews 4–6.

83 **Check** and discuss homework.

Review ch. 4–6 for Test 6 (Semester Exam) in les. 85, using important concepts from Chapter Reviews 4–6.

HW: Continue studying ch. 1–9 for Test 6 (Semester Exam) in les. 85. Answer p. 209, Review Exercises 8–15.

Note: Assign 5–8 additional items from Chapter Reviews 7 and 8.

84 **Check** and discuss homework.

Review ch. 7–9 for Test 6 (Semester Exam) in next lesson, using important concepts from Chapter Reviews 7–9.

HW: Study ch. 1–9 for Test 6 (Semester Exam) in next lesson.

85 **Administer Test 6** (Semester Exam) over ch. 1–9.

HW: Read pp. 210–214. Answer p. 214, questions 1–4. Briefly read *Science in Action* ch. 4, pp. 91–100, and bring book to class. Investigation, Journal, and first draft of Investigation Followup due les. 91 (ch. 10).

Teacher Notes

Chapter 9 Overview. This chapter focuses on chemical bonds, which bind atoms together into compounds, and intermolecular forces, which bind molecules together to form solids and liquids. The chapter begins by introducing and explaining the different types of chemical bonds, followed by a discussion of how the chemical bonds in a molecule determine the molecule's shape and properties. Intermolecular forces are then introduced and explained, and the chapter concludes with a brief discussion of crystals.

Chapter opener photos (pp. 184–185). The photo on p. 184 is the Hope Diamond, a famous 45-carat blue diamond kept at the Smithsonian Institution.

The photo on p. 185 is a closeup of the Yokohama Bay Bridge, Yokohama, Japan.

The octet rule (9.1, p. 186). Although the octet rule applies in the vast majority of cases, there are a few exceptions. The most obvious exceptions, of course, are hydrogen and helium, which seek to have two electrons rather than eight because their valence shell (1*s*) can hold only two electrons. Such elements as sulfur, phosphorus, iodine, and boron also exhibit non-octet behavior in a few compounds:

More than 8 valence electrons:	
• phosphorus pentachloride (PCl_5)— P has 10 valence electrons	[Lewis structure of PCl_5]
• sulfur hexafluoride (SF_6)— S has 12 valence electrons	[Lewis structure of SF_6]
• tetrachloroiodate ion (ICl_4^-)— I has 12 valence electrons	[Lewis structure of ICl_4^-]
Less than 8 valence electrons:	
• NO (N has 5 valence electrons)	·N̈—Ö:
• BF_3 (B has 6 valence electrons)	[Lewis structure of BF_3]

The reasons for this behavior are beyond the scope of this discussion, but they have to do with the particular outer-shell electron configurations of the atoms in question (see "Atomic orbitals and molecular geometry" on p. 56 of this Teacher Guide). The octet rule still holds true for the vast majority of compounds, however.

Metals, nonmetals, and ionic bonds (9.1, p. 188). Keep in mind that the tendency of metal-nonmetal compounds to contain ionic, rather than covalent, bonds is a generalization, not a rule. Although the principle holds true in most cases, metals and nonmetals that are *close together in the periodic table* tend to form molecules with a significantly covalent character (e.g., $AlCl_3$; see Fig. 9.8).

Bonding and group number (9.1, pp. 186–189). The number of electrons gained or lost in ionic bonding and the number of covalent bonds formed in simple covalent bonding are both related to the group number of the periodic table in which the element is found. For example, calcium belongs to group IIA and must *lose two* electrons to satisfy the octet rule. Similarly, oxygen (group VIA) has six valence electrons and must *gain two* electrons to obtain an octet. It can do this either by gaining two electrons outright (forming the O^{2-} ion) or by forming two covalent bonds with another atom or pair of atoms.

Covalent bonds (9.1, p. 189). The origin of the word *covalent* (*co-* + *valence*) makes it easy to remember that this type of bond involves the sharing of valence electrons.

Metallic bonding (9.1, pp. 191–192). In some ways, the metallic bond is similar to both covalent and ionic bonds. Like covalent bonds, metallic bonds involve the sharing of valence electrons with other atoms, rather than a complete transfer (i.e., a metal does not consist of cations and anions). But like ionic bonds, metallic bonds do not simply bond one atom to another; rather, each metal atom is attracted to all the metal atoms around it.

The unique character of metallic bonds results from the fact that the shared electrons are shared with not one atom, but many atoms *(delocalized),* forming an electron cloud that spreads throughout the metal. The mutual attraction of the metal atoms for their shared electrons bonds all the metals together into a single "molecule." British chemist Roger Peters defines a *metal* as follows:

> A metal consists of a giant covalent structure, in which each atom has contributed one or more of its valence electrons to the formation of omnidirectional, delocalized covalent bonds that extend throughout the structure.[1]

[1]Roger Peters, "Introduction—Metallic Bonding," *Aufbau1,* n.d., <http://www.netcomuk.co.uk/~rpeters1/aufl mbd.htm> (4/3/2000).

Metals, nonmetals, and bond character (9.1, pp. 192–193). When a nonmetal reacts with another nonmetal, the bond will almost always be covalent; when a metal reacts with another metal, the bond will always be metallic.

Polar covalent bonds (9.1, pp. 193–194). It may be helpful to visualize the atoms in a polar covalent bond as playing "tug-of-war" with the shared electron pair(s);

Chapter 9

the "stronger" (more electronegative) atom pulls the electrons closer toward itself, giving it a stronger negative charge.

Similarity in Lewis structures (9.2, pp. 195–196). Since elements in the same group have the same number of valence electrons, we may predict that similar molecular compounds (e.g., CH_4 and SiH_4) will have similar Lewis structures.

Resonance hybrids (9.2, pp. 196–197). It may be helpful to think of resonance hybrids in terms of an analogy. A mule is a hybrid animal that is a cross between a donkey and a horse. It is *always* a mule, having specific characteristics, not a horse one moment and a donkey the next. Similarly, a molecule with delocalized electrons does not switch back and forth between single bonds and double bonds; rather, the bonds are identical and stable.

Molecular models (9.2, pp. 197–198). Molecular models can greatly aid student comprehension in this section. Simple models can be made from materials purchased at a craft store (polystyrene foam balls, small dowels, glue, and paint); molecular model kits are also available from scientific supply companies.

Atomic orbitals and molecular geometry (9.2, p. 197). Perceptive students may notice a seeming contradiction between chapter 7 (where it was said that the overall electron cloud of an atom is spherical) and the nonspherical cloud arrangements on pp. 197–198. Some may also wonder how an atom can have a tetrahedral or trigonal planar geometry, since no *s, p, d,* or even *f* orbital has such a shape. At this level, you may wish to simply point out that even though the *overall* electron cloud of an atom is spherical, the configuration of the *valence* electrons of an atom is not necessarily so. Visualizing the atom as a sphere with one to six "sticky spots" on its surface where it tends to bond with other atoms may be helpful.

The geometry of the bonding electrons (tetragonal, trigonal planar, linear, etc.) is determined by a phenomenon called *orbital hybridization,* in which electrons "spill over" into adjacent unfilled shells to create a "hybrid" orbital with a different shape. For example, a carbon atom has four valence electrons—two in the $2s$ orbital, one in the $2p_x$ orbital, and one in the $2p_y$ orbital; the $2p_z$ orbital is empty. From the standpoint of chemical bonding, the four valence electrons can be thought of as "spilling over" slightly into the empty $2p_z$ orbital, forming four identical "hybrid" electron clouds that no longer have standard *s* and *p* orbital shapes, but rather have the tetrahedral structure shown on p. 197, Fig. 9.11a. Each of these clouds contains one unpaired electron that can form a chemical bond with another atom.

The bonding geometry of any atom is determined by the type of orbital hybridization it undergoes:

geometry	description	example
linear (*sp* hybridization)	two *s* electrons "spill over" into empty p_x orbital, forming two "*sp*" orbitals 180° apart	beryllium in BeF_2 (Fig. 9.14)
trigonal planar (sp^2 hybridization)	two *s* electrons and one p_x electron "spill over" into empty *p* orbitals, forming three "sp^2" orbitals 120° apart	boron in BF_3 (Fig. 9.15)
tetragonal (sp^3 hybridization)	two *s* electrons, one p_x electron, and one p_y electron "spill over" into empty p_z orbital, forming four "sp^3" orbitals 109.5° apart containing one electron each	carbon in CH_4 (Fig. 9.11)
trigonal pyramidal (sp^3 hybridization)	two *s* electrons "spill over" into half-filled p_x, p_y, and p_z orbitals, forming four "sp^3" orbitals 105°–109° apart; one contains two electrons (a nonbonding pair) and three contain one electron each (bonding)	nitrogen in NH_3 (Fig. 9.12)
angular (sp^3 hybridization)	two *s* electrons and two p_x electrons "spill over" into half-filled p_y and p_z orbitals, forming four "sp^3" orbitals 105°–109° apart; two contain two electrons each (nonbonding pairs) and two contain one electron each (bonding)	oxygen in H_2O (Fig. 9.13)
octahedral (sp^3d^2 hybridization)	two *s* electrons and five *p* electrons "spill over" into two empty *d* orbitals, forming six "sp^3d^2" orbitals 90° apart; all six contain one electron each (bonding)	sulfur in SF_6 (not shown)

For more information on orbital hybridization, you consult an up-to-date college chemistry text under the heading "valence bond theory" or "hybridization" (see Chapter 9 Resource List).

Intermolecular forces (9.3, p. 200). Intermolecular forces may also be referred to as *van der Waals* [vän′dĕr väls′] *forces.*

Hydrogen bonds (9.3, pp. 202–203). By definition, hydrogen bonding can occur *only* between molecules containing hydrogen covalently bonded to nitrogen, oxygen, or fluorine (e.g., a molecule of HCl and a molecule of HF would attract each other by means of dipole-dipole and London forces, but not hydrogen bonds).

Hydrogen bonding between water molecules is responsible for the geometric crystal structure of ice (see p. 26, Fig. 1.18a). It is this regular, open structure that causes water to expand as it freezes.

Determining crystal structures (9.4, pp. 204–206). The actual crystal structure of a substance can be determined from the X-ray diffraction pattern, obtained when X-rays are passed through the crystal. A computer can infer the arrangement of ions, atoms, or molecules in the crystal by analyzing the spacing and arrangement of the dots in the pattern.

As a side note, this technique can also be used to determine the structure of complex molecules such as proteins; the models of the protein molecules on pp. 315 and 445 of the text were generated by X-ray diffraction studies.

A molecular model set (purchased or homemade) is also very useful in teaching this section.

Unit cells (9.4, pp. 204–205). Samples of wallpaper having various patterns may be used to illustrate unit cells; point out that the determination of the boundaries for the unit cell is arbitrary by defining it at several places on one sample. Unit cells may be demonstrated using polystyrene foam balls and toothpicks or models from scientific supply companies. Different methods of close packing may be demonstrated with a large number of identical spheres (marbles, table tennis balls, etc.) and an appropriately sized transparent container.

Lab 16 may be done as a demonstration here, if desired.

Lecture Demonstrations

Types of bonding (9.1, pp. 186–192). You may wish to have on display several compounds representing each type of bonding under discussion (e.g., table salt, table sugar, water, $KMnO_4$, I_2, Fe, Al).

Ionic and covalent bonding may be demonstrated by simple reactions. First, collect two (or more) bottles of oxygen by water displacement (see Lab 20). Ionic bonding may be demonstrated by burning a strip of magnesium in oxygen; ignite it in a burner first and immediately plunge it into the O_2. **CAUTION: *Do not look directly at the flame;*** permanent eye damage may result. To avoid potential eye injury to students, the bottle may be placed in a large metal can (to block direct line of sight) and the magnesium burned in a darkened room. However, if your eyes are partially dark-adapted, be especially careful not to look at or near the flame while trying to insert the burning ribbon into the jar.

Covalent bonding can be demonstrated by simply lighting a Bunsen burner (Fig 4.2; see reaction 4.5).

Molecular geometry (9.2, pp. 197–198). A model of the geometry of electron pairs about a central atom may be constructed from four round balloons (approx. 9" diameter) tied together at their necks or fastened together with string. Be sure to blow them up to the same size, but do not make them too rigid or it will be difficult to tie their necks together. Also be sure the necks of the balloons are pulled tightly together rather than just loosely connected. This inexpensive model can be useful in the discussion of tetrahedral, trigonal pyramidal, and angular geometries.

Chapter 9 Resource List

Silberberg, Martin. *Chemistry: The Molecular Nature of Matter and Change.* St. Louis: Mosby, 1996, pp. 385–390. A college-level chemistry text and useful reference on valence-bond theory (orbital hybridization); computer-generated electron cloud models make the presentation clearer.

Answers to Text Questions

Section Review 9.1 (pp. 194–195)

Concept Review

1. What is a chemical bond? *an attractive force between atoms that is strong enough to enable the group to act as a unit*
2. What is the octet rule? Why might this principle be considered the "driving force" that causes elements to react to form chemical bonds? *Elements will tend to react chemically so as to achieve a noble gas electron configuration, either by losing or by gaining electrons, or by sharing electrons with other atoms. This rule could be considered a "driving force" in chemical reactions because elements tend to react in ways that result in a complete octet.*
3. Define *ionic bond.* *a force of attraction (an electrostatic force) between oppositely charged ions which have been formed by a transfer of electrons*

Chapter 9

4. Give three properties of ionic compounds and three properties of covalent compounds.
Ionic compounds *(any three)*
• *crystalline solids with high melting and boiling points*
• *conduct electricity well when molten*
• *many are soluble in water*
• *water (aqueous) solutions conduct electricity well*
• *most are insoluble in nonpolar solvents (e.g., benzene)*
Covalent compounds *(any three)*
• *gases, liquids, or solids with low melting points*
• *liquid state does not conduct electricity*
• *many are insoluble in water*
• *aqueous solutions* usually *do not conduct electricity well*
• *most are soluble in nonpolar solvents*

5. Define *covalent bond.* *a chemical bond resulting from the sharing of one or more electron pairs between two atoms*

6. Give two examples of network covalent substances. *diamond, abrasive silicon carbide, quartz, etc.*

7. What is a metallic bond? *the force of attraction between metal cations and the surrounding cloud or "sea" of free, mobile electrons*

Application

8. **(a)** Give the Lewis structures of calcium and fluorine atoms. (You may refer to Fig. 7.26 on p. 157.) **(b)** If Ca and F atoms are allowed to react, what will be the electron configurations and Lewis structures of the resultant ions? **(c)** Show the reaction between Ca and F atoms by using Lewis structures.
a. Ca: :F:
b. Ca^{2+} $[:F:]^-$
c. Ca: 2 :F: ⟶ Ca^{2+}, 2 $[:F:]^-$

9. Which of the following compounds would you expect to contain ionic bonds?
a. SrI_2 **c.** Li_2O **e.** CsF
b. SO_2 **d.** BrCl **f.** $CaCl_2$
You would expect **a, c, e,** *and* **f** *to contain ionic bonds.*
Which one of the above compounds would you expect to have the most ionic character? *e. CsF*

10. Draw Lewis structures for each of the following.
a. an iodine atom :I:
b. an iodine molecule :I:I: or :I–I:
c. an HI molecule H:I or H–I:

11. Predict what type of bonding predominates in each of the following.
a. $AsCl_3$ *covalent* **g.** MnF_2 *ionic*
b. LiBr *ionic* **h.** HCN *ionic* or *covalent**
c. CuNi *metallic* **i.** Al_2O_3 *ionic*
d. SO_2 *covalent* **j.** KCl *ionic*
e. XeF_6 *covalent* **k.** O_2 *covalent*
f. Fe *metallic* **l.** Cr *metallic*
**Ionic between H^+ and CN^-; covalent between C and N.*

12. Tell whether the bonds between the following atoms are polar covalent or pure covalent bonds.
a. Si–Si *pure covalent* **e.** Cl–F *polar covalent*
b. H–O *polar covalent* **f.** Cl–Cl *pure covalent*
c. C–H *polar covalent* **g.** N–H *polar covalent*
d. C–O *polar covalent* **h.** O–O *pure covalent*

Section Review 9.2 (p. 200)

Concept Review

1. What are delocalized electrons? *electrons that circulate freely through the molecule instead of being bound to a single atom or pair of atoms*

2. What do we call a situation in which a Lewis structure cannot accurately represent the arrangement of valence electrons in a molecule? *resonance*

3. What do we mean when we describe a molecule as being polar? *the electrons are not shared equally between the bonded atoms*

Application

4. What shape would you expect a molecule to have that was based on an atom with only two bonding pairs of electrons? Three bonding pairs? Four?
a. two bonding pairs *linear molecule*
b. three bonding pairs *trigonal planar*
c. four bonding pairs *tetrahedral pyramidal*

5. Based on the Lewis structures you have already studied and the group similarities of the elements, give **(1)** the Lewis structure for each of the following molecules and **(2)** its shape.
a. SiH_4
H
|
H–Si–H *tetrahedral*
|
H
b. AlF_3
:F–Al–F:
|
:F: *trigonal planar*
c. H_2S
H
|
H–S: *angular*

d. HBr $H-\ddot{Br}:$ *linear*

e. $SeCl_2$:Cl–Se: (with :Cl: above Se) *angular*

f. O_3 :O=O–O: ⟷ :O–O=O: *angular*

g. PI_3 :I–P–I: (with :I: below P) *trigonal pyramidal*

h. CCl_4 :Cl–C–Cl: (with :Cl: above and below C) *tetrahedral*

6. What conditions must exist for a polyatomic molecule to be nonpolar? *The molecule must have a symmetrical distribution of polar (or nonpolar) bonds, resulting in no net dipole.*

Section Review 9.3 (p. 204)

Concept Review

1. How are intermolecular forces different from chemical bonds? *Chemical bonds show how elements combine, whereas intermolecular forces occur between the electrons in the molecule and determine the state of that molecule.*
2. Explain the dipole-dipole force. *a force between neighboring polar molecules due to the attraction of oppositely charged ends*
3. What causes London forces? *instantaneous dipoles in molecules*
4. Explain the difference between hydrogen bonds and dipole-dipole forces. *The hydrogen bond is the strongest of the three intermolecular bonds and the dipole-dipole bond is the weakest bond. Hydrogen bonds occur only in those molecules containing a bond between hydrogen and N, O, or F.*

Application

5. Tell which intermolecular force(s) would exist between molecules of the following substances.
   - **a.** H_2S (polar) *London force + dipole-dipole force*
   - **b.** H_2O *London force + hydrogen bond*
   - **c.** O_2 *London force only*
   - **d.** SiH_4 (nonpolar) *London forces*
   - **e.** HCl *London force + dipole-dipole force*
   - **f.** CH_3Cl (polar) *London force + dipole-dipole force*
   - **g.** CO_2 (nonpolar) *London force*
   - **h.** NH_3 *London force + hydrogen bond*

Section Review 9.4 (p. 207)

1. Differentiate between amorphous solids and crystalline solids; give an example of each. *An amorphous solid has no ordered arrangement or pattern for the particles in it, whereas a crystalline solid has a regular, repeated, three-dimensional pattern for the particles composing it. (Examples will vary.)*
2. What is a unit cell? What is meant by the statement that unit cells do not actually exist in a crystal? *A unit cell is the simplest repeating unit in a crystal. They do not exist as separate and distinct parts of the crystal but are only models which aid in our visualization of the structure.*
3. What types of close-packed unit cells do most metals assume? *hexagonal close packed structure and cubic close packing (face-centered cubic)*
4. In what way(s) does a liquid crystal have characteristics of both liquids and solids? *A liquid crystal is like a solid because of the orderly arrangement of its molecules, but like a liquid in the flexibility and movement of the substance itself.*

Chapter 9 Review (p. 209)

1. What is a *chemical bond*? How does a chemical bond differ from an intermolecular force? *A chemical bond is an attractive force between atoms that is strong enough to enable the group to act as a unit. An intermolecular force occurs between molecules, while a chemical bond occurs within molecules.*
2. State the octet rule. *Elements will tend to react chemically so as to achieve a noble gas electron configuration, either by losing or gaining electrons, or by sharing electrons with other atoms.*
3. Distinguish between ionic and covalent bonds in terms of the electron rearrangements involved. *In ionic bonding, electrons are transferred; in covalent bonding, electrons are shared.*
4. What is the difference between single, double, and triple covalent bonds? *the number of pairs of electrons that are shared between the atoms*
5. Why do network covalent substances such as diamond and silicon carbide tend to be very hard? *Trillions of atoms are joined into one unit by strong covalent bonds. For example, a diamond may actually be considered as one macromolecule, regardless of its size.*

6. What is the primary difference between covalent and metallic bonds? *Covalent bonding involves the sharing of electrons; metallic bonding involves the sharing of (delocalized) electrons among large numbers of atoms.*
7. Predict what type of bonding predominates in each of the following substances.
   a. I_2 *covalent*
   b. V *metallic*
   c. CsI *ionic*
   d. NaF *ionic*
   e. CO_2 *covalent*
   f. Fe_3Al *metallic*
8. What type of covalent bond can make a molecule a dipole? *pure covalent bond*
9. What are delocalized electrons? *electrons that circulate freely through a molecule (or metal) instead of being bound to a single atom or pair of atoms*
10. What do we call a situation in which Lewis symbols cannot accurately represent a molecule's electron arrangement? *resonance*
11. Draw the Lewis structure and predict the shape of antimony trichloride, ($SbCl_3$), a soft solid used as a flame retardant. :C̈l̤–S̈b–C̈l̤: with :C̤l̤: below Sb — *trigonal pyramidal*
12. Which type of intermolecular force is the strongest? Which type is the weakest? *hydrogen bonds; London force*
13. Name the only intermolecular force that affects nonpolar molecules. *London force*
14. Which type(s) of intermolecular force would exist in a liquid made up of each of the following molecules?
   a. H—Ge—H (with H above and H below Ge) *London forces*
   b. H—Ö—F̈: *hydrogen bond; dipole-dipole force, London force*
   c. :C̈l: bonded to :C̤—Ö: *dipole-dipole force, London force*
15. What is the difference between crystalline and amorphous solids at the molecular level? How does this affect the properties of the substance? *A crystalline solid is characterized by a regular and repeated three-dimensional pattern of arrangement of the particles composing it. Crystalline solids have a definite melting point or very narrow melting temperature range. Amorphous solids have no ordered arrangement or pattern for the particles composing them; amorphous solids have no definite melting point.*

Chapter 10 (pp. 210–243)

Selected Nonmetals and Their Compounds

Suggested Daily Pacing

86 **Check** homework.

Return and go over graded Test 6.

Introduce ch. 10, Selected Nonmetals and Their Compounds.

Discuss homework.

Teach pp. **211–214,** introduction and sec. **10.1** Hydrogen.

Review lesson.

SP: Discuss the science project exhibit again in more detail, using *Science in Action* ch. 4, pp. 91–100. Students will use their exhibit in their oral presentation.

HW: Read pp. 214–219. Answer p. 219, questions 1–10. Investigation, Journal, and first draft of Investigation Followup due les. 91.

87 **Check** and discuss homework.

Review pp. 211–214.

Teach pp. **214–219,** sec. **10.2** Oxygen.

Review lesson.

HW: Read pp. 219–223. Answer p. 224, questions 1–11.

88 **Give Quiz 16** (over pp. 211–219).

Check and discuss homework.

Review pp. 214–219.

Teach pp. **219–223,** sec. **10.3** Nitrogen.

Review lesson.

HW: Read *Lab Manual* Lab 17 and complete Prelab Assignment. Investigation, Journal, and the first draft of Followup Report due les. 91.

89 **Check** and discuss homework.

Conduct Lab 17: Preparation and Properties of Oxygen.

HW: Complete Lab 17 Report Sheet. Read pp. 224–227. Answer p. 228, questions 1–7.

90 **Check** and discuss homework.

Review pp. 219–223.

Teach pp. **224–227,** sec. **10.4** Phosphorus.

Review lesson.

HW: Read pp. 228–231. Answer p. 232, questions 1–4. Complete Investigation, Journal, and the first draft of Investigation Followup. Bring *Science in Action.*

91 **SP:** Collect and grade investigation journals.

Note: Grade journals only for completeness and format. Content will be part of the oral presentation grading.

Check **Investigation Followup first draft,** making suggestions as needed. (Have students answer text p. 232, questions 5–8.) Use *Science in Action* pp. 79–82 to remind students how to prepare the final draft of the Followup Report, which is due in les. 96 (ch. 11). Go over the sample Investigation Followup on *Science in Action* pp. 83–89. Also remind each student of the oral presentation date for which he signed up in les. 66 (ch. 8). Oral presentations begin in les. 102 (ch. 12).

Check and discuss p. 232, questions 1–8.

Review pp. 224–227.

Teach pp. **228–231,** sec. **10.5** Sulfur.

Review lesson.

HW: Read *Lab Manual* Lab 18 and complete Prelab Assignment. Final draft of Investigation Followup due les. 96 (ch. 11).

92 **Check** and discuss homework.

Conduct Lab 18: Allotropes of Sulfur.

HW: Complete Lab 18 Report Sheet. Read pp. 232–235, up to Uses of Chlorine.

93 **Check** and discuss homework.

Review pp. 228–231.

Teach pp. **232–235,** sec. **10.6** Halogens, up to Uses of Chlorine.

Review lesson.

HW: Read pp. 235–241. Answer p. 239, questions 1–6 and p. 241, questions 1–2. Final draft of Investigation Followup due les. 96 (ch. 11).

94 **Give** "pop" reading quiz over pp. 235–241:

1. Which of the halogens appears in either the preparation of most medicines or in the actual medicine itself? *chlorine*
2. Name two uses for neon. *Any two of the following: neon signs, airport lights, and checkout scanners.*
3. Halons, firefighting chemicals, are formed from which halogen? *bromine*
4. True or False: Due to the unreactive nature of the noble gases, no compounds of them have ever been produced in a laboratory. *false*
5. Which of the halogens is often used as a bleaching agent? *chlorine*

Check and discuss homework.

Review pp. 232–235.

Teach pp. **235–241,** sec. **10.6** (cont.)—**10.7** Noble Gases.

Review lesson.

HW: Read pp. 244–248. Answer p. 246, questions 1–4 and 249, questions 1–4. Bring *Science in Action* to class.

Teacher Notes

Chapter 10 Overview. This chapter is the first of two descriptive chemistry chapters dealing with the occurrence, properties, preparation, reactions, and uses of a number of elements. Chapter 10 discusses the nonmetals hydrogen, oxygen, nitrogen, phosphorus, sulfur, the halogens, and the noble gases.

Although the primary focus of the chapter is to show students how chemistry is applied in everyday life, the chapter can also serve as grounds for additional practice in classifying equations and for reviewing concepts taught in previous chapters.

Abundance of tritium (10.1, p. 212). Natural hydrogen is about 10^{-7}% $^{3}_{1}H$ (tritium).

Hydrogen and the *Hindenburg* disaster (10.1, p. 212). At 803 feet long and 135 feet across, the *Hindenburg* was 123 feet longer and 27 feet broader than a WWII *South Dakota*-class battleship. Only the ship's bridge protruded beneath the hull; the staterooms, dining hall, crew quarters, fuel bunkers, storerooms, and other accommodations were located inside the hull itself. The airship had been flying safely for more than a year before the disaster, making 18 safe transatlantic voyages and carrying more than a thousand passengers.

It has recently been proposed that the primary cause of the *Hindenburg* disaster may not have been leaking hydrogen. Recent research has revealed that the doping compound used to waterproof and strengthen the airship's fabric skin consisted of cellulose acetate (highly flammable), nitrocellulose (modern "gunpowder"), aluminum powder (used as a fuel in solid rockets), and red iron oxide (used as a catalyst in solid rockets to regulate the burn rate). It is possible that the combustible skin of the *Hindenburg* was ignited by an electrical discharge caused by the stormy weather conditions, although hydrogen undoubtedly contributed to the resulting fire.

Producing hydrogen from algae (10.1, pp. 212–213). Some researchers are studying ways to use photosynthetic bacteria or algae to produce hydrogen commercially. One approach involves the green algae *Chlamydomonas reinhardtii,* which releases hydrogen when deprived of sulfur.

A hydrogen economy (10.1, p. 213). Many environmentalists have extolled the virtues of a hydrogen-based economy, in which hydrogen would be the primary transportation and industrial fuel. Such an economy would produce very little pollution, as the primary combustion product is water vapor. Hydrogen is also a versatile fuel that can be used in piston engines, jets and other gas turbines, and rockets; it can also replace coal and natural gas in ironmaking. Unfortunately, many "hydrogen economy" proposals tend to start with hydrogen and work from there, glossing over the energy required to *make* hydrogen. A hydrogen economy might be feasible if the ultimate power source were nuclear (chapter 17) or hydroelectric, but the sources of energy typically proposed—solar and wind power—seem woefully inadequate to provide the amount of energy necessary.

Uses of deuterium and tritium (10.1, p. 213). Nuclear-related uses of deuterium and tritium will be discussed further in chapter 17. A photo of a tritium-containing watch is found on p. 392.

Toxicity of heavy water (10.1, p. 213). Toxic effects from drinking "heavy water" would appear only if several liters of D_2O were ingested; D_2O has to replace a relatively large percentage of the body's H_2O in order to cause ill effects.

Metallic hydrogen (10.1, p. 214). The metallic hydrogen that composes much of the planet Jupiter is probably in a molten state because of the high temperature inside Jupiter (as much as 20,000 K).

Odor of ozone (10.2, p. 215). The sharp odor encountered near high voltage sources, electric trains, etc. is largely due to ozone, but oxides of nitrogen (NO_x) also play a part. The ozone is formed when an electric arc ("spark") breaks down an O_2 molecule into atomic oxygen (O), which may then combine with an intact O_2 molecule to form O_3.

Liquid oxygen and submarines (10.2, p. 216). Large tanks of liquid oxygen (LOX) are carried on board some nonnuclear submarines (such as the Swedish *Gotland* class) to allow a small kerosene- or ethanol-powered electrical generator to recharge the submarine's batteries while the sub is deeply submerged.

Hydrogen peroxide as high-energy fuel (10.2, pp. 218–219). Concentrated hydrogen peroxide (80–98%) has been used as a high-energy propellant for over 50 years, both in rocket engines and gas turbines. One of the most interesting applications was an experimental rocket backpack built by Bell Aerospace for U.S. Army special forces in the 1960s. The rocket "burned" concentrated H_2O_2 over a silver catalyst grid to produce oxygen and high-temperature steam that was exhausted through two rocket nozzles, allowing the wearer to fly. Unfortunately, the backpack contained only 25 seconds' worth of fuel, making it impractical for military use. Other notable propulsion uses of H_2O_2 include the German Me-163B Komet fighter of World War II (methanol-hydrazine / H_2O_2); the U.S. Air Force "Black Horse" air-refueled spaceplane concept of the 1990s (jet fuel / H_2O_2); the large Beal Aerospace BA-2 space booster (jet fuel / H_2O_2); and the USAF/NASA X-37 spaceplane.

Dissolving power of ammonia (10.3, pp. 221–222). An interesting property of liquid NH_3 (*not* aqueous NH_3) is its ability to dissolve many alkali and alkaline earth metals, producing blue solutions. In the process, the metal atoms give up electrons to become cations.

Nitrogen oxides (10.3, p. 222). Nitrogen oxides are produced by high-temperature combustion in air, such as occurs in automobile and aircraft engines. NO_x emissions from cars can be controlled by means of computerized engine management and catalytic converters (section 13.4).

Volume increase of nitroglycerin (10.3, p. 223). Note that the figure given in the text is the volume of the product gases *after* they have been cooled to 25 °C. Since the gases would be very hot (hundreds of degrees C) immediately after detonation, the initial product volume could be double or triple the figure given.

Other nitrated high-energy compounds (10.3, p. 223). Other high-energy nitrogen compounds not mentioned in the text include *nitromethane,* used as a racing fuel in NHRA "Top Fuel" dragsters (enabling them to accelerate from 0–300 mph in 5 seconds); *nitrocellulose* (cellulose trinitrate), the primary component of modern "gunpowder"; *pentaerythritol tetranitrate* (PETN), a common military explosive; and *triaminotrinitrobenzene* (TATB), a shock- and fire-resistant explosive used in the primaries of modern nuclear weapons (Fig. 17.26).

CL-20, developed by the U.S. Navy, is also known by the tongue-twisting chemical name *hexanitrohexaazaisowurtzitane.* Like RDX, CL-20 makes an excellent solid-rocket fuel.

Nitrate-based explosives that are even more powerful are thought to be feasible [e.g., *octonitrocubane,* $C_8(NO_2)_8$], but have not yet been synthesized in quantities larger than a few micrograms.

Nitrate-fueled rockets (10.3, p. 223). The missile in the photo on p. 223 is a U.S. Army SAM-N-25 Nike Hercules, a 1960s vintage antiaircraft missile

Chapter 10

with a limited antiballistic missile capability; the first-stage solid rocket fuel was a mixture of nitrocellulose and nitroglycerin. A descendant of this missile, the LIM-49A Spartan or Nike-EX, protected the central United States from rogue ICBM attacks for a short time until Congress ordered the system deactivated in 1974.

Although less efficient than liquid-fueled rockets (p. 213), solid-fueled rockets can be designed for much greater acceleration because their combustion rate is not limited by a pump's ability to deliver fuel to the combustion chamber. One solid-fueled anti-ICBM missile known as Sprint (deployed alongside Spartan) could accelerate from 0 to 7400 mi/h (Mach 10) in under 5 seconds. An experimental Sprint variant known as HiBEX was even quicker, accelerating from zero to Mach 5 or more in $^1/_2$ second.

Malathion toxicity (10.4, p. 227). Malathion and other organophosphates kill insects by interfering with the transmission of impulses in their motor nerves.

Some anti-pesticide activists have claimed that malathion is dangerous, citing a 1976 incident in which 3 deaths and a number of injuries were attributed to a pesticide mixture containing malathion. However, investigators discovered that the deaths and injuries were caused by another chemical in that particular mixture known as trimethyl phosphorothiolate, which is extremely toxic (less than 1 gram could kill a 140-lb human). Purified malathion, by contrast, is relatively nontoxic (LD_{50} = 12,500 mg/kg); a 140-lb human would have to ingest nearly 1.8 *pounds* of purified malathion to receive a lethal dose. This makes pure malathion considerably less toxic than many "organic" pesticides such as pyrethrin (pyrethrum, obtained from the chrysanthemum plant), nicotine sulfate, and even sulfur. (See Chapter 10 Resource List for further information.)

Pesticide Toxicity in Perspective

substance	lethal dose (oral LD_{50}) (per kg body weight)	(for 140-lb human)
C. botulinum toxin	0.000 01 mg	6×10^{-7} g
Sarin (nerve gas)	0.1 mg	0.006 g
nicotine*	53 mg	3.4 g
caffeine	150 mg	9.5 g
pyrethrum*	1500 mg	95 g
aspirin	1680 mg	107 g
malathion (typical mix)	2800 mg	180 g
sulfur*	5000 mg	320 g
malathion (purified)	12,500 mg	795 g

*Substance used and classified as "organic" pesticide.

Natural organophosphates (10.4, p. 227). Not all organophosphate neurotoxins are man-made. The common soil bacterium *Streptomyces antibioticus* produces an organophosphate that is one of the most effective nerve poisons known.[1] Like other organophosphates, it blocks nerve transmission by deactivating the enzyme *acetylcholinesterase,* causing a rapid buildup of neurotransmitters in the synapse and thereby jamming the synapse.

[1]Neumann and Peter, "Insecticidal Organophosphates: Nature Made Them First," *Experientia* **43**:1235–1237 (1987), quoted in Thomas Miller, "Organophosphorus Insecticides," *Chemistry and Toxicology of Insecticides* (1996), <http://insects.ucr.edu/ent128/ops.html> (accessed 4/4/2000).

Thiols and natural gas (10.5, p. 231). Because of its strong odor, a thiol known as *ethyl mercaptan* (C_2H_5SH) is added to natural gas (methane / ethane) and LP gas (propane / butane) to allow gas leaks to be detected by odor. The smell of ethyl mercaptan is said to be so potent that if a single drop were evenly distributed through the air of a moderate-sized warehouse, a human could smell it.

Ethyl mercaptan reacts with rust to form a nonvolatile solid, so that methane or propane stored in a rusty tank can quickly lose all odor (making it an explosion hazard since a leak could not be detected by smell). Once the tank has been filled a few times times, however, the walls of the tank become saturated with the mercaptan and will no longer react.

Mercaptans and other sulfur compounds are responsible for the odors of rotten eggs (hydrogen sulfide), garlic, onions, and halitosis (which can often be treated with oxidizing toothpastes containing H_2O_2 and baking soda).

Neutralizing skunk scent (10.5, p. 231). Skunk scent is nearly impossible to wash away, but it can be quickly and easily neutralized using chemical principles. If the area sprayed by the skunk is soaked with a mild oxidizing agent (such as a mixture of 3% hydrogen peroxide, baking soda, and a little detergent),[2] the thiols responsible for the scent will quickly be oxidized to odorless sulfones, completely neutralizing the odor. A typical reaction is as follows:

$$\underset{\text{strong-smelling thiol}}{C_4H_7SH(l)} + 3\,H_2O_2(aq) \xrightarrow{NaHCO_3} \underset{\text{odorless sulfone}}{C_4H_7SO_2OH(l)} + 3\,H_2O(l)$$

The above formulation is mild enough to be used on pets, though it may change hair color; it must be used immediately, however, since H_2O_2 decomposes rapidly when mixed with other substances. Thiols in contaminated clothing can be similarly oxidized by washing them with bleach.

[2]William F. Wood, "Deodorize Skunk Spray" (20 July 1998), <http://sorrel.humboldt.edu/~wfw2/deodorize.shtml> (accessed 4/4/2000).

Plastics (10.6, p. 234). Plastics such as Teflon® and PVC will be discussed further in chapter 18.

Perfluorocarbons and diving (10.6, p. 234). Several scientists have raised the possibility of breathing an oxygen-saturated perfluorocarbon liquid as a means to very deep underwater diving. Much research along these lines was conducted in the 1980s and 1990s using an oxygenated perfluorocarbon fluid containing encapsulated granules of lithium hydroxide to absorb excess CO_2. In theory, if a closed-circuit scuba-type system using a perfluorocarbon as a working fluid were developed, it would allow a human to breathe oxygen at ordinary partial pressures even at tremendous depths; it would also prevent the "bends" (decompression sickness) by preventing the dissolution of gases into the blood. Perfluorocarbon-breathing mice have safely endured ambient pressures of nearly 25 kPa (3600 psi), corresponding to an ocean diving depth of about 8000 feet, and much greater depths may be possible.

Malaria cases and DDT (10.6, pp. 236–237). It is estimated that since its introduction in the early 1940s, DDT has saved the lives of as many as 500 million people that otherwise would have died of malaria.[3]

[3] J. Gordon Edwards and Steven Milloy, "100 Things You Should Know about DDT" (1999), <http://www.junkscience.com/ddtfaq.htm> (accessed 4/4/2000).

Water chlorination (10.6, pp. 237–238). According to the World Health Organization, an estimated 25,000 children worldwide are killed *every day* by pathogens carried by nonchlorinated drinking water. This tragic figure should help us keep the hypothetical one-in-a-million or one-in-a-billion cancer risk from chlorinated water in perspective.

Halons (10.6, p. 238). Halon-1301 (CF_3Br) has long been considered the only known chemical that can reliably quench an explosion in a tightly enclosed space (such as an airplane cockpit or the inside of a tank or submarine) without harming the people inside. As of 2000, the U.S. military was still using Halon-1301 in critical applications.

Helium and deep diving (10.6, p. 238). For the deepest dives, deep-sea and "technical" divers often use a mixture of 49.5% helium, 49.5% hydrogen, and 1% oxygen (hydroheliox) to help prevent problems that can result from high-pressure helium.

Lecture Demonstrations

Preparation of hydrogen (10.1, pp. 212–213). Small amounts of hydrogen may be generated and collected by using the setup shown below. In a large test tube (25- × 200-mm) clamped to a support stand, place several pieces of mossy zinc; cover with 6*M* HCl and immediately stopper the test tube with a one-hole stopper containing a length of bent glass tubing. Allow the reaction to proceed for several seconds before collecting a test tube full of H_2 as shown. Since H_2 has such a low density, it will displace air from the tube. (A simpler but still effective method is to drop several calcium metal "turnings" into a beaker of H_2O and invert a water-filled test tube over each fragment.)

Test for the presence of H_2 by holding a lighted splint at the mouth of the tube while it is held downward. A "pop" or "bark" will be heard unless the test tube contains pure H_2, in which case the H_2 should burn quietly around the mouth of the tube. Droplets of water produced by the reaction may sometimes condense on the test tube walls. Allowing a longer time for the tube to fill with H_2 will increase the purity of H_2 in it, or the method of water displacement may be used. **Do not point the mouth of the tube at anyone!** The reaction may be stopped by filling the tube with tap water. The dilute acid may be flushed down the drain with water; the remaining zinc may be rinsed and reused.

If the flame test is performed in a darkened room, students may see a pale flash as the hydrogen burns. The test must be performed quickly because hydrogen diffuses faster than any other gas (equation 5.15).

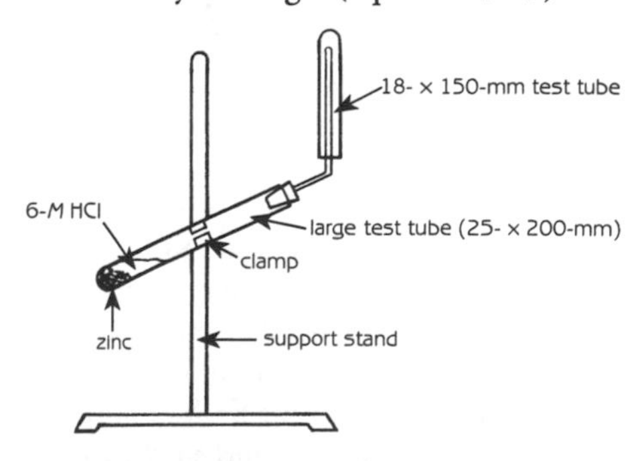

Preparation of oxygen (10.2, pp. 214–216). Small amounts of oxygen may be generated in a manner similar to that used for generating hydrogen, but the large test tube should contain 3% H_2O_2 and a pinch of MnO_2. Collecting O_2 produced by the apparatus using water displacement (Lab 17 and Fig. 10.4) is preferred since the densities of air and O_2 do not differ

Chapter 10

greatly. The glowing splint test for oxygen may be demonstrated by lighting a wooden splint, blowing out the flame, and thrusting the glowing splint into the tube of O_2; it should burst into flame.

Preparation of nitrogen oxides (10.3, p. 222). CAUTION: Perform only in a fume hood! NO_2 is toxic and highly irritating to the respiratory system. Concentrated HNO_3 is a strong acid and a strong oxidizing agent. If a fume hood is available, you may wish to demonstrate the production of brown, ***toxic*** NO_2 gas by reacting copper metal with concentrated nitric acid. Setting up the reaction in a 250-mL Erlenmeyer flask, stoppered as shown in the figure, will allow you to bubble the NO_2 gas through a test tube of water; after several minutes, test the water with litmus paper to show that the water is acidic due to the formation of HNO_3 (reaction 10.22).

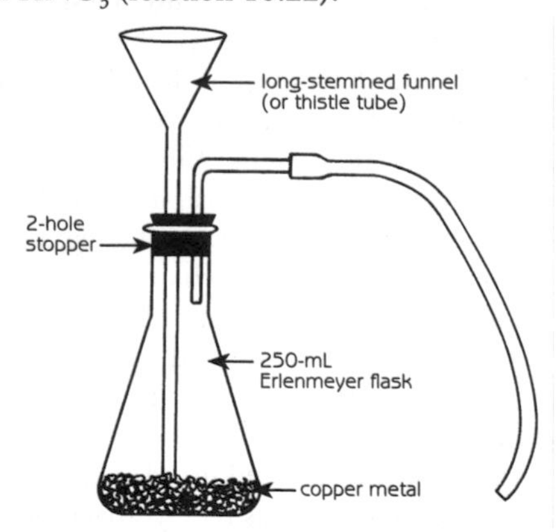

Additionally, colorless NO gas can be produced **in a fume hood** by reacting 8.0 *M* HNO_3 with copper metal (light turnings preferred); cover the metal with the acid and be sure the end of the long-stemmed funnel (or thistle tube) is below the surface of the acid. Initially, the gas produced is reddish brown, due to the reaction between the NO produced and the O_2 trapped in the flask. When the NO_2 has been flushed from the generating flask, collect a bottle or flask of colorless NO by water displacement (see Lab 17 for procedure); allow a small amount of water to remain in the bottle or flask. Stop the flask or bottle and place it in front of a white background ***in the hood.*** Stop the NO gas generation by filling the flask containing the copper and nitric acid with water. Remove the stopper from the container of NO for several seconds; reddish-brown NO_2 will form in the neck. Replace the stopper and shake the container to dissolve the NO_2. Repeat the opening, stoppering, and shaking procedure several times. Each successive time the container should fill more rapidly with reddish-brown NO_2 due to the partial vacuum produced by the NO_2 dissolution. Reactions 11.21 and 11.35 can be thus demonstrated. The copper in the generating flask can be rinsed, dried, and reused; the NO in the other flask can be allowed to react with air in a hood and the resulting HNO_3 (when shaken with water) rinsed down the drain. Neutralize any spills with $NaHCO_3$ before wiping them up.

Formation of phosphorus oxides (10.5, pp. 225–226). The combustion of phosphorus to form P_4O_6 and P_4O_{10} may be demonstrated by burning red phosphorus in oxygen. Collect one or more bottles of O_2 by water displacement (Lab 17). Using a burner, heat a small amount of red phosphorus (about the size of a pea) in a deflagrating spoon until the phosphorus ignites; immediately thrust the spoon into the bottle of O_2, keeping it covered as much as possible with a glass plate. Add several milliliters of water to the bottle, shake, and test the solution with litmus paper to show that it is acidic (blue litmus turns red); the acidity is due to the formation of H_3PO_3 (phosphorous acid) and H_3PO_4 (phosphoric acid) from P_4O_6 and P_4O_{10}, respectively.

The reaction of phosphorus with a halogen may be demonstrated by adding 0.3 g P_4 from a spatula to 1 mL Br_2 in an evaporating dish ***in a fume hood.*** A bright yellow flame and large amounts of "smoke" are produced immediately. The PBr_3 produced hydrolyzes in moist air to form H_3PO_3 and HBr, both irritants. **CAUTION: Wear rubber or plastic gloves when handling Br_2; a fume hood must be used since the vapor is toxic.** Unreacted Br_2 may be reacted with a solution of $Na_2S_2O_3$ or $NaHSO_3$ and the colorless result then flushed down the drain.

Chemistry of sulfur; sulfuric acid (10.5, pp. 228–231). If Lab 18 is not being done by students, it may be done as a demonstration during the discussion of this section. Sulfur may also be burned in a bottle of oxygen and the result shaken with water and tested with litmus to show that an acidic solution is produced.

Reaction 10.50 (Fig. 10.21) may be demonstrated by putting about 10 g table sugar (sucrose) into a small (50-mL) beaker; **carefully** pour about an equal volume of concentrated sulfuric acid over the sugar and stir briefly with a glass stirring rod. **CAUTION: Do not breathe the steam produced since it may contain sulfuric acid; perform only in a hood or in a well-ventilated area. Concentrated H_2SO_4 is a powerful dehydrating agent and can cause severe burns.** Spills should be neutralized with $NaHCO_3$ before being wiped up. When cool, *thoroughly* rinse the solid black residue with water and discard it in the trash can.

An alternative demonstration is to put a small amount of concentrated H_2SO_4 into a small beaker and gently drop a crumpled piece of tissue paper into the beaker; the reaction will be similar to the sucrose reaction since paper is made of cellulose, a glucose polymer; the same precautions apply.

The dehydrating ability of concentrated H_2SO_4 may also be demonstrated by placing a large crystal of $CuSO_4 \cdot 5\ H_2O$ in a few mL of H_2SO_4; note the appearance of white $CuSO_4$ (anhydrous) on its surface after a short time. The same precautions apply.

Chapter 10 Resource List

Note: Internet sources are given **for the teacher's reference.** Address or content may have changed since this publication of this teacher guide. Be sure to thoroughly review the location and content of any site yourself and check your school policy before recommending the site to your students.

Metallic Hydrogen

- Nellis, William. "Jumpin' Jupiter! Metallic Hydrogen" (1996). <http://www-phys.llnl.gov/H_Div/GG/Nellis.html> (accessed 4/5/2000). A description of the experiment that first produced metallic hydrogen, written by one of the researchers involved; also discusses some of the properties of metallic hydrogen and its abundance in the solar system.

Ozone Layer Controversy

- Science and Environmental Policy Project. "Stratospheric Ozone" (1998). <http://www.sepp.org/ozone/ozone.html> (accessed 4/5/2000). A collection of articles generally skeptical of the CFC-ozone-depletion hypothesis.
- Parson, Robert, ed. "The Ozone Depletion FAQ" (12/20/1997). <http://www.cs.uu.nl/wais/html/nadir/ozone-depletion/intro.html>; text files also archived at <ftp://rtfm.mit.edu/pub/usenet/news.answers/ozone-depletion/> under filenames ***intro, stratcl, antarctic,*** and ***uv*** (accessed 4/5/2000). Written by a physical chemist with an extensive meteorological background. Generally supports the CFC-ozone-depletion hypothesis, but does not support many of the extravagant claims of some environmental activists.

Pesticides

- Edwards, J. Gordon, and Milloy, Steven. "100 Things You Should Know about DDT" (1999). <http://www.junkscience.com/ddtfaq.htm> (accessed 4/4/2000). A discussion of many misunderstandings about DDT, including many positive facts not widely known.
- Miller, Thomas. *Chemistry and Toxicology of Insecticides* (1996). <http://insects.ucr.edu/ent128/lec_outl.html> (accessed 4/4/2000). A thorough discussion of the chemistry, mode of action, and safety of the various classes of pesticides (organophosphates, carbamates. etc.); includes structural formulas of individual compounds.
- Ames, B.; Profet, M.; and Gold, L. "Nature's Chemicals and Synthetic Chemicals: Comparative Toxicology." *Proceedings of the National Academy of Sciences USA,* 7782–7786 (1990). Archived at <http://socrates.berkeley.edu/mutagen/ames.PNASIII.html> (accessed 5/4/2000). Article comparing the toxicity of natural and synthetic chemicals; coauthored by Dr. Bruce N. Ames, inventor of the Ames test and director of the University of California Environmental Health Sciences Center.

Answers to Text Questions

Section Review 10.1 (p. 214)

1. What is the most important commercial method of preparation of hydrogen in the U.S.? *steam reforming*
2. What is one laboratory method of preparing hydrogen? *either by electrolysis or by reacting zinc with an acid such as HCl*
3. Write balanced equations showing the reactions between hydrogen and each of the following elements.
   a. potassium $2\,K(s) + H_2(g) \xrightarrow{\Delta} 2\,KH(s)$
   b. fluorine $H_2(g) + F_2(g) \xrightarrow{\Delta} 2\,HF(g)$
   c. sulfur $H_2(g) + S(s) \xrightarrow{\Delta} H_2S(g)$
4. List two important uses of hydrogen. *Any two of the following: synthesis of ammonia; hydrogenation of vegetable oils; rocket fuel; oxyhydrogen torch; self-luminous items (tritium)*

Section Review 10.2 (p. 219)

1. Sand is the oxide of what element? *silicon*
2. What is an allotrope? *two or more forms of the same element which differ in their properties but exist in the same physical state*
3. How is oxygen most often prepared commercially? *by distilling liquid air or by filtering air through a molecular sieve*
4. What is photosynthesis? Give the equation for the overall reaction if glucose is a product. *Photosynthesis is the process in which plants use energy from sunlight to convert $CO_2(g)$ and $H_2O(l)$ into $O_2(g)$ and carbohydrates.*
   $6\,CO_2(g) + 6\,H_2O(l) \xrightarrow[\text{chloroplasts}]{\text{light}} C_6H_{12}O_6(s) + 6\,O_2(g)$
5. How would you prepare some $O_2(g)$ in the laboratory? *heat $KClO_3(s)$ with $MnO_2(s)$, react Na_2O_2 with water, or electrolyze water*

Chapter 10

6. Differentiate between an oxide, a peroxide, and a superoxide. *An oxide contains the O^{2-} ion, a peroxide contains the O_2^{2-} ion, and a superoxide contains the O_2^- ion.*
7. Write a balanced equation for the combustion of butane, $C_4H_{10}(l)$.
$$2\ C_4H_{10}(l) + 13\ O_2(g) \xrightarrow{\Delta} 8\ CO_2(g) + 10\ H_2O\ (g)$$
8. List five uses of oxygen and two uses of ozone.
oxygen: *used for blast furnaces for steel manufacture; medical uses; breathing apparatuses; oxyhydrogen and oxyacetylene torches (welding); oxidizer in liquid-fueled rockets; metabolism*
ozone: *purification of drinking water; deodorizing air and sewage gases; bleaching textiles, waxes, and oils*
9. Give the formula for hydrogen peroxide and list two of its uses. *H_2O_2; antiseptic, bleach, rocket fuel*
10. Write the equation showing the decomposition of hydrogen peroxide.
$$2\ H_2O_2(aq) \longrightarrow 2\ H_2O(l) + O_2(g)$$

Section Review 10.3 (p. 224)

1. Though both nitrogen and oxygen are diatomic gases, nitrogen is far less reactive than oxygen. Why? *Nitrogen has a strong triple covalent bond whereas oxygen has a double bond.*
2. List three uses for nitrogen. *Any 3 of the following: production of ammonia for fertilizers; inert atmosphere for some foods and reactive chemicals; manufacture of explosives and rocket fuels; liquid nitrogen: fast-freezing foods; refrigerating foods and biological specimens*
3. Define the term ***nitrogen fixation.*** *conversion of atmospheric N_2 to compounds plants can use*
4. List the names of three important nitrogen fertilizers with their formulas. *Any 3 of the following:*
urea $[(NH_2)_2CO]$
ammonium nitrate (NH_4NO_3)
ammonia (NH_3)
ammonium sulfate $[(NH_4)_2SO_4]$
ammonium dihydrogen phosphate $(NH_4H_2PO_4)$
5. What is meant by the designation 15-10-7 on a bag of fertilizer? *15% nitrogen, 10% P_2O_5 equivalent, and 7% K_2O equivalent*
6. **(a)** What name is given to the process used to synthesize ammonia commercially? **(b)** Write a balanced equation for this reaction.
a. Haber process
b. $N_2(g) + 3\ H_2(g) \xrightarrow[\text{catalyst}]{\text{300 atm, 500–600 °C}} 2\ NH_3(g)$
7. How would you prepare each of the following in the laboratory?
a. N_2O $\quad NH_4NO_3(s) \xrightarrow{\Delta} N_2O(g) + 2\ H_2O(g)$
b. NO_2 $\quad Cu(s) + 4\ HNO_3(aq) \xrightarrow{\Delta} Cu(NO_3)_2(aq) + 2\ NO_2(g) + 2\ H_2O(l)$
8. List two uses of nitrous oxide. *anesthetic in minor surgery; propellant for food products (whipped cream); oxidizer in high-performance engines*
9. **(a)** Give the name for the process used to synthesize nitric acid commercially. **(b)** Write the balanced equations describing this process.
a. Ostwald process
b. $4\ NH_3(g) + 5\ O_2(g) \xrightarrow[\text{Pt-Rh catalyst}]{\text{1000 °C}} 4\ NO(g) + 6\ H_2O(l)$
$2\ NO(g) + O_2(g) \xrightarrow{\Delta} 2\ NO_2(g)$
$3\ NO_2(g) + H_2O(l) \xrightarrow{\Delta} 2\ HNO_3(aq) + NO(g)$
10. Why are old solutions of nitric acid a brownish or yellow color? *HNO_3 decomposes in light to form brown NO_2; NO_2 is present in old solutions*
11. List four commercial uses for nitric acid. *manufacture of fertilizers, drugs, dyes, and explosives; etching and photoengraving processes*

Section Review 10.4 (p. 228)

1. **(a)** What are the two major allotropes of phosphorus? **(b)** Explain how their structures differ from each other.
a. white phosphorus and red phosphorus
b. White phosphorus is P_4 and tetrahedral in structure; red phosphorus is a polymer consisting of chains of P_4 subunits.
2. How is phosphorus prepared? Write the balanced equation for this reaction. *Elemental phosphorus (P_4) is commercially obtained from phosphate rock by heating it to more than 1000 °C with coke (carbon) and silica sand (SiO_2).*
$$2\ Ca_3(PO_4)_2(s) + 10\ C(s) + 6\ SiO_2(s) \xrightarrow{\Delta} 6\ CaSiO_3(l) + 10\ CO(g) + P_4(g)$$
3. List four uses for phosphorus. *synthesis of phosphoric acid and other phosphorus compounds; manufacture of matches and specialized military ammunition*

4. Give five uses of phosphates, either as the acid (H_3PO_4) or as one of its salts. *fertilizers; acidity regulators and emulsifiers in foods; baking powder; toothpastes; water softeners; crop-protection chemicals (pesticides); metabolism*

5. Write the balanced equation for the reaction occurring when baking powder is heated.

$$Ca(H_2PO_4)_2 + 2\ NaHCO_3(s) \xrightarrow{\Delta} 2\ CO_2(g) + 2\ H_2O(g) + CaHPO_4(s) + Na_2HPO_4(s)$$

6. How do safety matches differ from strike-anywhere matches? *Safety matches need to be ignited by the friction on red phosphorus found on a special striking surface. Strike-anywhere matches have all the necessary components for ignition in the head of the match.*

Section Review 10.5 (p. 232)

1. Describe what happens to sulfur as it is heated from room temperature to about 250 °C; mention the various allotropes encountered. *Heating rhombic sulfur to above 96 °C converts it to monoclinic sulfur, which melts at 119 °C to form a pale yellow liquid. Viscosity increases with continued heating to about 150–187 °C and the color changes to reddish brown; by 187 °C it is very viscous. Continued heating to above 250 °C reduces the viscosity once again.*

2. **(a)** Describe the Frasch process for mining sulfur. **(b)** Why must the water be superheated?
   - ***a.*** *Superheated water melts the underground sulfur; compressed air forced into the molten sulfur forms a foamy mixture which is forced out of the ground and allowed to solidify.*
   - ***b.*** *The water will not melt the sulfur unless the water's temperature is above the melting point of sulfur (119 °C); since water's normal boiling point is 100 °C, pressure must be applied to the water to prevent boiling so that the temperature will rise sufficiently.*

3. List five uses for sulfur, including its most important use. *Five of the following:* ***synthesis of sulfuric acid*** *(most important use); vulcanization of rubber; preparation of insecticides, fungicides, pharmaceuticals, gunpowder, dyes, photographic materials, and textiles*

4. Give the equations showing the steps involved in synthesizing sulfuric acid by the contact process.

$$S(s) + O_2(g) \longrightarrow SO_2(g)$$

$$2\ SO_2(g) + O_2(g) \xrightarrow[V_2O_5]{\Delta} 2\ SO_3(g)$$

$$SO_3(g) + H_2SO_4(aq) + H_2O(l) \longrightarrow 2\ H_2SO_4(aq)$$

5. List five commercial uses of sulfuric acid. *Five of the following: production of fertilizers, fibers, plastics, dyes, paints, and detergents; petroleum refining; metal refining; dehydrating agent*

6. Why is skin damaged severely by concentrated H_2SO_4? *Answers will vary. Essentially, its effects on skin would be broadly similar to its effects on carbohydrates (Fig. 10.21); it is such a strong dehydrating agent that it reacts with many compounds to remove hydrogen and oxygen in a 2:1 ratio. The result would be carbonization of the skin—a severe chemical burn.*

7. List two uses for sulfur dioxide. *two of the following: manufacture of* H_2SO_4*; bleaching agent for paper products, oils, and starch; food preservative; fungicide*

8. What causes silver to tarnish? H_2S *reacts with silver and atmospheric oxygen to form black* Ag_2S *(tarnish) and water.*

Section Review 10.6 (p. 239)

1. Give equations showing the commercial methods for preparation of the halogens (F_2, Cl_2, Br_2, and I_2).

F_2: $H_2SO_4(aq) + CaF_2(s) \xrightarrow{\Delta} 2\ HF(g) + CaSO_4(s)$

$$2\ HF \xrightarrow[KF]{\text{electric current}} H_2(g) + F_2(g)$$

Cl_2: $2\ NaCl(l) \xrightarrow{\text{electric current}} 2\ Na(l) + Cl_2(g)$

Br_2: $2\ NaBr(aq) + Cl_2(g) \longrightarrow 2\ NaCl(aq) + Br_2(l)$

I_2: $2\ NaIO_3(aq) + 6\ NaHSO_3(aq) \longrightarrow 2\ NaI(aq) + 3\ Na_2SO_4(aq) + 3\ H_2SO_4(aq)$

$$5\ NaI(aq) + NaIO_3(aq) + 3\ H_2SO_4(aq) \longrightarrow 3\ I_2(s) + 3\ Na_2SO_4(aq) + 3\ H_2O(l)$$

2. Tell how you would prepare chlorine gas in the laboratory.

$$2\ H_2SO_4(aq) + MnO_2(s) + 2\ NaCl(s) \xrightarrow{\Delta} Cl_2(g) + MnSO_4(aq) + Na_2SO_4(aq) + 2\ H_2O(l)$$

or

$$4\ HCl(aq) + MnO_2(s) \rightarrow 2\ H_2O(l) + MnCl_2(aq) + Cl_2(g)$$

3. List three uses for each of the halogens fluorine, chlorine, and bromine; and two uses for iodine.

F_2: *fluoridation of water; toothpastes; manufacture of refrigerants, Teflon®, and perfluorocarbons; nuclear fuel refining; glass etching; lasers*

Chapter 10

Cl_2: bleaches and disinfectants; plastics; medicines; crop-protection chemicals

Br_2: agricultural fumigants; firefighting chemicals (halons); dyes and pharmaceuticals; fire retardants; photography; perfluorocarbons

I_2: antiseptic, iodized salt, photographic emulsions; some refrigerants; lasers

4. **(a)** What is Teflon®? **(b)** Give three uses for Teflon®.
   a. *polytetrafluoroethylene (a polymer of tetrafluoroethene)*
   b. *electrical insulators, high-temperature plastics, cookware, nonlubricated valves and bearings*
5. What is the antibacterial agent in swimming pools? *hypochlorous acid (HOCl)*
6. What is the basis for the bleaching action of household bleach? *HOCl adds to double bonds, converting them to colorless single bonds.*

Section Review 10.7 (p. 241)

1. What is the major source of helium? *natural gas wells*
2. List three uses found for the noble gases.
   He: *lifting gas in balloons and airships; cryogenic coolant; diving mixtures; inert atmosphere for welding; diluent for gaseous anesthetics; lasers*
   Ne: *neon signs; airport runway lights; lasers*
   Ar: *light bulbs; inert atmosphere for metallurgy and welding; flushing O_2 from molten metals; lasers*
   Kr: *airport runway lighting, high intensity flash-light bulbs*
   Xe: *photographic flash tubes; arc lamps*
   Rn: *radioactive tracer; cancer treatment (declining)*

Chapter 10 Review (p. 243)

1. What is the most abundant element in the universe? *hydrogen*
2. What is the most abundant element in the earth's crust? *oxygen*
3. Name the two primary ways in which hydrogen is produced commercially. *steam reforming and the petroleum refining process*
4. What is ***hydrogenation?*** Why is it used in some food products? *Hydrogenation is the addition of hydrogen to double (or triple) bonds. Hydrogenation is used to make oils more solid and thus more suitable for certain foods.*
5. What is an ***allotrope?*** *another form of an element that differs in its properties but exists in the same physical state*
6. Chemically speaking, what is ***combustion?*** *a burning reaction involving oxygen*
7. What is the purpose of the ozone layer? *to block most harmful ultraviolet rays from reaching the earth's surface*
8. **(a)** What element is the major component of air? **(b)** What percentage does it constitute?
   nitrogen; 78%
9. Most of the nitrogen produced in the United States each year is used to produce what compound? Name the process by which this compound is produced. *ammonia; Haber process*
10. Why is nitrogen fixation important to agriculture? *Nitrogen is an essential element to living organisms, but plants cannot use nitrogen directly from the air. It must first be fixed, or converted to compounds plants can use.*
11. The Ostwald process is used to produce what industrial chemical? *nitric acid*
12. Name three high-energy nitrate compounds. *three of the following: nitroglycerin (dynamite), TNT, RDX, CL-20; many others not mentioned in the text*
13. Name the two allotropes of phosphorous. Which one is more stable? *white phosphorous and red phosphorous; red phosphorous is more stable*
14. List three uses of phosphates. *fertilizers; acidity regulators and emulsifiers in foods; baking powder; toothpastes; water softeners; crop-protection chemicals (pesticides); metabolism*
15. What is the main use of sulfur? *to produce sulfuric acid, H_2SO_4*
16. What is the most reactive halogen? *fluorine*
17. What is the composition of household bleach? *5% sodium hypochlorite (NaOCL)*
18. Which one of the noble gases is the most common in the atmosphere? *argon*
19. Write formulas for the following substances:
   a. ammonia NH_3
   b. nitric acid HNO_3
   c. sulfuric acid H_2SO_4
   d. sodium nitrite $NaNO_2$
   e. ozone O_3
   f. cesium superoxide CsO_2

g. phosphoric acid *H_3PO_4*
h. ammonium nitrate *NH_4NO_3*
i. sodium hypochlorite *NaOCl*

20. Balance the following equations.

a. $XeF_4(s) + H_2O(l) \rightarrow XeO_3(s) + Xe(g) + HF(g)$
$3\,XeF_4(s) + 6\,H_2O(l) \rightarrow 2\,XeO_3(s) + Xe(g) + 12\,HF(g)$

b. $H_3PO_3(aq) \xrightarrow{\Delta} H_3PO_4(aq) + PH_3(g)$
$4\,H_3PO_3(aq) \xrightarrow{\Delta} 3\,H_3PO_4(aq) + PH_3(g)$

c. $NH_3(g) + H_3PO_4(aq) \rightarrow (NH_4)_2HPO_4(s)$
$2\,NH_3(g) + H_3PO_4(aq) \rightarrow (NH_4)_2HPO_4(s)$

d. $Ca_3(PO_4)_2(s) + H_2SO_4(aq) \longrightarrow Ca(H_2PO_4)_2(s) + CaSO_4(s)$
$Ca_3(PO_4)_2(s) + 2\,H_2SO_4(aq) \longrightarrow Ca(H_2PO_4)_2(s) + 2\,CaSO_4(s)$

21. Give a balanced equation for the combustion of the hydrocarbon heptane, $C_7H_{16}(l)$. (See reac-tion 10.16.)

$C_7H_{16}(l) + 11\,O_2(g) \longrightarrow 7\,CO_2(g) + 8\,H_2O(g)$

22. In 1992, 44.4 million tons of H_2SO_4 were produced in the United States. How many moles of H_2SO_4 is this?

$$4.44 \times 10^7 \text{ tons} \times \frac{2000 \text{ lb}}{1 \text{ ton}} \times \frac{1 \text{ kg}}{2.2046 \text{ lb}} \times \frac{1000 \text{ g}}{1 \text{ kg}} \times \frac{1 \text{ mol } H_2SO_4}{98.08 \text{ g/mol}} \approx \mathbf{4.11 \times 10^{11} \text{ moles}}$$

Chapter 10

Chapter 11 (pp. 244–271)

Selected Metals and Semimetals

Suggested Daily Pacing

95 **Check** homework.

Review pp. 235–241.

Introduce ch. 11, Selected Metals and Semimetals.

Give "pop" reading quiz over pp. 245–248:

1. Give the term for the extraction of metals from their naturally occurring materials and the preparation of them for use. *metallurgy*
2. What was the widely used separation method mentioned in the text? *flotation*

3–4. List two of the four general steps in the production of a useful metal from an ore. *(Any two of these: concentrate, reduce, refine, shape)*

5. What is a mixture of two or more metals that are usually melted together? *alloy*

Discuss homework.

Teach pp. **245–248,** introduction and sec. **11.1** Metallurgy—**11.2** Alkali Metals.

Review lesson.

SP: Use *Science in Action* ch. 5, pp. 101–103, to explain how to prepare for oral presentations. Also refer to *Science in Action* pp. 91–92 to remind students how to prepare their Science Project Notebook for their oral presentation day. Oral presentations begin in les. 102 (ch. 12).

HW: Read pp. 249–255, up to Steel Refining. Answer p. 252, questions 1–6. Complete Investigation Followup final draft. Bring Followup Grade Form and *Science in Action.*

96 **SP:** Collect Investigation Followup final draft. Grade the Investigation Followup and return in next lesson (see note.)

Note: This grading is intended to be a quick check for completion (all parts included) and neatness (follows format). The actual content will be the same basic material that is incorporated into the display board and oral presentation and will therefore be reflected in the presentation grade.

Since the Investigation Followup is to be included in the Science Project Notebook on oral presentation day, give priority in your grading of the Followup to the students whose oral presentation is to be given first.

Use *Science in Action* ch. 5, pp. 101–103, to briefly remind students how to prepare for the oral presentations, which begin in lesson 102 (ch. 12). Also remind students what to bring on the day of their oral presentation: Presentation Grade Form, Science Project Exhibit, Exhibit Grade Form, and their Science Project Notebook.

Check and discuss homework.

Review pp. 245–248.

Teach pp. **249–255,** sec. **11.3** Alkaline Earth Metals—**11.4** Iron, up to Steel Refining.

Review lesson.

HW: Read pp. 255–258. Answer p. 257, questions 1–7 and p. 259, questions 1–3.

97 **Give** "pop" reading quiz over pp. 255–258:

1. Name one of the two processes for refining steel mentioned in the text. *One of the following: basic oxygen process or electric arc process*
2. Name the process used to remove the internal stress of steel created by cooling it. *annealing*
3. What process can be used to make the steel both hard and tough? *case hardening*
4. True or False: Copper is the best electrical and heat conductor. *false*
5. What other element combines with iron to form steel? *carbon*

Check and discuss homework.

Review pp. 249–255.

Teach pp. **255–258,** sec. **11.4** (cont.)—**11.5** Copper.

Review lesson.

HW: Read pp. 259–263. Answer p. 260, questions 1–6 and p. 264, questions 1–5.

98 **Check** and discuss homework.

Review pp. 255–258.

Teach pp. **259–263,** sec. **11.6** Precious Metals—**11.7** Aluminum and Other Metals.

Review lesson.

HW: Read pp. 264–269. Answer p. 269, questions 1–8. First oral presentations due les. 102 (ch. 12).

99 **Check** and discuss homework.

Review pp. 259–263.

Teach pp. **264–269,** sec. **11.8** Important Semimetals and Their Compounds.

Review lesson.

HW: Begin studying ch. 10–11 for Test 7 in les. 101. Answer p. 243, Review Exercises 19–21; also answer p. 271, Review Exercises 9–14 and 22.

100 **Give Quiz 17** (over pp. 259–269).

Check and discuss homework.

Review ch. 10–11 for Test 7 in next lesson, using Chapter Reviews 10–11 on pp. 242–243 and 270–271.

HW: Study ch. 10–11 for Test 7 in next lesson.

101 **Administer Test** 7 (over ch. 10–11).

Note: You may choose to have the science project grade replace Test 7.

HW: Read pp. 272–276, up to Solvent-Solute Interaction. Answer p. 278, questions 1–4. Prepare for first oral presentations.

Teacher Notes

Chapter 11 Overview. This chapter, the second of the descriptive chemistry chapters, discusses the properties and practical uses of selected metals and semimetals. The alkali metals are discussed first, followed by the alkaline earth metals. Iron, the most widely used metal, comes next, followed by copper, the precious metals, and aluminum. Lead, titanium, and uranium are briefly discussed, followed by the semimetals silicon, germanium, and boron.

Although the primary focus of this chapter is to show students how chemistry is applied in everyday life (like chapter 10), this chapter can also serve as grounds for reviewing concepts taught in previous chapters.

Chapter opener photos (pp. 244–245). A continuous caster (p. 244) works by extruding molten steel through a rectangular opening while simultaneously cooling the extruded material to below the freezing point, causing the steel to solidify into a slab as it leaves the caster. The length of the slab is limited only by the supply of molten steel available and the physical length of the steel plant. Many plants incorporate hot-rollers, cold-rollers, and other shaping equipment "downstream" from the continuous caster in order to produce steel plate or sheet metal. When the steel reaches the end of the line, powerful cutting torches (or lasers, in some cases) slice it into manageable lengths for shipment.

According to Boeing, each 747-400 (p. 245) contains 73.5 tons (147,000 lb) of high-strength aluminum alloy. The maximum takeoff weight of a 747-400 is 417.5 tons, including 57,000 gallons of fuel and as many as 524 passengers.

Sodium-vapor lamps (11.2, p. 247). Sodium-vapor lamps are quite common in parking-lot and roadway lighting because they are unusually efficient at converting electricity to visible light (up to twice as efficient as fluorescent lamps and up to seven times as efficient as incandescent lamps). Low-pressure sodium lamps are quite yellow, whereas high-pressure sodium lamps may have a pink or rose-colored tint. However, if the light is blazing white or has a bluish tint, it is probably a metal halide lamp or (in older fixtures) a mercury-vapor lamp, rather than a sodium-vapor lamp.

Limestone caves (11.3, p. 250). The cavern in the photo is the "Sand Passage" in Kabul Cave, part of the Chiquibul cave system in the Central American country of Belize.

The world's largest known cavern is the Sarawak Chamber in Lobang Nasib Bagus (Good Luck Cave), Mulu National Park, Malaysia. Located deep underground beneath a mountain, the chamber is a single room as large as 17 football fields; its sandy, sloping floor measures 2300 ft × 1480 ft (700 m × 450 m), and the ceiling is never less than 230 ft (70 m, about 20 stories) above the floor.

Cement kilns as hazardous-waste incinerators (11.3, p. 251). The very high temperatures inside cement kilns makes them attractive as hazardous waste incinerators. Since both the temperature and the residence time in a kiln are even greater than in most purpose-built waste incinerators, kilns can do an excellent job of destroying these wastes. Burning combustible wastes such as old tires and used motor oil can actually reduce the cost of making cement in some cases, since they can serve as an inexpensive fuel.

Cast iron *vs.* wrought iron (11.4, p. 254). In the past (until the mid-1800s), the only way to make ductile, malleable iron was to reheat cast iron (pig iron) red hot for several hours or days in an oxygen-containing atmosphere, periodically removing it from the furnace to hammer it (either by hand or by special industrial equipment). The prolonged heating caused the dissolved carbon to react with oxygen to form carbon dioxide, while the hammering flattened and stretched the slag impurities into long fibers within the iron. This process produced a much tougher and more malleable iron called *wrought iron* that was nearly carbon-free and relatively corrosion resistant. Wrought iron was gradually replaced by steel after industrial-scale steelmaking processes were invented in the mid-1850s.

Iron *vs.* steel (11.4, p. 255). The difference between *iron* (the metal, not the element) and *steel* lies in the refining process. The reduction of iron ore to iron metal takes place at a temperature *below* the melting point of pure elemental iron; this is possible because the various impurities in the iron significantly lower the melting point. Steel, by contrast, is produced at temperatures *above* the melting point of pure elemental iron. Steel refining also starts with a relatively pure product (pig iron or better), whereas iron ore refining does not.

High-carbon steel (11.4, p. 255). It should be noted that despite its name, high-carbon steel still contains far less carbon than pig iron or cast iron (1.5% *vs.* 7–8%, respectively). It does contain more carbon than wrought iron, however, which has been treated to remove as much of the carbon as possible.

Cold working (11.4, p. 257). By rearranging the crystal structure, cold working causes distortions in the crystal to migrate and become "pinned" so that they can no longer move, making the metal harder and stronger. A side effect, of course, is that the metal also becomes more brittle (less able to bend without breaking). Excessive cold working can also break the metal. For this reason, an object requiring extensive cold working is often annealed to prevent excessive brittleness.

A commonly cited example of cold working is the repeated bending of a paper clip wire (which is usually made of soft, low-carbon steel). When the *straight part* of a paper clip wire is first bent, it bends relatively easily, but bending it the second and third time in the same place is somewhat more difficult. With continued bending, however, the wire becomes brittle, weakens, and breaks in half. (This effect is not seen in the curved parts of the wire, because there the wire has already been bent.) If the paper clip wire were bent several times and then annealed before it broke, it would regain its strength and become easily workable once again.

Quenching *vs.* tempering (11.4, p. 257). Note that rapid cooling of hot steel by immersion in a liquid is called quenching, not tempering; tempering refers to a mild annealing process that may occur after heat treatment. Though the two terms are often confused, quenching makes a metal harder and *more* brittle, whereas tempering makes it *less* brittle and is not a hardening process.

Heat-treated steels in ancient times (11.4, p. 257). Hardening steel by heat treatment was practiced in Roman times in order to make high-quality swords; many of these techniques were independently discovered by Asian swordsmiths as well. Some of the most advanced metalsmiths of the ancient world were the swordsmiths of Japan. The blades of Japanese swords *(katana)* were made from several different pieces of steel, with different compositions, that were hammered together to form a single blade. The cutting edge consisted of high-carbon steel that was heat-treated (by quenching) to an extreme hardness. The hard, brittle cutting edge was then hammer-welded to a tough core consisting of resilient, low-carbon steel; this assembly was then reinforced by layers of medium-carbon steel hammer-welded to the sides and back. The resulting composite blade was then polished to a mirror finish and fitted with a handle. This process resulted in a very tough, lightweight sword with an extremely hard cutting edge.

Copper alloys in coins (11.5, p. 258). All current United States coins in general circulation are composed mostly of copper (except, ironically, the penny, which is 97.5% zinc and is only copper plated). The nickel is the only homogeneous coin, consisting of a solid ingot of copper-nickel alloy (75% Cu/25% Ni). All other U.S. silver-colored coins (dime, quarter, half-dollar, and the discontinued Susan B. Anthony dollar) consist of a copper core faced with a copper-nickel alloy (91.7% Cu/8.3% Ni); the copper core can often be seen by carefully examining the coin's edge. The much newer gold-colored Sacagawea dollar (first issued in 2000) consists of a copper core faced with a special manganese-nickel brass (77% Cu, 12% Zn, 7% Mn, 4% Ni) that looks remarkably like 14-karat gold. The copper and zinc provide the color, the nickel provides tarnish resistance, and the manganese gives the proper electrical resistance for vending machine purposes.

Precious metals (11.6, pp. 259–260). Quantities of gold, silver, and other precious metals are commonly measured in *troy ounces,* an FPS unit equal to exactly $^1/_{12}$ pound, or $1^1/_3$ ounce avoirdupois (the common FPS ounce). In mid-2000, gold was valued at roughly $300 per troy ounce, and silver roughly $5 per troy ounce. The value fluctuates greatly, however; gold prices of over $800 per troy ounce (much more in today's dollars) were seen in the 1970s, when soaring inflation led to an increased demand for gold investments.

A huge, high-security vault located deep underground beneath the Federal Reserve Bank on Wall Street, New York City, contains over 13,000 tons (315 million troy ounces) of gold bullion.

Reactivity of aluminum with oxygen (11.7, p. 262). The high reactivity of aluminum with oxygen can be seen if aluminum is amalgamated with mercury. The aluminum oxide that forms cannot stick to the aluminum surface and protect it, so the underlying aluminum very quickly reacts with atmospheric oxygen and flakes off as the oxide.

Uranium (11.7, p. 263). Uranium is one of the densest natural elements, being roughly the same density as pure gold and only slightly less dense than osmium (the densest element). A 2-liter soda bottle full of solid uranium would weigh about 84 lb, compared to 50 lb for 2 liters of lead, 12 lb for 2 liters of aluminum, and 4.4 lb for 2 liters of water.

Uranium used for non-nuclear purposes has been processed to remove the valuable U-235 isotope for use in nuclear reactor fuel. For this reason, non-nuclear uranium is often called "depleted uranium" or "DU." Each Boeing 747-400 contains about 3300 lb of DU counterweights in its control surfaces. Another use for depleted uranium is radiation shielding; because of its density, uranium is even more effective than lead at blocking nuclear radiation (section 17.3). DU has also been used in flywheels, gyroscopes, high-performance yachts, and oil-well sinker bars. Uranium alloys used in armor and projectiles contain a small percentage of molybdenum or titanium for added strength; heat treatment includes both quenching and annealing to provide both hardness and toughness.

Coal contains trace amounts of a wide variety of elements, including uranium. In fact, a piece of coal contains more potential energy in the form of uranium than in the form of combustible hydrocarbons. In other words, when coal is burned, more energy leaves the furnace as uranium waste than as heat.

Uranium armor in action (11.7, p. 263). The uranium-armored tank in Fig. 11.17 is an American M1A2 Abrams, originally designed by Chrysler and manufactured by General Dynamics Land Systems. The exact composition of the M1A2's armor is classified, but it is thought to consist of several layers (including polymers and ceramic plates) that allow it to resist a variety of projectiles. The uranium layer consists of hardened uranium mesh encased in a thin layer of steel alloy.

During the 1991 Persian Gulf War, one M1 became hopelessly stuck in a morass of mud and (while stuck) took at least three direct frontal hits from 125-mm armor-piercing rounds fired at point-blank range by a trio of Iraqi tanks. Fortunately for the crew, the M1's uranium composite armor stopped all three rounds with only a notch or two on the turret face to show for it, saving the crew and allowing them to return fire. After friendly forces arrived, it was decided to destroy the stuck tank to prevent it from falling into unfriendly hands. A second M1 fired repeatedly at the stuck tank's ammunition magazine at close range, but two shots bounced harmlessly off, and a third detonated the magazine but left the tank still operational, thanks to blowout panels and a halon fire suppression system (chapter 10). The tank was eventually pulled from the mud, had its turret replaced, and went back into combat.

Properties of glass (11.8, p. 267). Glasses are examples of amorphous solids (section 9.4) because the atoms and ions in glass have a random and disordered structure instead of being regularly arranged (Fig. 9.23). Like other amorphous solids, glasses do not have a definite melting point, but rather soften and become less and less viscous over a broad temperature range until they become liquid. The midpoint of this temperature range is referred to as the *transition temperature.* The transition temperature for window glass and borosilicate glass is about 550 °C (1000 °F); that of fused silica is about 1200 °C (2200 °F).

It was once thought that glass flows very slowly even at ordinary temperatures (far below the transition temperature) over a time scale of centuries. However, detailed studies have now shown that glass cannot flow at all (even on a time scale of millennia) unless the temperature is close to the transition temperature of the glass.

Heat-resistant glass (11.8, p. 267). Although borosilicate and aluminosilicate glasses are not as heat-resistant as fused silica, they are much easier and cheaper to manufacture.

Although fused silica is resistant to high temperatures, halogen light bulbs often contain a warning not to install the bulb with one's bare hands because it will shorten the life of the bulb. This phenomenon occurs because (1) sodium ions from salt in perspiration will diffuse into the silica, weakening its structure, and (2) skin oils quickly carbonize when the bulb is lit, forming deposits of black carbon that soak up radiant heat from the filament. This process creates localized "hot spots" in the glass that can cause it to crack.

Lecture Demonstrations

Thermal decomposition of sodium bicarbonate (11.2, p. 248). The decomposition of $NaHCO_3$ can be demonstrated by putting about 3 g $NaHCO_3$ in a Pyrex® test tube and heating it with a burner flame. The decomposition reaction is

$$2\ NaHCO_3(s) \xrightarrow{\Delta} Na_2CO_3(s) + CO_2(g) + H_2O(l)$$

(Because it is a residue produced by thermal decomposition, Na_2CO_3 [sodium carbonate] is sometimes called "soda ash.") If the test tube is fitted with a one-hole stopper containing a length of bent glass tubing, you can bubble the CO_2 through limewater [saturated aqueous $Ca(OH)_2$] to produce a white precipitate or cloudiness due to insoluble $CaCO_3$ (calcium carbonate or limestone).

Production of slaked lime (11.3, p. 251). Slaked lime, $Ca(OH)_2$, is produced from calcium oxide ("lime" or "quicklime") by reacting it with water according to the reaction

$$CaO(s) + H_2O(l) \longrightarrow Ca(OH)_2(s)$$

The exothermic, volume-increasing nature of this reaction may be demonstrated by placing about 50 g of CaO lumps into a 150-mL beaker and adding about 25–30 mL H_2O. Steam will be produced after a short time and the volume will increase noticeably.

Flame tests (11.3, p. 252). Flame tests for calcium and strontium may be demonstrated here unless the students have done Lab 13; in any case, they could still be performed, even if only as a review.

Iron and steel (11.4, pp. 253–257). A field trip to a metal refining plant might be of benefit if one is in your vicinity. Also, having samples of cold-forged, heat-treated, or case-hardened items would be helpful in your discussion of hardening methods. Many high-quality wrenches are marked "cold forged," and drill bits, padlocks, etc. are commonly case hardened or heat treated. Many auto parts (wheel bearings, engine bearings, internal gears, etc.) are also heat-treated or case-hardened; you may be able to find inexpensive examples at a local auto parts store or salvage yard (be sure to clean any salvaged examples thoroughly).

Production of copper (11.5, p. 258). The reduction of copper(II) oxide to copper may be illustrated as follows. Either begin with black CuO or heat a piece of copper metal in a burner flame using tongs until it is covered with black CuO. Using a heavy glass Pyrex tube or an ignition tube to avoid melting the glass, set up the demonstration as shown in the figure below. (**CAUTION:** Wear eye protection.) With the air intake on the burner closed, turn on the gas, light the burner, and wait until the flame is a luminous yellow color. (This indicates that the air is flushed out.) Open the air intake to obtain a hot blue flame and begin to heat the tube in the region of the CuO, gently at first, then strongly. You should move the burner around periodically to avoid overheating in one spot. Heat until the black CuO has been reduced to Cu. Remove the burner from the tube and allow the tube to cool; then turn off the gas.

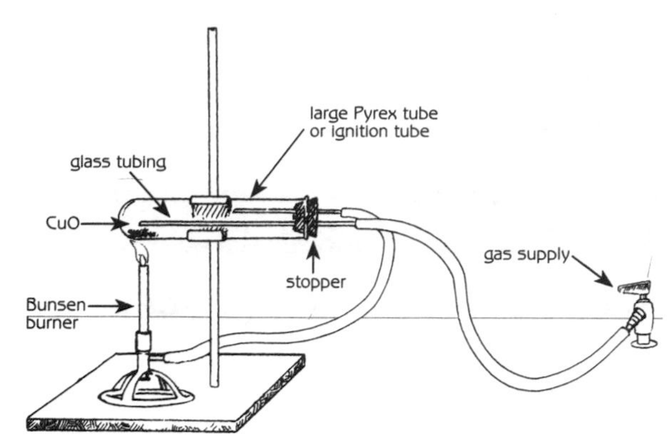

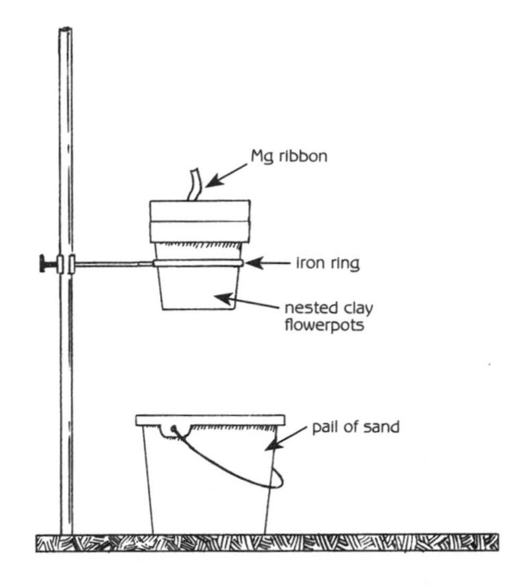

The thermite reaction (p. 262). The thermite reaction is a highly dramatic reaction that students will remember. However, because of the energy and temperatures involved, it must be performed very carefully. This reaction must be performed *outdoors* in an area where it will not pose a fire hazard; keep students at a safe distance. Intense heat, sparks, smoke, and molten metal are produced. Do not underestimate the fire hazard; the reaction produces molten iron at several thousand degrees Fahrenheit that will instantly ignite almost any flammable material.

Thermite and thermite starter are both commercially available from science supply companies such as Frey Scientific, but thermite can also be prepared from iron(III) ("ferric") oxide powder and aluminum powder by mixing 50–55 g Fe_2O_3 and 15 g Al powder (325 mesh or finer). Place this mixture in a *clay* flowerpot (about 2 1/2" inside top diameter) which has a piece of paper towel or filter paper covering the hole in the bottom (see figure). Place this clay pot inside another of the same size; place them inside an iron support ring clamped near the top of a support stand. A bucket of sand, about half full, should be beneath the pots to catch the molten iron that runs through the holes in the pots. Follow either option 1 or option 2. **CAUTION:** Do not stare or look directly at the thermite (or the magnesium ribbon in option 1) as it burns. The heat and UV radiation produced may be sufficient to cause eye damage.

Option 1: Make a cone-shaped indentation in the thermite mixture and fill it with thermite starter (about 1 teaspoon). Place a strip of magnesium ribbon (about 6 cm) in the starter. To begin the reaction, ignite the Mg ribbon using a burner or match and *stand back.* In a matter of seconds the thermite mixture will ignite and produce intense heat and molten iron. If the thermite fails to ignite, repeat by adding more starter and a new piece of Mg ribbon.

Option 2: Make a cone-shaped depression in the thermite, about $^3/_4$" deep and about $^1/_2$" – $^3/_4$" wide; fill with about 20 g $KMnO_4$ crystals. Make a small depression in the $KMnO_4$ crystals and add 5 mL glycerol to the depression; *stand back.* After 15–60 seconds, the glycerol-$KMnO_4$ mixture should ignite; seconds later the thermite should ignite. If ignition of the thermite fails, wait for 1–2 minutes before adding more $KMnO_4$ and glycerol. If the glycerol-$KMnO_4$ mixture fails to ignite, add more glycerol.

When the reaction has ceased, pick up the red-hot iron with tongs to show the students; cool the iron in a large beaker full of water before touching it.

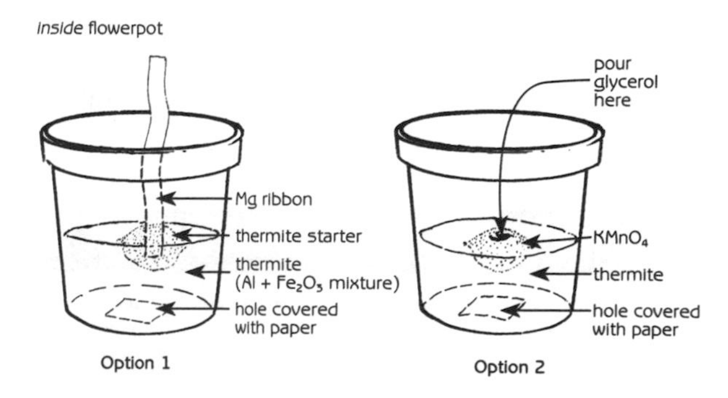

Dissolution of aluminum (11.7, p. 262). Demonstrate that aluminum dissolves in both acid (HCl) and base (NaOH; reactions 11.27 and 11.28) by adding strips of aluminum foil (heavy duty is best) to separate test tubes containing 6 *M* HCl and 6 *M* NaOH. Show that the gas produced is hydrogen in each case by inserting a lighted wooden splint; a "pop" or "bark" is a positive test.

Silicon and integrated circuits (11.8, pp. 264–265). *At press time,* factory-reject 3-inch silicon wafers etched with computer chips, similar to the larger wafer in Fig. 11.18c, were available from some electronics supply companies such as the Electronic Goldmine (see Ch. 11 Resource List) for only a few dollars each; they were discarded by the manufacturer due to small manufacturing defects. Such a wafer can be quite useful when teaching this section; not only do students get to see what purified silicon looks like, but they also gain an understanding of how chips are manufactured. (If your class is very small, you might even be able to examine the etched surface of the wafer under a dissecting microscope.) You may need to check several sources for these as continued availability is uncertain.

If you are unable to find a wafer, you may be able to obtain a burned-out or obsolete chip module (such as a microprocessor or EPROM) from a local computer repair store; if you are careful, you can often crack or pry open the case so that the chip is visible. EPROMs often have a window so that the chip is visible without opening the case.

Properties of silicates (11.8, pp. 265–266). Show samples of the minerals asbestos, mica, and talc (available from Frey, Sargent-Welch, and others) to demonstrate their properties. Be sure not to allow the asbestos to become frayed; the fibers produced can be hazardous to the lungs.

Contrast the ways in which a piece of window glass and a piece of mica cleave when they are fractured to show the amorphous (*vs.* crystalline) nature of glass.

Silicones (11.8, p. 268). You may wish to display or demonstrate the properties of representative silicones, such as silicone grease or spray, silicone rubber, "Silly Putty®" and a "Superball®."

Chapter 11 Resource List

Note: Internet sources are given **for the teacher's reference.** Address or content may have changed since this publication of this teacher guide. Be sure to thoroughly review the location and content of any site yourself and check your school policy before recommending the site to your students.

Iron and Steel Production

Bethlehem Steel Corporation, <http://www.bethsteel.com>. Steel industry web site.

U.S. Steel Group, <http://www.usx.com/ussteel/>. Steel industry web site.

Silicon Wafers

The Electronic Goldmine (electronics supply company), <http://www.goldmine-elec.com>. At press time, etched 3-inch silicon wafers were available from the catalog only (they were not featured as an online item). Catalogs may be downloaded from the site; printed catalogs were also available by request. **Note:** ***Continued availability is uncertain.***

Answers to Text Questions

Section Review 11.1 (p. 246)

1. What is ***metallurgy?*** *the science of extracting metals from their naturally occurring materials and preparing them for use*
2. What is an ***ore?*** *a naturally occurring material containing a metal in sufficient concentration to make its extraction profitable*
3. List the four general steps in the production of a useful metal from an ore. *concentration, reduction, refining, shaping*
4. What process of ore separation involves first mixing crushed rock with oil, water, and detergent and agitating? *flotation*

Section Review 11.2 (p. 249)

1. Explain why the reactivity of the alkali metals increases with increasing atomic number. *Answers will vary. The outer-shell electron becomes farther away from the nucleus as atomic number increases. The electron is therefore more easily lost, making the element more prone to undergo chemical reactions.*
2. **(a)** How are alkali metals generally prepared? **(b)** Write a balanced equation for the preparation of K by this method.
   a. *electrolysis of their molten chloride salts*
   b. $2\,KCl(l) \xrightarrow{electrolysis} 2\,K(l) + Cl_2(g)$
3. List four uses for the element sodium. *Any 4 of the following:*
   - *manufacture of drugs and dyes*
   - *metallurgy of some metals*
   - *heat-transfer liquid in some nuclear reactors*
   - *street lamps*
   - *sodium compounds (many possible answers, including those in Table 11.3)*
4. Give names and formulas for each of the following.
   a. caustic soda *sodium hydroxide,* $NaOH$
   b. soda ash *sodium carbonate,* Na_2CO_3

Section Review 11.3 (p. 252)

1. Differentiate between the causes of temporary hard water and of permanent hard water. *(Wording may vary.) Permanent hard water contains the sulfate of calcium, magnesium, or iron(II), whereas temporary hard water contains the bicarbonate.*
2. Show by an equation one cause of boiler scale.
   $Ca(HCO_3)_2(aq) \xrightarrow{\Delta} CaCO_3(s) + CO_2(g) + H_2O(l)$
3. Explain how a cation-exchange resin softens water. *Positively charged ions such as Ca^{2+}, Fe^{2+}, and Mg^{2+} in water are exchanged on the resin for Na^+ or H^+ ions.*
4. Give one use for each alkaline earth metal (Be through Sr). *Answers may include some of the following ideas:*

   beryllium: *x-ray tubes; structural materials; alloys used in aircraft, springs, and nonsparking tools; corrosion-resistant ship parts; (also nuclear weapons—ch. 17)*

   magnesium: *incendiary bombs; fireworks; old-fashioned flashbulbs; lightweight alloys (used in wheels, ladders, metal furniture, aircraft, and spacecraft)*

   calcium: *important nutrient (bones, teeth; nerve excitation, vision, muscle contraction); compounds used in building materials (limestone, cement, concrete, gypsum)*

   strontium: *metal form not listed; compounds used in signal flares and fireworks*
5. Give the chemical formula of each of the following substances.
   a. lime *CaO*
   b. slaked lime *$Ca(OH)_2$*
   c. limestone *$CaCO_3$*
   d. milk of magnesia *$Mg(OH)_2$*
   e. Epsom salts *$MgSO_4 \cdot 7\,H_2O$*
   f. magnesia *MgO*
6. Give one compound of each alkaline earth metal and its use. *Answers may vary; some compounds mentioned in the text are as follows:*

   beryllium: *no compounds mentioned, but alloys have many uses*

   CaO *(lime),* ***$Ca(OH)_2$*** *(slaked lime): many industrial uses*

   $CaCo_3$: *building material (limestone); iron ore reduction; cement manufacturing; pollution control*

   $Mg(OH)_2$ *(milk of magnesia): antacids; laxatives*

   $MgSO_4 \cdot 7\,H_2O$ *(Epsom salts): treatment of bruises and sprains; laxatives and cathartics*

   MgO *(magnesia): heat-resistant brick; insulators*

   $Sr(NO_3)_2$: *signal flares; fireworks*

   $BaSO_4$: *X-rays of GI tract; white paints*

   $Ba(NO_3)_2$: *pyrotechnics (fireworks)*

Section Review 11.4 (p. 257)

1. Tell by equations how pig iron is produced in the blast furnace.

   $2\,C(coke) + O_2(g) \xrightarrow{\Delta} 2\,CO(g) + heat$

   $3\,CO(g) + Fe_2O_3(s) \xrightarrow{\Delta} 2\,Fe(l) + 3\,CO_2(g)$

   $Fe_2O_3(s) + 3\,C\,(Coke) \xrightarrow{\Delta} 2\,Fe(l) + 3\,CO(g)$
2. **(a)** Give balanced equations for the production of slag in the blast furnace. **(b)** List two uses for slag.
   a. $CaCO_3(s) \xrightarrow{\Delta} CaO(s) + CO_2(g)$
   $CaO(s) + SiO_2(s) \xrightarrow{\Delta} CaSiO_3(l)$
   b. *manufacture of cinder block, concrete, and asphalt; support material for railroad ties; mineral wool (insulation, ceiling tiles)*
3. How does direct iron reduction differ from blast furnace reduction? *Direct iron reduction does not require the use of coke for the reduction process, but uses natural gas instead; the iron is also produced in solid form (sponge iron) rather than as a liquid.*
4. Describe the basic oxygen process for iron refining. *(Wording will vary.) In a high-temperature furnace, a supersonic blast of pure oxygen is blown against the surface of the molten iron, oxidizing the impurities; no external heat source is necessary. Lime and other fluxes are added to convert oxidized silicon impurities to slag; alloying metals or carbon may also be added.*
5. How does the electric-arc process differ from the basic oxygen process? *The electric-arc process uses an electric arc between giant carbon electrodes to provide heat to melt the charge, whereas the basic oxygen process uses a powerful blast of oxygen to oxidize impurities. Use of the electric arc process results in greater purity of the metal due to the higher temperature.*
6. Name three ways to increase the hardness of a piece of steel. *cold working, heat treatment, case hardening*
7. What process can be used to make a piece of heat-treated steel less brittle? *tempering*

Section Review 11.5 (p. 259)

1. List the five steps involved in the refining of copper from chalcopyrite ore.
   (1) flotation to concentrate ore
   (2) roasting in air (to convert iron impurities to FeO)
   (3) adding silica to remove FeO as slag
   (4) strong heating to produce molten copper metal
   (5) electrolytic purification
2. Give three uses of copper. *electrical wiring; cookware; piping; roofing materials; brass (screws, rings, nuts, bolts, jewelry, nozzles); bronze (corrosion-resistant parts)*
3. Differentiate between the composition of bronze and of brass. *Bronze is an alloy of tin and copper; brass is an alloy of zinc and copper.*

Section Review 11.6 (p. 260)

1. List the three primary precious metals. *gold, silver, platinum*
2. What property of gold allows it to be separated from sand or crushed ore by panning or sluicing? *its high density*
3. What chemical process is used today to extract gold from low-grade ores? *cyanide process*
4. What percentage gold is in 10 K gold? (Use 3 significant figures.)
   $$\frac{10 \text{ parts Au}}{24 \text{ parts metal}} \times 100\% = 41.7\% \text{ Au}$$
5. What is sterling silver? *silver-copper alloy (92.5% Ag, 7.5% Cu)*
6. Give three uses for gold, three uses for silver, and two uses for platinum.
   gold: *jewelry; dentistry (i.e., crowns) and medicine; microcircuitry; investment/financial reserve*
   silver: *coins; jewelry; dental fillings; photographic emulsions*
   platinum: *catalyst in pollution-control devices and petroleum production; electronic devices; spark plugs; surgical tools; dental work; investment (bullion); compounds used as anticancer drugs*

Section Review 11.7 (p. 264)

1. Give formulas for each of the following substances.
   a. alumina Al_2O_3
   b. bauxite $Al_2O_3 \cdot n\, H_2O$
   c. cryolite Na_3AlF_6
2. What is the role of cryolite in aluminum purification? *In its molten form it dissolves the bauxite, allowing aluminum to be produced electrolytically at reasonable temperatures.*
3. Write the balanced equation for the thermite reaction.
   $Fe_2O_3(s) + 2\,Al(s) \xrightarrow{\Delta} 2\,Fe(l) + Al_2O_3(s) + heat$
4. Why should basic solutions [e.g., NaOH(*aq*)] not be placed in aluminum containers? *They dissolve aluminum.*
5. Name one use for each of the following elements: lead, titanium, and uranium.
   lead: *car and truck batteries; weights; small arms ammunition; radiation shielding*
   titanium: *helicopters; airplanes; spacecraft*
   uranium: *fuel in nuclear power plants; counterweights; protective armor for military tanks; armor-piercing projectiles; radiation shielding*

Section Review 11.8 (p. 269)

1. What is meant by the term ***semiconductor?*** *a substance having electrical conductivity that is intermediate between insulators and conductors*
2. How is silicon prepared and purified? *Silicon is prepared by heating silica in an electric furnace with coke. To further purify the element, it is reacted with HCl(g) to form trichlorosilane, which can be further purified by fractional distillation.*
3. Account for the differences in the properties of the silicates asbestos and mica on the basis of chemical structure. *Asbestos contains polyanion silicate chains,* $Si_4O_{11}^{6-}$*, making it fibrous, whereas mica contains two-dimensional silicate sheets,* $Si_2O_5^{2-}$*, allowing it to be separated easily into sheets.*
4. Differentiate between a glass and a crystal. *(Wording may vary.) A glass is an amorphous solid (usually made of silica); although glasses are hard and do not flow, they have a random arrangement of molecules. A crystal, on the other hand, is characterized by a regular and repeating arrangement of molecules (section 9.4).*
5. What substances mix to form window glass (soda lime glass)? *It is a mixture of sodium and calcium silicates.*
6. How is glass made heat-resistant? *Boron and aluminum oxides are used in place of some sodium and calcium compounds.*

7. What are silicones? *polymers with a general formula* $(R_2SiO)_n$ *(in which two oxygen atoms in a silicate chain have been replaced by –OH or hydrocarbon groups)*
8. Give two uses of boron.

   boron: *borosilicate glass; laundry detergents; fire retardants; insecticides; fertilizers; abrasives; neutron absorbers; high-temperature alloys and ceramics*

Chapter 11 Review (p. 271)

1. List three general physical properties that distinguish metals from semimetals.
   - *high electrical and thermal conductivity*
   - *malleable and ductile*
   - *bright, shiny metallic luster*
2. What is an ***alloy?*** *a mixture of two or more metals, usually melted together*
3. Which two of the alkali metals are the most abundant? *sodium and potassium*
4. What commonly used material is made by heating limestone and clay in a kiln and mixing the resulting product with gypsum? When this material is mixed with water, sand, and crushed rock or gravel, what material results? *cement; concrete*
5. What is the most abundant metal in the earth's crust? The second most abundant metal? Which is more widely used? *aluminum; iron; iron*
6. Give the name and formula for the most commonly used iron ore. *hematite;* Fe_2O_3
7. What is the most common method for reducing iron ore to iron metal? What newer method does not involve coke? *blast furnace; direct iron reduction*
8. Name two common methods for refining iron into steel. *basic oxygen process; electric arc process*
9. How does heat treatment affect the hardness and toughness of steel? *Heat treatment makes the steel less malleable but far stronger and harder.*
10. Name the one metal that conducts electricity better than copper. *silver*
11. Name two well-known alloys of copper. *brass, bronze*
12. What is the most malleable metal? *gold*
13. What is an ***amalgam?*** *a mercury alloy*
14. What precious metal is commonly used as a catalyst in pollution-control devices and industrial processes? *platinum*
15. What property of aluminum makes it attractive for use as an alloy in aircraft, spacecraft, and structural materials? *its low density*
16. Why are copper (and its alloys) and aluminum resistant to atmospheric corrosion, whereas iron is not? *When copper (and its alloys) and aluminum are exposed to air, they react to form a layer of corrosion that protects the metal from further corrosion. The layer of rust formed when iron reacts to the air, on the other hand, is crumbly, and therefore fresh layers of the iron are constantly being exposed to the air.*
17. What is the primary use of lead? Of uranium? *car and truck batteries; fuel in nuclear power plants*
18. What is the most abundant element in the earth's crust? The second most abundant element? *oxygen; silicon*
19. What element is most commonly used as the basis of computer chips? *silicon*
20. What is ***asbestos?*** *a natural polysilicate mineral formed by heat and pressure within the earth's crust*
21. What is ***glass?*** *a transparent amorphous solid formed by cooling molten silica*
22. Distinguish between silicon, silica, silicates, and silicones.

    silicon—*an element, classified as a semimetal*

    silica—SiO_2 *(quartz, sand, etc.)*

    silicates—*compounds containing metals and silicon-oxygen groups*

    silicone—*a silicon-containing polymer with the general formula* $(R_2SiO)_n$

Chapter 12 (pp. 272–301)
Solutions and Colloids

Suggested Daily Pacing

102 **Return** and go over graded Test 7.

Check homework.

Introduce ch. 12, Solutions and Colloids.

Discuss homework.

Teach pp. **273–276,** introduction and sec. **12.1** Introduction to Solutions, up to Solvent–Solute Interaction.

Review lesson.

SP: Hear 3 oral presentations. Grade presentations on the day given, using grade forms from Appendix A.

HW: Read pp. 276–278. Answer p. 278, question 5. Prepare for next oral presentations.

103 **Review** pp. 273–276.

Teach pp. **276–278,** sec. **12.1** (cont.).

Review lesson.

Give Quiz 18 (over pp. 274–278).

SP: Hear 2–3 oral presentations.

HW: Read pp. 278–282. Answer p. 282, questions 1–6. Prepare for next oral presentations.

104 **Give** "pop" reading quiz over pp. 278–282:

1. What kind of solution contains all the solute possible under equilibrium conditions at a given temperature? *saturated solution*
2. What term refers to the total heat energy absorbed or released when one substance dissolves in another? *heat of solution*
3. In what type of equilibrium are reverse processes constantly occurring at equal rates? *dynamic*
4. True or False: The solubilities of gases increase with increasing temperature. *false*
5. What will happen to the solubility of a gas at a given temperature as the partial pressure of that gas increases? *Its solubility will increase.*

Check and discuss homework.

Review pp. 276–278.

Teach pp. **278–282,** sec. **12.2** Behavior of Solutions.

Review lesson.

SP: Hear 1–2 oral presentations.

HW: Read pp. 282–286. Answer pp. 286–287, questions 1–5. Prepare for next oral presentations.

105 **Check** and discuss homework.

Review pp. 278–282.

Teach pp. **282–286,** sec. **12.3** Measuring Solution Concentration.

Review lesson.

SP: Hear 2–3 oral presentations.

HW: Read pp. 287–289 up to Electrolytes and Colligative Properties. Answer p. 293, questions 1 and 2. Prepare for next oral presentations.

106 **Check** and discuss homework.

Review pp. 282–286.

Teach pp. **287–289,** sec. **12.4** Colligative Properties, up to Electrolytes and Colligative Properties.

Review lesson.

SP: Hear 2–3 oral presentations.

HW: Read *Lab Manual* Lab 19 and complete Prelab Assignment.

107 **Check** and discuss homework.

Conduct Lab 19: Colligative Properties: Determination of Boiling Point Elevation.

HW: Complete Lab 19 Report Sheet. Read pp. 290–293. Answer p. 293, questions 3–5. Prepare for next oral presentations.

108 **Check** and discuss homework.

Review pp. 287–289.

Teach pp. **290–293,** sec. **12.4** (cont.).

Review lesson.

SP: Hear 3 oral presentations.

HW: Read pp. 294–296, up to Types of Colloids. Prepare for next oral presentations.

109 **Give Quiz 19** (over pp. 287–293).

Review pp. 290–293.

Teach pp. **294–296,** sec. **12.5** Colloids, up to Types of Colloids.

Review lesson.

SP: Hear 3 oral presentations.

HW: Read pp. 296–298. Answer p. 299, questions 1–6. Prepare for next oral presentations.

110 **Check** and discuss homework.

Review pp. 294–296.

Teach pp. **296–298,** sec. **12.5** (cont.).

Review lesson.

SP: Hear 2–3 oral presentations.

HW: Read *Lab Manual* Lab 20 and complete Prelab Assignment.

111 **Check** and discuss homework.

Conduct Lab 20: Colloids.

HW: Complete Lab 20 Report Sheet. Read pp. 302–305. Answer p. 305, questions 1–4. Prepare for next oral presentations.

Teacher Notes

Chapter 12 Overview. Mixtures, briefly mentioned in chapter 3, are the subject of this chapter, which focuses on two particular types of mixtures: solutions and colloids. After introducing some basic terminology and reviewing different types of solutions, the chapter explains the solution process, various factors that can affect solution rate, and the interactions at the molecular level that cause one substance to dissolve in another. The behavior of solutions is then discussed, including such topics as solution equilibrium, factors that affect solubility, and thermodynamic changes that occur when a solute dissolves in a solvent. The concept of concentration is then introduced, and various ways to measure it are explained. Colligative properties of solutions, which depend primarily on concentration, are then discussed, including an explanation of osmosis. The section concludes with a look at a special class of mixtures called colloids, which are very common in everyday life.

The solution process (12.1, p. 275). Because water is the most familiar solvent and the most commonly encountered in everyday life, it is the primary solvent discussed in this chapter. However, keep in mind that practically any liquid can act as a solvent.

Hydration *vs.* solvation (12.1, p. 275). Point out the differences and similarities in the terms *hydrated* and *solvated;* hydration is a particular type of solvation. Discuss the process of solvation.

"Like dissolves like" (12.1, p. 277). The rule "like dissolves like" is a rule of thumb rather than a scientific law; it is sometimes difficult to predict the solubility of a given compound based solely on the type of intermolecular forces involved. However, it is accurate enough for our purposes here.

Solubility of ionic compounds (12.1, p. 277). If you wish, you may test your students' understanding of Table 12.2 by asking them whether the following ionic compounds would be soluble in water:

K_2CO_3 *yes*	$Mg(OH)_2$ *no*
$Fe(NO_3)_3$ *yes*	MnS *no*
$Ca_3(PO_4)_2$ *no*	AgI *no*
$PbSO_4$ *no*	$NH_4C_2H_3O_2$ *yes*
$CuSO_4$ *yes*	$Zn(C_2H_3O_2)_2$ *yes*
Na_2S *yes*	$SrSO_4$ *no*
$CsOH$ *yes*	CaS *yes*

Chapter 12

Molar concentration (12.3, pp. 283–284). Molarity (moles per liter) serves as the link between *volume* and *moles* since it contains both of those units.

Vapor pressure lowering (12.4, p. 288). The lowering of vapor pressure is primarily the result of intermolecular forces between solute and solvent particles. Although at first glance it might seem as if the solute particles at the surface simply "crowd out" the solvent molecules, thereby reducing the evaporation rate, by far the largest effect is the strong *attraction* the solvent has for the solute. Remember that for the solute to dissolve in the solvent in the first place, the solvent molecules must be even more strongly attracted to the solute particles than they are to each other (otherwise the solvent would just "close ranks" due to surface tension and exclude the solute, as when oil and water are mixed). The strong attraction for the solute particles acts like a "glue" that binds the solvent together more tightly, thereby lessening the tendency of solvent molecules to escape.

Colloidal particles (12.5, p. 294). Though the actual dimensions of colloidal particles are not clearly defined, it is generally agreed that at least one of its dimensions (length, width, or thickness) must be between 1 nm and 100 nm. Mixtures containing particles having all of their dimensions larger than about 100 nm are considered *suspensions,* and those with particles having all their dimensions smaller than about 1 nm are considered true solutions (see Table 12.9). Colloidal particles may occur in a wide variety of shapes, ranging from spheres (milk) to long fibers (gelatin).

Blue sky and the Tyndall effect (12.5, p. 294). It is a common misconception in scientific circles that the sky is blue (and sunsets red) because of colloidal scattering due to the Tyndall effect. Actually, the sky would be blue even if it contained no dust or colloidal particles whatsoever. It is true that light is scattered as it passes through the atmosphere, and that short wavelengths are scattered more than longer wavelengths, but most of this scattering comes from relativistic interactions between photons of light and the valence electrons of nitrogen and other atoms in air molecules, rather than from Tyndall-effect scattering from colloidal particles.

A smaller amount of colloidal scattering does occur in the air (from dust particles, etc.), but usually contributes less to sky color than does the atomic scattering described above. However, significant colloidal scattering can occur if the fine dust (or smoke) content of the atmosphere is dramatically increased. For example, the cataclysmic eruption of the volcano Krakatau (Krakatoa) in 1883 and the multi-megaton airburst of an asteroid or comet over Tunguska, Siberia, in 1908 both injected millions of tons of dust into the upper atmosphere that spread around the world, causing dramatically colored sunrises and sunsets for many months after each event.

Lecture Demonstrations

Solubility and miscibility (12.1, pp. 274–278). You can demonstrate the usage of the terms (1) miscible, (2) immiscible, (3) soluble, and (4) insoluble by mixing (1) ethanol (or methanol, isopropanol, car antifreeze) and water, (2) vegetable oil and water, (3) $CuSO_4$ (small amount) and water, and (4) I_2 and water, respectively.

Factors affecting solution rate (12.1, p. 275). You can illustrate how stirring and increasing the temperature of a solvent increase the rate of solution as follows. Add a crystal of $KMnO_4$ to each of two 50-mL beakers containing about 30 mL water; stir one and not the other. Add a similar-sized crystal of $KMnO_4$ to each of two 50-mL beakers, one containing very hot water and the other containing cold or room-temperature water; do not stir. Note the relative rates of solution in each case.

A similar demonstration can be done with table salt or table sugar. If sugar is used, be careful not to add too much in demonstration (2), or else it may cake together and greatly slow the dissolving process.

"Like dissolves like" (12.1, p. 277). You can demonstrate the principle of "like dissolves like" by adding a few crystals of $KMnO_4$ (ionic) and I_2 (nonpolar covalent) to separate test tubes each containing about 8 mL H_2O (polar covalent) and 8 mL dichloroethane (nonpolar covalent). Ask students prior to the demonstration to predict which liquid each solute will dissolve in.

Stopper both tubes and shake them vigorously. When the phases separate after shaking, the $KMNO_4$ color will occur in the H_2O layer of first test tube, while the I_2 color will occur in the $C_2H_2Cl_2$ layer of the second test tube.

For a simpler and less expensive demonstration, add table salt and paraffin wax to each of two clear plastic cups containing (1) water and (2) kerosene. Stirring may be necessary to dissolve the paraffin.

Supersaturated solutions (12.2, p. 279). Supersaturation may be demonstrated by either of the following demonstrations.

1. Prior to class time, fill a large (25- × 200-mm) test tube about 1/2 to 2/3 full of sodium thiosulfate pentahydrate ($Na_2S_2O_3 \cdot 5\ H_2O$) and heat carefully in a burner flame or in a boiling water bath until a clear liquid is obtained. Clamp the tube in an upright position on a support stand and allow to cool to room temperature. Do not disturb it during this time. (You may wish to prepare 2 or 3 such tubes.) This liquid is a supersaturated solution which may be crystallized by the addition of a crystal of $Na_2S_2O_3 \cdot 5\ H_2O$. Note that the crystallization process is exothermic. The tube may be stoppered and reused repeatedly. Use of a new, unscratched tube will help prevent premature crystallization.

2. Prior to class time, heat a mixture of 87.5 g $NaC_2H_3O_2 \cdot 3\ H_2O$ and 25 mL deionized water in a 250-mL Erlenmeyer flask using a boiling water bath; swirl the flask periodically and heat until a clear solution is obtained. Cover the mouth of the flask with a 150-mL beaker and allow to cool undisturbed until it reaches room temperature (several hours). For the demonstration, place a few crystals of $NaC_2H_3O_2 \cdot 3\ H_2O$ on a clean piece of hardboard or a piece of plate glass. Slowly pour the supersaturated solution onto the crystals; crystallization occurs immediately, trapping all the water inside the solid, and heat is liberated. You may make pillars of different sizes or shapes or "draw" different patterns as you pour the solution. The solid may be reused repeatedly (until it is contaminated) by cutting it up and returning it to the flask; stopper the flask if it is to be reused. Losses of water by evaporation occur after several cycles; this can be replaced by adding a *small* amount of water.

Gas solubility and pressure (12.2, pp. 280–281). Henry's law can be demonstrated by removing the label from a fresh 2-liter bottle of carbonated soft drink, shaking it, and then loosening the cap to release the pressure. As soon as the pressure is released, a significant amount of CO_2 comes out of solution, causing a large amount of fizzing (CO_2 bubbles).

This demonstration can sometimes be messy; perform over a sink if possible (or pour off some of the soda before class to minimize spattering). The more vigorously the soda is shaken before opening, the more CO_2 is released. You may wish to experiment between clear sodas /colas and regular/diet sodas to find out what works best. Note that warm soda usually fizzes more than refrigerated soda (because gas solubility decreases with increasing temperature).

Gas solubility and temperature (12.2, p. 280). The effect of temperature on the solubility of a gas in a liquid can be demonstrated by opening two identical cans of soft drink—one cold and the other warm—and pouring them into separate glasses. The warm one will usually effervesce more due to the lower solubility of CO_2 at the higher temperature. Likewise, heating a beaker of soda over a Bunsen burner will drive off the CO_2, leaving the soda very "flat" when it is cooled; clear soda works best since the formation of CO_2 bubbles during heating is more apparent.

Solid solubility and temperature (12.2, p. 281). You may demonstrate the decrease in solubility of $Ca(C_2H_3O_2)_2$ with increasing temperature by heating a solution containing 8 g $Ca(C_2H_3O_2)_2$ in 25 mL H_2O. A precipitate of the salt forms. Note that decreasing solubility with increased temperature is the *exception* to the rule; most solid solutes become more soluble, not less, as the temperature of the solution is increased.

Heats of solution (12.2, pp. 281–282). Demonstrate ΔH_{soln} by measuring 40 g $CaCl_2$ and 30 g NH_4NO_3 into separate capped reagent bottles. Add 100 mL water to each and shake to dissolve the solids. Note the enthalpy changes in each case. **CAUTION:** The bottle containing $CaCl_2$ gets quite hot; be cautious of getting burned. You may wish to vent the hot bottle before passing it around the class since air pressure builds up inside due to the increased temperature.

Epsom salt ($MgSO_4 \cdot 7\ H_2O$) also produces a large amount of heat when it is first dehydrated and then added to water. (Dehydrate the salt by heating an amount of the hydrate in a crucible.)

Dilutions (12.3, pp. 284–285). Demonstrate the fact that dilution of a solution does not change the number of *moles* of solute, only its *concentration,* as follows. Dissolve a few crystals of $KMnO_4$ in 10 mL H_2O (dark purple). Dilute to about 100 mL so there is a noticeable lightening of the color. The number of moles of $KMnO_4$ does not change, but its concentration does.

Freezing point depression (12.4, p. 289). Demonstrate the freezing point lowering of an ionic solute as follows. Allow the temperature of an ice-water mixture to equilibrate in two separate 400-mL beakers; record the temperature of each on the chalkboard. (Be sure you have enough ice in equilibrium with the water so that the added salt does not melt all the ice.) Add 50 g $CaCl_2$ to one of the beakers, stir, wait for the temperature to equilibrate, and record the temperature. (Sodium chloride may also be used.) Ice-cream churns for making homemade ice cream are typically packed with a mixture of ice and rock salt (NaCl) to produce a lower temperature.

This demonstration also helps explain why icy streets and sidewalks are "salted" in the winter. Both $CaCl_2$ and NaCl may be used for "salting"; $CaCl_2$ is more potent because it produces three ions when it dissolves rather than two, but NaCl is much cheaper and is therefore more widely used.

Conductivity of electrolytes (12.4, p. 290). A conductivity apparatus may be purchased from a science supply company (e.g., Frey, Sargent-Welch). If you have such an apparatus, you may wish to test the conductivity of a number of solutions for the class, such as deionized water, tap water, ethanol, methanol, acetone, 0.1 *M* NaCl, 0.1 *M* $HC_2H_3O_2$, 0.1 *M* HCl, 0.1 *M* NH_3, 0.1 *M* NaOH, 0.1 *M* H_2SO_4, 0.1 *M* sucrose, 0.1 *M* ascorbic acid or oxalic acid (both diprotic), 0.1 *M* $CuSO_4$. Be sure to ***unplug the apparatus*** (or switch it off, if it is so equipped) and rinse the electrodes using a wash bottle after each test.

If you are experienced at safely designing and wiring 120-volt electrical circuits, you may wish to assemble your own conductivity apparatus from supplies locally available at hardware stores (see figure). One advantage of the constructed apparatus is the ability to test conductivities in a greater variety of solutions with better qualitative results. That is, all three lamps light up in strong electrolytes; weak electrolytes may need to have the 40-W lamp unscrewed from the socket so that the 10-W and 1-W (or 4-W) lamps will be able to light. Very weak electrolytes will be able to light up only the 1-W (or 4-W) lamp with the 40-W and 10-W lamps partially unscrewed. Nonelectrolytes will not light even the 1-W (or 4-W) lamp. For best results, use bulbs of the same type (i.e., all frosted or all unfrosted). **CAUTION:** To avoid electrical shock, **do not touch the electrodes when the apparatus is plugged in.** 120-volt AC current is quite capable of triggering ventricular fibrillation, resulting in sudden cardiac death.

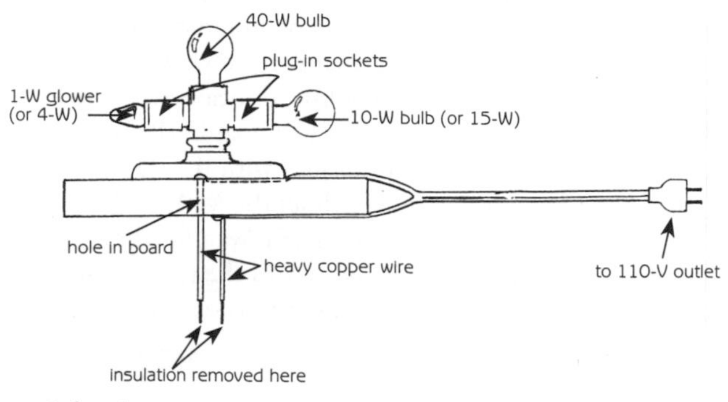

Osmotic pressure (12.4, p. 291). Demonstrate osmotic pressure by boring a large hole in a potato or carrot, adding enough saturated sugar solution or molasses to the hole to nearly fill it, stoppering it tightly with a one-hole stopper fitted with a foot-long piece of glass tubing, and placing the assembly into a beaker of water. The level of liquid in the potato should be such that it is just seen at the top of the stopper. (Food coloring may be added to make the colorless sugar solution more visible). The high sugar concentration will cause water to pass by osmosis from the potato into the reservoir beneath the stopper, causing the colored liquid in the glass tube to rise. Results can usually be seen within an hour. (You may wish to try this before class to get an idea of what results to expect.)

The Tyndall effect (12.5, p. 294). Demonstrate the Tyndall effect as follows. Prior to class, tape a heavy piece of paper with a single hole punched in it over the end of a powerful flashlight, or use a setup like Fig. 13.15 where a one-hole stopper is placed in front of the lens of a slide projector. This will provide a narrow beam of light. In class, dissolve 5 g $Na_2S_2O_3 \cdot 5\ H_2O$ in about 700 mL deionized H_2O in a large beaker (1 L). Place the beaker of solution in front of the beam of light in a darkened room to show that no scattering of light occurs. Add 5 mL of concentrated HCl and mix well; note what happens. As colloidal sulfur forms, the light is scattered. Tell the students to observe the colors of the scattered *and* the transmitted beams as the reaction proceeds. The color of the transmitted beam on the wall should change colors, as in a sunset, until the sulfur particles become so concentrated that light cannot pass through. Colors can be seen in the beaker as well, depending on the angle of observation.

For a quicker and less expensive demonstration, use the same setup as above, but add a teaspoon of milk to the water instead of $Na_2S_2O_3 \cdot 5\ H_2O$ and HCl.

Lab 22 may also be done as a demonstration in this section.

Brownian motion (p. 295). Various types of apparatus for demonstrating Brownian motion are available from science supply companies (e.g., Frey Scientific).

Answers to Text Questions

Section Review 12.1 (p. 278)

1. In each of the following solutions, indicate which substance is the solute and which is the solvent.
   a. a solution containing 5.6 g KBr and 55.4 g H_2O *solvent = water; solute = KBr*
   b. a solution containing 3.9 g paraffin wax and 100. g benzene
   solvent = benzene; solute = paraffin wax
   c. a solution containing 25.0 g methanol and 15.0 g H_2O
   solvent = methanol; solute = water
   d. a solution containing 50.0 g silver and 13.0 g mercury *either way is acceptable; hardened dental amalgam can be considered a mercury-in-silver alloy (Table 12.1), but a liquid amalgam can be considered a silver-in-mercury solution.*
2. Describe the behavior of the following pairs of substances as soluble, insoluble, miscible, or immiscible.
   a. 1.00 g AgCl is shaken with 100.0 g H_2O to give a milky mixture which separates into a clear liquid and a white sediment. *insoluble*
   b. 10.0 g $CuSO_4 \cdot 5\ H_2O$ and 150 g H_2O are mixed to give a blue solution that is clear (i.e., not cloudy) and of one phase. *soluble*
   c. 10.0 g chloroform and 25.0 g H_2O are shaken together; the mixture quickly separates into two layers. *immiscible*
   d. 500 g ethylene glycol and 500 g H_2O are shaken together; the mixture is clear and colorless and does not separate into layers. *miscible*
3. What is meant by each of the following terms?
   a. solvated *The solute particles are surrounded by solvent molecules.*
   b. hydrated *The solute particles are surrounded by water molecules.*
4. Differentiate between ***dissociation*** and ***ionization.*** *(Wording will vary.)*
   Dissociation *involves the physical separation of preexisting ions that occurs when an ionic compound is solvated; it does not form new ions.*
   Ionization *involves the formation of new ions and occurs when certain covalent compounds are solvated*
5. List three things that could be done to hasten the rate of solution of a large crystal of $CuSO_4 \cdot 5\ H_2O$ in water. *grind it; stir the water after adding the crystal; use warmer water*

Section Review 12.2 (p. 282)

1. What is meant by the term ***solution equilibrium?*** *a state of dynamic equilibrium that exists when the rate of crystallization is equal to the rate of dissolution*
2. What is a dynamic equilibrium? *a situation in which two processes are continually occurring in opposite directions at equal rates, resulting in no net change in conditions.*
3. What is meant when a solution is described as saturated, unsaturated, and supersaturated, respectively?
   saturated solution: *a solution which contains all the solute possible under equilibrium conditions at a given temperature*
   unsaturated solution: *a solution which contains less solute than it could at equilibrium at a specific temperature*
   supersaturated solution: *a solution which contains more solute than it could under equilibrium conditions*
4. Relating pressure to solubility, explain why deep-sea divers often replace the nitrogen in their air tanks with helium. *The solubility of gases increases with increased pressure. Deep-sea divers often use helium because it is less soluble than nitrogen and thus dissolves less in the bloodstream.*
5. Based on what you have read, would you expect the cool waters of the Atlantic Ocean to contain more or less dissolved oxygen than the waters of a tropical lagoon? What effect might this have on the abundance of sea life? *One would expect that the Atlantic Ocean would have more dissolved oxygen due to the colder water temperature (p. 280); this could allow it to support more sea life than would a tropical lagoon. (This is indeed the case.)*
6. What is meant by the term ***heat of solution?*** *the total heat energy absorbed or released when one substance dissolves in another*

Section Review 12.3 (pp. 286–287)

Example 12.1

1. The normal average concentration of sodium ions in human blood plasma is about 3.3 g/L. Calculate the molarity of Na^+ in human blood plasma.

$$\frac{3.3\ g\ Na^+}{1\ L} \times \frac{1\ mol\ Na^+}{22.99\ g\ Na^+} = \mathbf{0.14\ M}$$

2. Calculate the molarities of solutions prepared by dissolving the following solutes in sufficient water to produce the given volumes of solution.

Chapter 12

a. 16.0 g SO_3 in 2.00 L solution

$$\frac{16.0\ g\ SO_3}{2.00\ L} \times \frac{1\ mol\ SO_3}{80.06\ g\ SO_3}$$

$= \mathbf{9.99 \times 10^{-2}\ M\ H_2SO_4}\ (SO_3 + H_2O \rightarrow H_2SO_4)$

b. 16.7 g $CaCl_2$ in 400.0 mL solution

$$\frac{16.7\ g\ CaCl_2}{400.0\ mL} \times \frac{1\ mol\ Na_2CO_3}{105.99\ g\ Na_2CO_3} \times \frac{1\ mL}{10^{-3} L}$$

$= \mathbf{0.376\ M\ CaCl_2}$

Example 12.3

3. Tell how you would prepare the following solutions from the given stock solutions.

a. 3.00 L of 0.500 M H_2SO_4 from 18.0 M H_2SO_4 ("concentrated H_2SO_4")

$$V_1 = \frac{(3.00\ L)(0.500\ M\ H_2SO_4)}{18.0\ M\ H_2SO_4}$$

$= 0.0833\ L \approx 83.3\ mL$

Carefully add water to ***83.3 mL*** *of 18.0 M H_2SO_4 to make 3.00 L of solution.*

b. 100.0 mL of 2.5 M HCl from 11.8 M HCl

$$V_1 = \frac{(100.0\ mL)(2.5\ M\ HCl)}{11.8\ M\ HCl} = 21\ mL$$

Carefully add water to ***21 mL*** *of 2.5 M HCl to make 100.0 mL of solution.*

4. Calculate the molarity of the following solutions (see Table 12.6).

a. 15.0 mL of concentrated H_2SO_4 diluted to 2.00 L

$$M_2 = \frac{1\ L}{1000\ mL} \times \frac{(15.0\ mL)(18.0\ M\ H_2SO_4)}{2.00\ L}$$

$= \mathbf{0.135\ M\ H_2SO_4}$

b. 1.5 mL of glacial acetic acid diluted to 350.0 mL

$$M_2 = \frac{(1.5\ mL)(17.5\ M\ HC_2H_3O_2)}{350.0\ mL}$$

$= \mathbf{0.075\ M\ HC_2H_3O_2}$

Example 12.4

5. Calculate the molality of the following solutions.

a. battery acid containing 368 g H_2SO_4 in 857 g H_2O

$$m = \frac{368\ g\ H_2SO_4}{857\ g\ H_2O} \times \frac{10_3\ g\ H_2O}{1\ kg\ H_2O} \times \frac{1\ mol\ H_2SO_4}{98.08\ g\ H_2SO_4}$$

$= \mathbf{4.38\ m\ H_2SO_4}$

b. salt water containing 15.8 g NaCl in 150. g H_2O

$$m = \frac{15.8\ g\ NaCl}{150.g\ H_2O} \times \frac{10_3\ g\ H_2O}{1\ kg\ H_2O} \times \frac{1\ mol\ NaCl}{58.44\ g\ NaCl}$$

$= \mathbf{1.80\ m\ NaCl}$

Section Review 12.4 (p. 293)

1. What are colligative properties? Name three colligative properties discussed in the text. *Colligative properties are properties of a solution that depend on the number of particles present rather than on the identity or properties of the particles. Examples would be vapor pressure lowering, freezing point depression, boiling point elevation, and osmotic pressure.*
2. How does a nonvolatile solute act to lower the vapor pressure of a solvent? *(Wording will vary.) A nonvolatile solute is said (1) to decrease the concentration of solvent at the liquid surface, thereby hindering evaporation; and (2) to increase the attraction between solvent molecules and the solution, thereby "holding" the solvent molecules in the solution and reducing their tendency to escape. (Mechanism #2 is thought to be most important.)*
3. Differentiate between the terms ***nonelectrolyte*** and ***electrolyte***. *A nonelectrolyte remains nonionized in aqueous solution, whereas an electrolyte ionizes to varying degrees in aqueous solution.*
4. List three strong electrolytes, three weak electrolytes, and three nonelectrolytes.
   Strong electrolytes: *hydrochloric acid, sulfuric acid, sodium chloride, sodium nitrate, ammonium chloride, sodium hydroxide, nitric acid*
   Weak electrolytes: *acetic acid, aqueous ammonia, phosphoric acid, carbonic acid, formic acid, sulfurous acid, hypochlorous acid*
   Nonelectrolytes: *ethanol, methanol, water, ethylene glycol, glycerol, urea, sucrose, glucose*
5. Why are freezing point depressions greater for electrolytes than they are for nonelectrolytes? *Electrolytes produce more particles in solution than do nonelectrolytes on a mole-for-mole basis.*

Section Review 12.5 (p. 299)

1. What is a *colloid?* *a mixture containing tiny clumps or particles that remain suspended within the mixture*
2. Why is there no such thing as a gas-in-gas colloid? *Gas molecules are always tiny enough to form true solutions with other gases; they always form homogeneous mixtures of one phase.*
3. Give 5 examples of colloids and identify the type, the dispersed substance, and the dispersing medium. *Answers will vary; see Table 12.10 on p. 296 for examples.*
4. What is *Brownian motion?* *the random motion of colloidal particles due to their bombardment by solvent molecules*

5. How may a colloid and a true solution be differentiated? *One method is to observe a beam of light passed through the substance at right angles to it; a colloid will scatter the light by the Tyndale effect, while a solution will not.*
6. Explain how soap removes greasy dirt from clothing. *The nonpolar end of the soap molecule dissolves in the grease; the charged polar end protrudes and is attracted and solvated by water molecules, allowing the grease to be lifted and forming a micelle.*

Chapter 12 Review (p. 301)

1. In a solution, which substance is the *solute?* The *solvent? The solute is the substance that is dissolved; the solvent is the substance that does the dissolving.*
2. Give one example from each of the following categories of solutions. Identify the solute and solvent in each example you give.
   - **a.** solid-in-solid solution
   - **b.** solid-in-liquid solution
   - **c.** gas-in-liquid solution
   - **d.** liquid-in-gas solution
   - **e.** gas-in-gas solution

   Answers will vary; see Table 12.1 on p. 274 for examples.
3. What do we mean when we describe two substances as *miscible? Those two substances are completely soluble in each other in all proportions.*
4. Distinguish between *solvation* and *dissociation. Solvation (hydration) is the process in which solute molecules or ions are surrounded by solvent (water) molecules; dissociation is the separation of ions from each other that occurs when an ionic compound is solvated.*
5. When you drop a sugar cube into a cup of tea, it begins to slowly dissolve as the sugar molecules become solvated. Suggest three ways to make the sugar cube dissolve more quickly. *stirring, crushing/grinding, increasing the temperature*
6. What is meant by the principle "like dissolves like"? *The more alike two molecules are (in terms of bonding and intermolecular forces), the more likely they are to form a solution.*
7. In your own words, explain what it means when a solution of sodium chloride in water is said to be *saturated. At a given temperature, that solution contains all of the sodium chloride that it can possibly contain under equilibrium conditions.*
8. As a rule, what effect does increased pressure have on the solubility of a substance? Increased temperature? *(Wording will vary.) Increased pressure has little effect on solid or liquid solutes but increases the solubility of gases (Henry's law). Increased temperature generally increases the solubility of solid and liquid solutes but decreases the solubility of gases.*
9. Distinguish between ***molarity*** and ***molality*** and give the abbreviation for each. *Molarity or molar concentration (**M**) is the number of moles of solute per liter of solution; molality or molar concentration (**m**) is the number of moles of solute per kilogram of solvent.*
10. Calculate the molarity of the solution that would result if you diluted 5.00 mL of concentrated nitric acid to 250.0 mL.

    $$M = \frac{(5.00\ mL)(15.8\ \mathrm{M}\ HNO_3)}{250.0\ mL} = \mathbf{0.316\ M\ HNO_3}$$
11. What is the *vapor pressure* of a liquid? What effect does increased temperature have on vapor pressure? *Vapor pressure is the measure of the escaping tendency of the molecules in the liquid. Increased temperature increases the vapor pressure.*
12. Would adding a tablespoon of sugar to a cup of water increase or decrease the vapor pressure of the water? *decrease*
13. What are *electrolytes? compounds that dissolve in water to produce ions which can conduct an electrical current*
14. In your own words, explain why distilled water and seawater separated by a semipermeable membrane would undergo osmosis. Toward which side of the membrane would the water molecules flow? *Osmosis can occur any time that there is a difference in concentrations of solutions on either side of a semipermeable membrane, and seawater is a more concentrated solution than distilled water. The flow in osmosis naturally occurs from the more dilute solution (the pure water) to the more concentrated solution (the salt water).*
15. Distinguish between a *solution* and a *colloid.* Give three everyday examples of colloids. *A **solution** is a (homogeneous) mixture in which the molecules of solvent and solute are thoroughly mixed. A **colloid** is a (heterogeneous) mixture consisting of tiny clumps or particles that remain suspended within the mixture and is therefore not evenly mixed. Examples of colloids are given in Table 12.10 on p. 296.*
16. Why is a solution of soap and water more effective than pure water at removing oily dirt from your hands? *Pure water is polar and would not be effective in dissolving nonpolar substances such as grease. If the water contains soap, the nonpolar ends of the soap molecules dissolve in the grease, emulsifying it and allowing the water to wash it away.*

Chapter 13 (pp. 302–319)

Chemical Kinetics

Suggested Daily Pacing

112 **Check** and discuss Lab 20 Report Sheet.

Check p. 305, questions 1–4.

Review pp. 296–298.

Introduce ch. 13, Chemical Kinetics.

Discuss p. 305, questions 1–4.

Teach pp. **303–305,** sec. **13.1** Introduction to Chemical Kinetics.

Review lesson.

SP: Hear 3 oral presentations.

HW: Read pp. 306–307. Answer p. 307, questions 1–4. Plan to finish oral presentations.

113 **Check** and discuss homework.

Review pp. 303–305.

Teach pp. **306–307,** sec. **13.2** Concentration, Temperature, and Reaction Rate.

Review lesson.

SP: Hear remaining oral presentations.

HW: Read pp. 307–309. Answer p. 310, questions 1–4.

114 **Give Quiz 20** (over pp. 303–307).

Check and discuss homework.

Review pp. 306–307.

Teach pp. **307–309,** sec. **13.3** Transition States and Energy Changes.

Review lesson.

HW: Read *Lab Manual* Lab 21 and complete Prelab Assignment.

115 **Check** and discuss homework.

Conduct Lab 21: Chemical Kinetics: A Clock Reaction.

HW: Complete Lab 21 Report Sheet. Read pp. 310–315, up to 13.5 Reaction Mechanisms. Answer p. 314, questions 1–4.

116 **Give** "pop" reading quiz over pp. 310–315:

1. What kind of catalyst is not in the same phase as the reactants? *heterogeneous*
2. Give the term for substances added to food to prevent catalysts from speeding up spoilage. *inhibitors*
3. True or False: A catalyst can make reactions possible that are normally impossible. *false*
4. What group of catalysts are found in living cells and organs? *enzymes*
5. What effect does a catalyst have on reaction rate? *increases reaction rate*

Check and discuss homework.

Review pp. 307–309.

Teach pp. **310–315,** sec. **13.4** Effects of a Catalyst.

Review lesson.

HW: Read pp. 315–317. Answer p. 317, questions 1–3.

117 **Check** and discuss homework.

Review pp. 310–315.

Teach pp. **315–317,** sec. **13.5** Reaction Mechanisms.

Review lesson.

HW: Begin studying ch. 12–13 for Test 8 in les. 119. Answer p. 301, Review Exercises 2 and 8–16; also answer p. 319, Review Exercises 7, 11, and 13–16.

118 **Check** and discuss homework.

Review ch. 12–13 for Test 8 in next lesson, using Chapter Reviews on pp. 299–301 and 318–319.

HW: Study ch. 12–13 for Test 8 in next lesson.

119 **Administer Test 8** over ch. 12–13.

HW: Read pp. 320–323, up to 14.2 Le Châtelier's Principle. Answer p. 323, questions 1–5.

Teacher Notes

Chapter 13 Overview. This chapter returns to the study of thermodynamics, exploring the factors that determine the rate at which a given reaction takes place. After introducing the concept of reaction rate, the chapter gives an overview of the collision theory, the foundation of chemical kinetics. The effects of concentration and temperature on reaction rate are discussed, followed by a look at transition state theory. Energy changes during endothermic and exothermic reactions are discussed in more detail than in chapter 6, and the effects of catalysts are explained. The chapter concludes with a brief introduction to reaction mechanisms and how they affect reaction rate.

Concentration, O_2, and combustion (13.2, p. 306). The increase in reaction rates at higher concentrations is easily seen in the case of O_2. Substances burn far faster in an atmosphere of 100% oxygen than they do in air, which is about 21% oxygen. In fact, some substances (e.g., hydrocarbon vapors) can ignite spontaneously in 100% oxygen and burn explosively. For these reasons, medical and industrial uses of oxygen involve safety precautions to prevent fire.

Explosive concentrations (13.2, p. 306). Although as a general rule the reaction rate increases as concentration increases, this does not hold true if the reactants are not present in the proper stoichiometric ratios. For example, a mixture of air and as little as 4% hydrogen is capable of explosive combustion. However, if *too* much hydrogen is present (such as 75% hydrogen / 25% air), the excess hydrogen squelches the reaction and the mixture will no longer explode.

This phenomenon makes sense if we view the reaction from the perspective of the *oxygen* concentration; as the hydrogen concentration increases beyond the stoichiometric ideal, the oxygen concentration *decreases* as oxygen is crowded out by the excess hydrogen. The oxygen concentration eventually drops to the point that the mixture will not even burn.

Reactions in confined spaces (13.2, pp. 306–307). When a reaction takes place in a confined space, the reaction itself may lead to conditions that increase the reaction rate exponentially. For example, consider common "gunpowder" (nitrocellulose). Unconfined nitrocellulose does not explode; rather, it burns rapidly with a hissing noise, producing heat and hot gases. However, if nitrocellulose is confined in a strong enclosure (such as in an artillery firing chamber or the chamber of a firearm), its behavior is quite different. As soon as it starts to burn, the initial combustion products increase the pressure and temperature inside the chamber. As the pressure and temperature rise, the reaction rate dramatically increases, producing still more heat and gases, which increase the reaction rate further, and so on. Within a few milliseconds of ignition, the conditions in the gun's chamber rise from room temperature and atmospheric pressure to 1800 °F (1000 °C) and 20,000–60,000 psi. As the temperature rises, the remaining nitrocellulose burns faster and faster, producing a controlled explosion rather than a slow burn.

Similar accelerated burning occurs inside automobile engines, jet engines, and rocket motors. In the combustion chambers of the space shuttle engines, for example (p. 213), hydrogen and oxygen burn furiously at temperatures exceeding 6000 °F (3300 °C) and pressures of more than 200 atm (3000 psi). Under these conditions, hydrogen and oxygen react so rapidly that each engine can burn 550 kg (1200 lb) of H_2/O_2 per second in a combustion chamber the size of a wastebasket.

Energy changes in chemical reactions (13.3, p. 309). Note that exothermic and endothermic reactions both have activation energies that must be overcome (an "energy hill" to climb) for a reaction to take place. What makes a reaction endothermic or exothermic is whether the difference between the energies of the reactants and products is positive or negative.

Catalysts (13.4, pp. 310–311). Stress that a catalyst makes only reactions that are *already* thermodynamically possible proceed more quickly; it cannot do the "impossible." A catalyst increases the rate by providing an easier "alternate route" for the reaction to occur.

Nitrogen oxides and pollution (13.4, p. 313). An internal combustion engine emits nitrogen oxides in the approximate ratio 90% NO and 10% NO_2. After these oxides are emitted, however, sunlight gradually converts NO to NO_2. Since the combined amount of NO and NO_2 does not change (only the ratios), they are commonly lumped together and referred to as NO_x in pollution-control discussions.

Enzyme inactivation (p. 314). Because enzymes are vitally important to living cells, inactivating or destroying a cell's enzymes will usually kill the cell. One of the simplest ways to inactivate an enzyme is by overheating it, which is why overly high fevers can be dangerous and why bacteria in food are killed by cooking.

Enzymes can also be inactivated by molecules that bind to the enzyme and block its active sites. If enough of the enzymes in a cell are shut down within a short time, the cell may become unable to carry out its assigned functions. Many poisons known to science are classified as poisons because they inactivate key enzymes.

The toxic thresholds of some enzyme-inhibiting compounds are very low. For example, mercury-containing substances are among the most toxic substances known; a single drop of dimethyl mercury ($Hg[CH_3]_2$) spilled on the skin can cause fatal brain damage. In 1997, a distinguished medical researcher at Dartmouth College died from a few drops of dimethyl mercury that she spilled on the *outside* of her latex glove; the fraction that soaked through the latex was enough to give a fatal dose.

Catalase and cellular H_2O_2 (13.4, p. 315). Catalase is not the only enzyme that breaks down hydrogen peroxide in the cell. H_2O_2 is also broken down by a selenium-containing enzyme known as *glutathione peroxidase.*

Lecture Demonstrations

Introducing reaction rate (13.1, pp. 303–305). The concept of reaction rate can be introduced by means of the following demonstration. Grind 5 g $KMnO_4$ finely using a mortar and pestle and place it in a crucible inside a large beaker; place 5 g $KMnO_4$ *crystals* into a second crucible inside a second large beaker. Place each beaker on a ceramic pad; you may wish to use a serving tray or aluminum foil to protect the tabletop. Make a depression in the center of each pile of $KMnO_4$; add 1 mL glycerol to each depression *simultaneously* and quickly stand back. If either fails to ignite after 2 minutes, add more glycerol. **CAUTION:** Wear appropriate protective attire, including eye protection. Flames and smoke are produced; have an appropriately rated fire extinguisher at hand, and perform in a well-ventilated area.

You can also use this reaction to discuss the effect of surface area on reaction rate (section 13.2).

Concentration and reaction rate (13.2, p. 306). The effects of oxygen concentration on combustion rate may be demonstrated by (a) placing a small piece of charcoal in a deflagrating spoon, lighting it, and then placing it in a bottle of oxygen, or (b) lighting a wooden splint and placing it in a bottle of pure oxygen; in both cases, point out the contrast between the rate in air and the rate in oxygen. (Students investigated this phenomenon for themselves in Lab 17.) Oxygen may be prepared using the method demonstrated in Lab 17.

Surface area and reaction rate (13.2, p. 306). The influence of surface area on reaction rate may be demonstrated by attempting to light a small pile of lycopodium powder (available from science supply companies) on a ceramfab wire gauze using a Bunsen burner; the powder burns poorly, if at all. Then raise the gauze about 18" above the burner and turn it over; a roaring flame results from the burning of the powder. (A darkened or dim room is best for this.) Discuss how the increased surface area of the falling dust increased the reaction rate; relate this to coal mine fires caused by coal dust and to grain elevator explosions.

Temperature and reaction rate (13.2, pp. 306–307). The effect of temperature on reaction rate may be demonstrated by comparing the rates of reaction of an Alka-Seltzer tablet placed simultaneously into each of three beakers of water at different temperatures: one an ice-water mixture, one at room temperature, and one very hot.

Effects of a catalyst (13.4, pp. 310–315). You may demonstrate the effects of a catalyst by means of the decomposition of H_2O_2 into H_2O and O_2. Point out that this reaction is already thermodynamically possible. A homogeneous catalyst may be demonstrated by adding about 1 mL of 0.1 *M* $FeCl_3$ or 0.1 *M* KI to a test tube half-filled with 3% H_2O_2 (reaction 13.8). Mix well and observe the formation of O_2 gas bubbles as the rate of the reaction increases noticeably. (Note that the I^- ion does not catalyze the reaction as quickly as Fe^{3+}.) A heterogeneous catalyst can be demonstrated by adding a pinch of MnO_2 to a test tube half-filled with 3% H_2O_2.

You can demonstrate the action of catalase (p. 315) by dropping one or more *freshly cut* pieces of fresh, uncooked liver (from a grocery store) into a beaker of 3% hydrogen peroxide; this reaction is fastest at room temperature. Mashing the liver with a mortar and pestle before adding it increases the reaction rate by making more catalase available.

Answers to Text Questions

Section Review 13.1 (p. 305)

1. Define *chemical kinetics.* *the study of rates of reactions (their speeds) and the pathway taken during the reaction (the mechanism of the reaction)*
2. In the following diagram, which curve represents the kinetic energy distribution of molecules at the *lower* temperature?

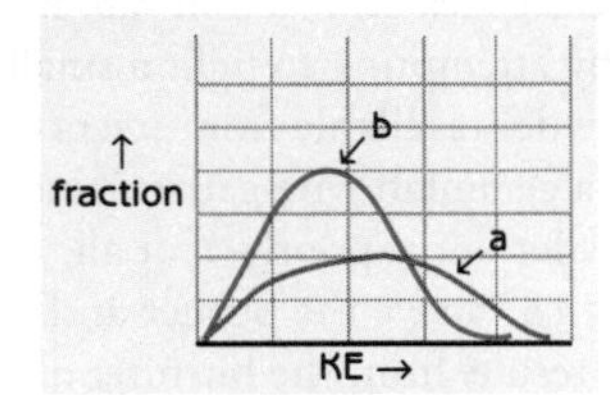

curve b

3. Explain why temperature affects reaction rate. *The higher the temperature, the greater the fraction of molecules having higher kinetic energies. As a result, molecules will collide more forcefully and will therefore be more likely to react.* *(Not mentioned in the text: The higher molecule speeds also result in more collisions in a given time, thereby resulting in a slight additional increase.)*
4. Explain in terms of the collision theory why orientation is important in chemical reactions. *Answers will vary; the key idea is that molecules must collide in such a way that the proper electron clouds come into contact with each other (i.e., the correct regions must collide). Some orientations are unfavorable for a reaction because the proper atoms do not come together.*

Section Review 13.2 (p. 307)

1. Explain in terms of the collision theory why concentration affects reaction rate. *The higher the concentration of reactant molecules, the more collisions there will be and the more likely reactions are to occur.*
2. A pile of starch is difficult to ignite but starch powder dusted into a flame will burn readily. Explain. *The surface area of the reactant is much greater in the form of dust than in the pile; the dust reacts with atmospheric oxygen more rapidly because the area of contact between reactants is greater.*
3. Why does powdered iron rust more rapidly than the same mass of iron in the form of a bar? *There is more surface area to react with atmospheric oxygen in powdered iron than in an iron bar.*
4. Explain what is meant by *activation energy.* *the minimum energy that a molecule must possess if it is to react*

Section Review 13.3 (p. 310)

1. What properties characterize the complex known in transition state theory as the *activated complex?* *It is a high-energy, short-lived, unstable arrangement of atoms, in which bonds are in the process of breaking and reforming.*
2. Sketch a potential energy diagram for **(a)** an exothermic reaction and **(b)** an endothermic reaction, labeling the axes and the points: reactants, products, activated complex, E_a, and ΔH.

(a) exothermic reaction

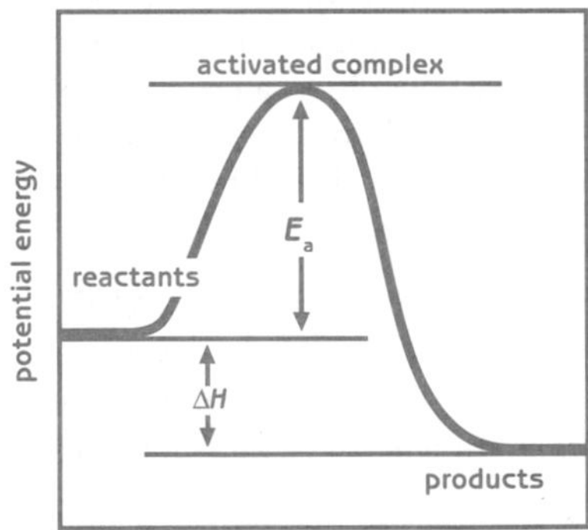

(b) endothermic reaction

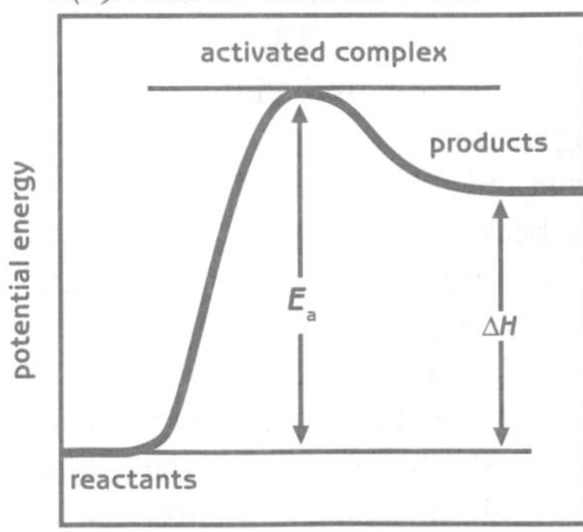

3. To answer the following questions, refer to the accompanying kinetic energy distribution diagrams which show activation energies for two reactions, A and B, at room temperature.

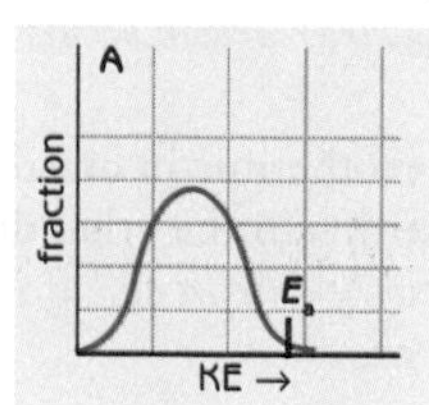

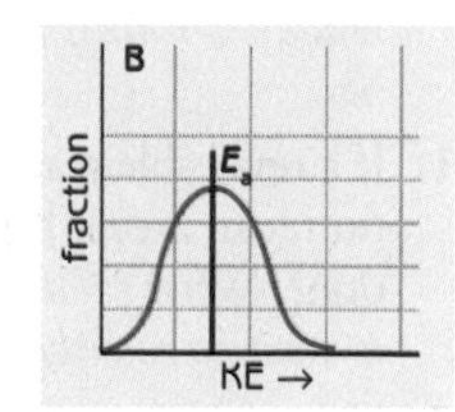

a. Which reaction will occur more rapidly at room temperature? *reaction* B

b. Which reaction will show a greater relative increase in rate by a temperature increase? Explain. *Reaction* A; *the area under the curve beyond* E_a *will increase proportionately more in reaction* A *than in reaction* B *when the temperature is increased.*

4. In a reversible reaction, how does the activation energy for the endothermic reaction compare with that of the exothermic reaction? *The activation energy is greater for the endothermic reaction than for the exothermic reaction.*

Section Review 13.4 (p. 314)

1. What is a catalyst? *a substance that alters the rate of a chemical reaction but is not permanently changed or consumed by the reaction*

2. How does a catalyst increase the rate of a chemical reaction? *The catalyst increases the rate of a chemical reaction by providing an "easier route" which has a lower activation energy.*

3. Tell whether each of the following is an example of a homogeneous catalyst or a heterogeneous catalyst.
   a. $MnO_2(s)$ in a mixture of $MnO_2(s)$ and $KClO_3(s)$ *homogeneous*
   b. the catalyst in an automobile catalytic converter *heterogeneous*
   c. finely divided nickel in the hydrogenation of vegetable oil *heterogeneous*

4. How do inhibitors preserve food? *They often bond to a catalyst, preventing it from doing its job of speeding up the decaying process.*

Section Review 13.5 (p. 317)

1. What is a ***reaction mechanism?*** *a series of steps which describes the way in which a reaction proceeds*

2. In the following chemical reaction, which is the rate-determining step?

   1. $Cl_2(g) \xrightarrow{\text{light}} 2\,Cl(g)$ *fast*
   2. $Cl(g) + CHCl_3(g) \longrightarrow HCl(g) + CCl_3(g)$ *slow*
   3. $CCl_3(g) + Cl(g) \longrightarrow CCl_4(g)$ *fast*

   net: $Cl_2(g) + CHCl_3(g) \longrightarrow HCl(g) + CCl_4(g)$

   Step 2 is the slowest step and therefore the rate-determining step.

3. Why is it impossible to predict either the rate or the mechanism of a chemical reaction from the balanced net equation? *The balanced net equation does not describe the rate of the reaction, nor does it tell how many other steps are involved in the reaction process.*

Chapter 13 Review (p. 319)

1. What two measurable quantities are used to define reaction rate? *change in molar concentration* and *time*

2. State the basic premise of the collision theory. *Collision between reactant molecules must occur for there to be a reaction; the greater the frequency and the greater the energy of collision between reactant particles, the greater the rate of reaction.*

3. How does raising the temperature of a substance affect the number of collisions between molecules? *the greater the temperature, the more number of collisions occur*

4. Why does the orientation of colliding molecules affect the likelihood of a chemical reaction between them? *Because molecules are made up of two or more atoms and these atoms have shape, the molecules colliding have various shapes. Therefore, some orientations would "encourage" a reaction, whereas if two molecules were to collide in a different orientation, they would simply bounce off one another unchanged.*

5. Explain why increased pressure increases the concentration of gaseous reactants but has little effect on liquid or solid reactants? *Gas is the only state of matter that has no definite volume. Since concentration is a measurement of the amount of a certain substance compared to total volume, then if the volume is decreased, the concentration is increased.*

6. Aspirin very slowly decomposes into acetic acid and salicylic acid over time. However, this decomposition occurs much more quickly if the bottle is stored in a hot place. Explain why this is so. *An increase in temperature increases the reac-*

tion rate. (An increase in temperature increases the kinetic energy of colliding molecules as well as the rate of collisions. The increase in kinetic energy makes a collision more likely to result in a reaction.)

7. **If a 10 °C rise doubles the rate of a certain reaction, by what factor will the rate of that reaction increase when the temperature is raised from 10 °C to 50 °C?** *A factor of 16; each 10 °C rise doubles the rate and there are doublings ($2 \times 2 \times 2 \times 2 = 16$).*
8. **List three factors affecting reaction rate and explain their effects on the basis of the kinetic-molecular theory or collision theory.** *concentration, surface area (heterogeneous reactions), temperature, and catalyst*
   concentration: *more collisions between molecules increase the likelihood of their reacting and hence the rate*
   surface area: *more contact is allowed between the reactants in different phases, allowing more collisions and a greater rate*
   temperature: *reactant molecules are moving faster at higher temperatures, producing more forceful collisions and a greater reaction rate*
   catalyst: *provides an alternate, lower energy pathway for the reaction so that more molecules have the necessary energy to react*
9. **What is the *activation energy* of a reaction? What happens when molecules collide with less energy than this?** *The activation energy of a reaction is the minimum energy necessary to react. Nothing happens when molecules collide with less energy than this.*
10. **In your own words, explain the role of a *transition state* (activated complex) in a chemical reaction.** *The transition state forms that critical period when atoms are splitting to form new compounds; the result determines whether a net reaction occurs or not.*
11. **If a reversible reaction is exothermic in one direction, can it ever be exothermic in the other direction? Why?** *No; if it is exothermic in one direction, it must be endothermic in the other.*
12. **How does a catalyst affect the activation energy of a chemical reaction? What effect does this change have on the reaction rate?** *A catalyst lowers the activation energy; the reaction rate will increase since it is now "easier" for a reaction to occur.*
13. **How does a catalyst affect the overall (net) energy change for a reaction?** *No effect; ΔH is a state function which does not depend on the route taken.*
14. **Distinguish between homogeneous and heterogeneous catalysts. Which type is found in automotive catalytic converters?** *A homogeneous catalyst exists in the same phase as the reactants, but a heterogeneous catalyst is not in the same phase as the reactants. Catalytic converters are heterogeneous catalysts.*
15. **What term is commonly used to refer to biological catalysts?** *enzymes*
16. **Why is the slowest reaction in a proposed reaction mechanism described as the rate-determining step?** *The rate of a reaction is limited by the rate of the slowest step.*

Chapter 14 (pp. 320–331)

Chemical Equilibrium

14.1 Reversible Reactions
14.2 Le Châtelier's Principle

Suggested Daily Pacing

120 **Return** and go over graded Test 8.

Check homework.

Introduce ch. 14, Chemical Equilibrium.

Discuss homework.

Teach pp. **321–323,** sec. **14.1** Reversible Reactions.

Review lesson.

HW: Read pp. 323–327, up to Temperature Changes. Answer p. 330, questions 1 and 2.

121 **Check** and discuss homework.

Review pp. 321–323.

Teach pp. **323–327,** sec. **14.2** Le Châtelier's Principle, up to Temperature Changes.

Review lesson.

HW: Read pp. 327–329. Answer p. 330, questions 3–6.

122 **Check** and discuss homework.

Review pp. 323–327.

Teach pp. **327–329,** sec. **14.2** (cont.).

Review lesson.

HW: Read *Lab Manual* Lab 22 and complete Prelab Assignment.

123 **Check** and discuss homework.

Conduct Lab 22: Equilibrium: Le Châtelier's Principle.

HW: Complete Lab 22 Report Sheet. Begin studying ch. 10–14 for Test 9 (Nine-Weeks Exam) in les. 126. Answer p. 331, Review Exercises 5–8.

124 **Give Quiz 21** (over pp. 321–328).

Check and discuss homework.

Review ch. 14 for Test 9 (Nine-Weeks Exam) in les. 126 using Concept Review 5: Le Châtelier's Principle. Discuss the most significant items from Chapter 14 Review on p. 331.

HW: Continue studying ch. 10–14 for Test 9 (Nine-Weeks Exam) in les. 126.
Note: Assign 10–15 items from Chapter Reviews 10–14.

125 **Check** and discuss homework.

Review ch. 10–14 for Test 9 in next lesson, using selected Chapter Reviews.

HW: Continue studying ch. 10–14 for Test 9 (Nine-Weeks Exam) in next lesson.

126 **Administer Test 9** (Nine-Weeks Exam) over ch. 10–14.

HW: Read pp. 332–336, up to Naming Acids. Answer p. 339, questions 1–3.

Teacher Notes

Chapter 14 Overview. This brief chapter focuses specifically on the dynamic equilibrium that occurs in reversible chemical reactions. The chapter begins with an introduction to reversible chemical reactions, followed by an explanation of chemical equilibrium. Le Châtelier's principle is then introduced, and the effects of changes in concentration, pressure, and temperature on the equilibrium point are discussed. The chapter closes with another look at catalysts from the standpoint of chemical equilibrium.

Chemical equilibrium (14.1, pp. 322–323). Recall that dynamic equilibrium was first introduced in section 12.2 (p. 279). You may find it helpful to refer back to this information.

Note that the forward and reverse reactions at equilibrium have not stopped; they are still occurring, but at equal rates so that it *appears* that no reaction is occurring. You may wish to reuse the analogy shown in Fig. 12.4 (p. 278); if the flow rates into and out of the bucket are equal, an observer of only the water level in the bucket might assume at first glance that no water was flowing since the water level was constant. In fact, however, the system maintains its seemingly static position through continual activity.

If you wish, reactions 14.4–14.6 can be made less abstract by referring students back to Fig. 13.8 on p. 307.

Le Châtelier history (14.2, pp. 323–324). Henri Louis Le Châtelier (1850–1936) was a French scientist, engineer, and college chemistry professor. He originally published his famous principle in 1884:

> Any system in stable chemical equilibrium, subjected to the influence of an external cause which tends to change either its temperature or its condensation (pressure, concentration, number of molecules in unit volume), either as a whole or in some of its parts, can only undergo such internal modifications as would, if produced alone, bring about a change of temperature or of condensation of opposite sign to that resulting from the external cause.[1]

He published a more concise explanation in 1888:

> Every change of one of the factors of an equilibrium [system] occasions a rearrangement of the system in such a direction that the factor in question experiences a change in a sense opposite to the original change.[2]

Interestingly, five years before the Haber process of ammonia production was successfully demonstrated, Henri Le Châtelier came very close to inventing it himself. Had it not been for an explosion that destroyed Le Châtelier's test equipment and discouraged him from continuing the project, the production of ammonia today would probably be called the "Le Châtelier process" rather than the "Haber process." Fritz Haber gave much credit to Le Châtelier for laying the groundwork for the discovery.

[1] H. L. Le Châtelier, *Comptes rendus*, **99**:786 (1884), quoted in John Oliver and Jim Kurtz, "Henri Louis Le Châtelier: A Man of Principle," <http://step.sdsc.edu/projects95/chem.in.history/essays/lechatelier.html>.

[2] Le Châtelier, *Annales des Mines*, **13(2)**:157 (1888), *op. cit.*

Understanding Le Châtelier's principle (14.2, pp. 323–328). One goal of this section is to give students sufficient understanding of Le Châtelier's principle to predict the effects (if any) of changes in temperature, pressure, and concentration on equilibrium concentrations. Be sure students understand what it means when they say that the equilibrium of a reaction "shifts left" or "shifts right" under a certain stress. If they fully understand the principle, they should be able to tell whether the concentration of reactants increases or decreases, whether the amount of products increases or decreases, etc.

Non-chemical applications of Le Châtelier's principle (14.2, pp. 323–328). Le Châtelier's principle has applications far beyond chemistry; it has been successfully applied in such widely varied fields as ecology (e.g., population equilibrium in predator-prey relationships) and economics. For example, if the population of mosquitoes in a given area is increased (initial stress), the population of dragonflies, bats, and other mosquito predators will subsequently increase to offset the initial stress. Similarly, if the government raises taxes on savings to generate revenue (initial stress), people will respond by putting less money in savings accounts, thereby reducing the revenue generated by the tax.

Lecture Demonstrations

Reversible reactions (14.1, pp. 321–322). A "reversible reaction" may be demonstrated as follows. Prior to class, dissolve 7 g NaOH in 350 mL H_2O in a 500-mL Erlenmeyer flask. In class, dissolve 7 g glucose in the NaOH solution and add 1–2 mL of 0.2% methylene blue solution. Stopper tightly and shake; the solution turns blue. Let it stand and the solution becomes colorless. This process may be repeated many times, but the mixture must be made up fresh on the day of intended usage.

The solution is blue at first because methylene blue forms an activated complex with the O_2 dissolved in the water. Glucose in solution is then oxidized by the O_2 and the solution becomes colorless when the O_2 is consumed. Shaking the flask mixes O_2 in the flask with the solution and it turns blue again. Upon standing, the color disappears. This may be repeated until the O_2 in the flask is used up; the stopper may then be removed for a time to admit more O_2 and the process repeated. Methylene blue acts as a catalyst in the air oxidation of glucose. (Note: Strictly speaking, only the reaction between methylene blue and NaOH is reversible in this reaction; the oxidation of glucose goes to completion.)

Reversible "clock reactions" (14.1, pp. 321–322). Several fascinating reversible reactions are known as "clock reactions" because of their regular oscillations as they approach equilibrium. Both of these demonstrations require a magnetic stirrer.

Reaction 1. *Prior to class time,* pour 375 mL of deionized water into a *clean* 600-mL beaker and slowly add, while stirring, 38 mL of concentrated H_2SO_4. **CAUTION: Sulfuric acid is dangerously caustic; use appropriate eye and skin protection. Very exothermic.** Allow the solution to cool to room temperature placing the beaker in a cold-water bath while adding the acid may help keep temperatures down. Also weigh out the required amounts of "malonic acid" (1,3-propanedioic acid, $CH_2[COOH]_2$), potassium bromate ($KBrO_3$), and $MnSO_4 \cdot H_2O$ (given in the next paragraph).

In class, place a magnetic stir bar in the beaker and place the beaker on the magnetic stirrer, adjusting the stirring rate to a medium speed. Dissolve 4.5 g malonic acid in the H_2SO_4 solution; then add 4 g $KBrO_3$. When the $KBrO_3$ is dissolved, add 0.9 g $MnSO_4 \cdot H_2O$; the solution becomes orange. After a short time, the solution becomes colorless and will oscillate between orange and colorless for at least 10 minutes. Though the chemistry is rather complex, you may tell them that (1) the Mn^{2+} serves as a catalyst, (2) the formation of Br_2 by the reaction of BrO_3^- and malonic acid results in the orange color, and (3) the kinetics of the reactions producing and consuming the Br_2 differ, resulting in the oscillatory appearance and disappearance of color.

Neutralize this solution with $NaHCO_3$ before flushing it down the sink with water.

Reaction 2. A similar but even more dramatic oscillating reaction is prepared as follows. Prior to class, dissolve 14.5 g KIO_3 in about 200 mL H_2O in a 600-mL beaker; add 4.3 mL of 6.0 *M* H_2SO_4. You may need to warm the mixture and stir it. Dilute to 250 mL with distilled water. This is solution A. To prepare solution B, dissolve 5.2 g malonic acid and 1.1 g $MnSO_4 \cdot H_2O$ in about 200 mL H_2O in another 600-mL beaker. In a 50-mL beaker, bring about 25 mL H_2O to a boil; add to it a mixture of 0.1 g starch in about 3 mL H_2O and heat and stir until the starch has "dissolved." Pour the starch "solution" into the $MnSO_4^-$malonic acid solution and dilute to 250 mL. In class, mix 200 mL of solution A and 200 mL of 3% H_2O_2 in a *clean* 1-L beaker which has been placed on the magnetic stirrer. Adjust the rate so that a large vortex is formed. Add 200 mL of solution B. The mixture will become amber, gradually deepen, then turn deep blue; the blue fades to colorless and the cycle is repeated for a number of minutes. In this case, I^- and I_2 are produced and the I_2 reacts with starch to form the characteristic blue-black coloration. Once again, Mn^{2+} functions as a catalyst.

Le Châtelier's principle (14.2, pp. 323–328). Lab 22 can help reinforce the material in this section.

The effect of concentration on equilibrium may be demonstrated as follows. Dissolve 2 g $CoCl_2 \cdot 6\,H_2O$ in 40 mL H_2O in a 100-mL graduated cylinder; add 60 mL of concentrated HCl and mix. Transfer half of this mixture to another 100-mL graduated cylinder. Add 35 mL H_2O to one and 35 mL 0.1 *M* $AgNO_3$ to the other. Discuss in terms of the equilibrium equation,

$$Co(H_2O)_6^{2+}(aq) + 4\,Cl^-(aq) \rightleftharpoons CoCl_4^{2-}(aq) + 6\,H_2O(l)$$

remembering that the precipitate is AgCl.

You may also wish to demonstrate the effect of temperature on the position of equilibrium, as in the opening photo. To produce the brownish NO_2 gas, *in a hood* (or in good ventilation) react concentrated HNO_3 with copper metal (shot or pieces) in a large test tube equipped with a one-hole stopper and bent glass tubing to direct the NO_2 into three flasks or vials which may be tightly capped or sealed. Allow the containers to fill with NO_2 by displacement of air (the glass tubing should reach to near the bottom of the container); be sure all vessels are the same depth of color before sealing each one tightly. Place one vessel in an ice-water bath, leave one at room temperature, and place the third in very hot water. After a short time, compare the colors. You may also wish to show reversibility by switching the vessels that were in the hot and cold baths and noting that the effects are the same as before. Use this demonstration to discuss the effect of temperature on equilibria, using Le Châtelier's principle, and how to determine if the reaction is exo- or endothermic, based on the shift observed.

The effect of pressure can be demonstrated by filling a large oral syringe (available from a pharmacy; see Ch. 5 Lecture Demonstrations) with NO_2 gas before sealing the tip. Apply pressure and note the lightening in the color. (NO_3 may be prepared in a fume hood by placing a piece of copper and a *small* amount of HNO_3 in an Erlenmeyer flask and capping the flask with a 1-hole stopper. Wait until all the air in the flask has been displaced, place the neck of the syringe in the hole, pull the plunger to fill the syringe with NO_2, and quickly cap the syringe.)

Answers to Text Questions

Section Review 14.1 (p. 323)

1. What is meant by a ***reversible reaction?*** *a reaction which may be made to go in either direction, i.e., either from products to reactants or from reactants to products*

2. (a) What can be said about the rate of a reaction that is in a state of chemical equilibrium? *The forward rate equals the reverse rate.*
   (b) Are the *amounts* of product and reactant equal at equilibrium? Explain. *Not necessarily; the* rates *of reaction in each direction are equal, but the* amounts *do not have to be equal.*
3. Under what condition will a reversible reaction go to completion? *in an open system; if a product is removed or escapes as it forms*
4. What substance(s) would need to be present initially in order for reaction 14.3 to reach a state of equilibrium in a closed system? *Fe and H_2O* **or** *Fe_3O_4 and H_2*
5. Give the term used for an equilibrium in which the forward and reverse reactions are constantly occurring. *chemical equilibrium (a type of dynamic equilibrium)*

Section Review 14.2 (p. 330)

1. Define Le Châtelier's principle. *If a stress is applied to a system at equilibrium, the system will react in such a way that the stress is at least partially offset.*
2. What kind of effect does an increase in concentration have on a reaction? *It increases the rate of reaction.*
3. Consider the reaction

   $$2\,NOCl(g) \rightarrow 2\,NO(g) + Cl_2(g) \quad \Delta H^\circ = 75\text{ kJ}$$

   a. Tell whether the equilibrium would shift to the right, shift to the left, or remain unchanged for each of the following changes.
   (1) the total pressure is increased *left*
   (2) NO is removed *right*
   (3) the temperature is increased *right*
   (4) [NOCl] is decreased *left*
   (5) [NO] is increased *left*
   (6) a catalyst is added *unchanged*

   b. Tell whether the equilibrium Cl_2 concentration would increase, decrease, or remain the same for each of the above changes.
   (1) decrease *(4) decrease*
   (2) increase *(5) decrease*
   (3) increase *(6) same*
4. For the following solution equilibrium,

   $$Ag_2SO_4(s) \rightleftharpoons 2\,Ag^+(aq) + SO_4^{2-}(aq)$$

   tell what happens to the mass of Ag_2SO_4 present when equilibrium is again established after the following changes.
   a. $Na_2SO_4(aq)$ is added *increases*
   b. $AgNO_3(aq)$ is added *increases*
   c. Ag^+ ions are removed by being reduced to metallic Ag *decreases*
5. Consider the reaction

   $$CO(g) + 2\,H_2(g) \rightleftharpoons CH_3OH(l) \quad \Delta H^\circ = -128\text{ kJ}$$

   and tell what happens to the mass of CH_3OH present at equilibrium when the following changes are made.
   a. the total pressure is increased *increases*
   b. CO is removed *decreases*
   c. the temperature is raised *decreases*
6. Consider the equilibrium system

   $$4\,HCl(g) + O_2(g) \rightleftharpoons 2\,Cl_2(g) + 2\,H_2O(g) \quad \Delta H^\circ = -114\text{ kJ}$$

   a. What stresses will increase the amount of Cl_2 produced if the temperature is held constant? *increase [HCl] and/or [O_2]; remove Cl_2 or H_2O as it forms; increase pressure*
   b. What effect on the equilibrium concentration of Cl_2 would an increase in temperature have? *decrease it*

Chapter 14 Review (p. 331)

1. Explain the difference between an open system and a closed system. *An open system is one that allows the products of a chemical reaction to escape into the atmosphere. A closed system is one in which neither the products nor the reactants can escape.*
2. Why must a closed system be used to achieve chemical equilibrium? *If an open system is used, some of the chemicals will escape into the atmosphere and the reaction may go to completion.*
3. Explain why continuous removal of one of the products of a chemical reaction causes the reaction to go to completion. *The reaction is under continuous stress to go toward the right to replace the product being removed. The reaction never reaches equilibrium, but continually produces product until one or more reactants are used up.*

4. Calcium fluoride (fluorspar or fluorite) is a partially soluble ionic compound used in metallurgy, particularly in aluminum and steel production. When placed in water, the solid is in equilibrium with its ions.
   a. Write a balanced equation to show this equilibrium.
      $CaF_2(s) \rightleftharpoons Ca^{2+}(aq) + 2\ F^-(aq)$
   b. What happens to the position of equilibrium if soluble calcium chloride is added to the solution of calcium fluoride? *It shifts left due to the addition of Ca^{2+} ions to the solution.*
   c. What will happen to the concentration of F^-? *decreases*
5. Tell how the equilibrium system given below shifts, if at all, for each of the following changes.
   $$Ni(s) + 4\ CO(g) \rightleftharpoons Ni(CO)_4(g) \quad \Delta H^\circ < 0 \text{ (exothermic)}$$
   a. add Ni(*s*) *right*
   b. decrease volume *right*
   c. add more CO(*g*) *right*
   d. increase the temperature *left*
6. The reaction
   $$CaCO_3(s) \rightleftharpoons CaO(s) + CO_2(g) \quad \Delta H^\circ = +178\ kJ$$
   is utilized in the production of lime for cements and the chemical industry.
   a. Under what conditions of temperature and pressure (high or low) would the reaction lie more toward the right? *low pressure, high temperature*
   b. What happens if the reaction is open to the atmosphere so that CO_2 can escape? *The reaction goes to completion.*
7. Gaseous ozone (O_3) may be formed from oxygen gas by passing an electric spark through oxygen.
   a. Write a balanced equation showing the equilibrium between O_3 and oxygen.
      $3\ O_2(g) \rightleftharpoons 2\ O_3(g)$
   b. If $\Delta H^\circ = +284$ kJ, tell what effect on ozone production each of the following would have.
      (1) increase temperature *increase*
      (2) remove O_3 as it forms *increase*
      (3) decrease the concentration of O_2 *decrease*
      (4) increase total pressure *increase*
8. Consider the reaction
   $$CO(g) + H_2(g) \rightleftharpoons C(s) + H_2O(l) \quad \Delta H^\circ = -131\ kJ$$
   and tell what would happen to **(1)** the equilibrium position and **(2)** the equilibrium concentration of H_2 for each of the following changes.
   a. more C is added
      (1) *no change (not gaseous)*
      (2) *no change*
   b. the total pressure is reduced
      (1) *left*
      (2) *increases*
   c. [CO] is increased
      (1) *right*
      (2) *decreases*
   d. [H_2O] is increased
      (1) *left*
      (2) *increases*
   e. a catalyst is added
      (1) *no change*
      (2) *no change*
   f. the temperature is reduced
      (1) *right*
      (2) *decreases*

Chapter 15 (pp. 332–361)

Acids, Bases, and Salts

Suggested Daily Pacing

127 **Check** homework.

Return and go over graded Test 9.

Introduce ch. 15, Acids, Bases, and Salts.

Discuss homework.

Teach pp. **333–336,** sec. **15.1** The Nature of Acids and Bases, up to Naming Acids.

Review lesson.

HW: Read pp. 336–339. Answer p. 339, questions 4–8.

128 **Check** and discuss homework.

Review pp. 333–336.

Teach pp. **336–339,** sec. **15.1** (cont.).

Review lesson.

HW: Read pp. 339–342. Answer p. 342, questions 1–5.

129 **Give Quiz 22** (over pp. 333–339).

Check and discuss homework.

Review pp. 336–339.

Teach pp. **339–342,** sec. **15.2** Strengths of Acids and Bases.

Review lesson.

HW: Read pp. 343–346. Answer p. 346, questions 1–4.

130 **Give** "pop" reading quiz over pp. 343–346:

1. The complete reaction between an acid and a base forms what two substances? *salt and water*
2. True or False: All soluble salts dissociate 100% into ions in aqueous solution. *true*
3. In what kind of equation do only the ions actually involved in the reaction appear? *net ionic equation*
4. Give the name of the listing in which metals are arranged in order of their ability to react with acids. *activity series*
5. What is an ionic compound composed of any cation except H^+ and any anion except OH^-? *a salt*

Check and discuss homework.

Review pp. 339–342.

Teach pp. **343–346,** sec. **15.3** Acids in Chemical Reactions.

Review lesson.

HW: Read pp. 346–351. Answer p. 348, questions 1–4 and p. 352, questions 1–8.

131 **Check** and discuss homework.

Review pp. 343–346.

Teach pp. **346–351,** sec. **15.4** Equivalents and Normality—**15.5** Ionic Equilibrium in Solution.

Review lesson.

HW: Read *Lab Manual* Lab 23 and complete Prelab Assignment.

132 **Check** and discuss homework.

Conduct Lab 23: pH Measurement.

HW: Complete Lab 23 Report Sheet. Read pp. 352–355, up to 15.7 Hydrolysis and Buffers. Answer p. 355, questions 1–4.

133 **Check** and discuss homework.

Review pp. 346–351.

Teach pp. **352–355,** sec. **15.6** Acid-Base Titrations.

Review lesson.

HW: Read *Lab Manual* Lab 24 and complete Prelab Assignment.

134 **Check** and discuss homework.

Conduct Lab 24: Acid-Base Titrations.

HW: Complete Lab 24 Report Sheet. Read pp. 355–359. Answer p. 359, questions 1–6.

135 **Check** and discuss homework.

Review pp. 352–355.

Teach pp. **355–359,** sec. **15.7** Hydrolysis and Buffers.

Review lesson.

HW: Begin studying ch. 15 for Test 10 in les. 137. Answer p. 361, Review Exercises 5–6 and 13–18.

136 **Check** and discuss homework.

Review ch. 15 for Test 10 in next lesson, using Chapter Review on pp. 360–361.

HW: Study ch. 15 for Test 10 in next lesson.

137 **Administer Test 10** over ch. 15.

HW: Read pp. 362–366. Answer p. 366, questions 1–6.

Teacher Notes

Chapter 15 Overview. This chapter discusses the chemistry of acids and bases. After surveying some well-known properties of acids and bases, the chapter defines the terms *acid* and *base* according to two different but complementary definitions, that of Arrhenius and that of Brønsted and Lowry. The concept of conjugate acids and bases is briefly presented, followed by an explanation of how acids are named, monoprotic and polyprotic acids, and acidic and basic anhydrides.

The strengths of various acids and bases are then discussed, followed by a survey of the chemical reactions acids and bases undergo and acid / base concentration. After a discussion of pH measurement and titration, the chapter concludes with an explanation of hydrolysis and buffers.

Chapter opener photo (p. 332). Each Alka-Seltzer® tablet contains 1.9 g (0.022 mol) of sodium bicarbonate and 1.0 g (0.005 mol) of citric acid. These reactants do not react in dry form. When the tablet is dropped into water, however, the citric acid and sodium bicarbonate react readily to form sodium citrate and carbon dioxide:

$$3\ \underset{\text{sodium bicarbonate}}{NaHCO_3(aq)} + \underset{\text{citric acid}}{H_3C_3H_5O_7(aq)} \longrightarrow \underset{\text{sodium citrate}}{Na_3C_3H_5O_7(aq)} + 3\ CO_2(g) + 3\ H_2O(l)$$

As the medicine in the tablet also dissolves, the combination of sodium citrate and excess bicarbonate ion *buffer* the solution (section 15.7), ensuring that it does not become too acidic or too basic. Some of the CO_2 produced also dissolves in the water, producing a carbonation effect that helps make the medicine more palatable.

Arrhenius concept (15.1, p. 334). Note that the Arrhenius definition of acids and bases applies only in water solution. However, it is probably the most commonly considered acid-base concept since water is the most common solvent.

Brønsted-Lowry concept (15.1, pp. 334–335). Note that the conjugate acid (having one *more* proton than the base) and the conjugate base (having one *less* proton than the acid) are found on the product side of the equation.

Note that one acid-base concept is not more correct than the other; both are "correct," but each explains different observations.

Naming acids (15.1, pp. 336–337). Students should be sufficiently familiar with Tables 15.2 and 15.3 to allow them to name both binary acids and oxyacids. They should also be able to recognize which acids and bases are classified as "strong" (Table 15.4).

Muriatic acid (15.1, pp. 336–337). The acid sold in hardware stores as "muriatic acid" is actually a hydrochloric acid solution (~8-*M* HCl).

Net ionic equations (15.3, p. 345). If you choose to spend extra time on net ionic equations, you may wish to have students memorize rules *a* through *c* on p. 345. Unless you provide "state labels" such as (*s*) or (*aq*), students will need Table 12.2 to determine which salts should be written as separate ions. Note that subscripts used to designate the number of a given ion must be written as coefficients in the ionic equation rather than as subscripts; for example, it would be incorrect to write 3 Ag^+ as "Al^{3+}" or to write 2 Al^{3+} as

"Al_2^{3+}." Some students may need to review the names and charges of ions (Table 3.2).

Equivalent masses (15.4, pp. 346–347). If some students have trouble calculating equivalent masses, you may wish to introduce the following dimensional analysis setup, which is less "condensed" than the version given in the text:

$$\text{eq mass of } H_3PO_4 = \frac{98.0 \text{ g}}{\text{mol}} \times \frac{1 \text{ mol}}{3 \text{ eq}} = 32.7 \text{ g/eq}$$

$$\text{eq mass of } Ba(OH)_2 = \frac{171 \text{ g}}{\text{mol}} \times \frac{1 \text{ mol}}{2 \text{ eq}} = 85.5 \text{ g/eq}$$

$$\text{eq mass of } HNO_3 = \frac{63.0 \text{ g}}{\text{mol}} \times \frac{1 \text{ mol}}{1 \text{ eq}} = 63.0 \text{ g/eq, etc.}$$

Normality (15.4, p. 347). Note that normality is always greater than or equal to molarity since the number of equivalents is always greater than or equal to the number of moles. (Equivalents and moles are related by small whole numbers.)

Invention of the pH scale (15.5, pp. 348–349). The concept of pH was introduced by the Danish chemist Søren Sørenson (1868–1939). In a now-famous paper,[1] Sørenson introduced the concept of the negative logarithm of the hydrogen molar concentration and called it "P_H"; the symbol has commonly been interpreted in English as "power [i.e., exponent] of hydrogen."

[1] S.P.L. Sørenson, "The Measurement and Meaning of Hydrogen Ion Concentration in Enzymatic Processes," *Biochemische Zeitschrift* **21**:131–200 (1909), archived at <http://www.dbhs.wvusd.k12.ca.us/Chem-History/Sorenson-article.html> (accessed 4/21/2000).

Neutral pH changes with temperature (15.5, pp. 348–349). In pure water at 25 °C, the product $[H_3O^+] \times [OH^-] = 1.00 \times 10^{-14}$. The solution is said to be *neutral* when $[H_3O^+]$ and $[OH^-]$ are equal to each other. Therefore, in a neutral solution at 25 °C, we can see that both $[H_3O^+]$ and $[OH^-]$ must have the value 1×10^{-7}. The exponent of the H_3O^+ concentration (–7) is made positive and taken as the pH; thus, at 25 °C, the pH of a neutral solution is 7.

Interestingly, these numerical relationships ***change with temperature*** because more water molecules dissociate as the temperature rises; thus, pH 7 is neutral only at 25 °C. At 37 °C (human body temperature), for example, the product $[H_3O^+] \times [OH^-]$ equals 2.5×10^{-14}, which can also be written $1 \times 10^{-13.6}$. Therefore, in a neutral solution at 37 °C, both $[H_3O^+]$ and $[OH^-]$ must have the value $1 \times 10^{-6.8}$; as a result, neutral pH at 37 °C is not 7, but rather 6.8. Similarly, neutral pH at 0 °C is 7.47 because fewer water molecules dissociate.

Lecture Demonstrations

Introducing acids and bases (15.1, p. 333). There are a number of demonstrations you can do to introduce the concept of acids and bases. You may wish to display a number of familiar substances that contain acids, bases, or salts (read labels); see Fig. 15.2 for ideas. You might test several acidic and basic solutions with litmus paper, or demonstrate the dissolution of a metal by a strong acid (e.g., Zn in HCl). If you conduct any lab using strong acids or bases, follow appropriate safety precautions.

Acidic anhydrides (15.1, p. 338). You can demonstrate the anhydride of sulfuric acid by burning a small amount of sulfur in a deflagrating spoon in a bottle of O_2 containing some water, as shown in Fig. 15.5; cover the mouth of the bottle with a glass square to minimize escape of SO_2. **CAUTION:** *Perform in a fume hood;* SO_2 is a powerful respiratory irritant. After shaking the bottle well to dissolve the SO_2, test the solution with litmus paper (see figure 16.5).

If a fume hood is available, you may also demonstrate the anhydride of nitric acid by bubbling NO_2 through water and testing the water with litmus. (See section 15.5 of teaching tips for suggestions on producing NO_2.) Any oxide of a group IA or IIA element may be added to water and the solution tested with litmus to demonstrate a basic anhydride.

Strong and weak acids and bases (15.2, pp. 339–341). If you purchased or constructed a conductivity apparatus for section 12.4 (Ch. 12 Lecture Demonstrations), you can also use it here to demonstrate the differences in conductivity of strong vs. weak acids and bases. Use the apparatus to test 0.1 *M* solutions of HCl (strong acid), $HC_2H_3O_2$ (weak acid), NaOH (strong base), and NH_3 (weak base). **CAUTION:** Follow the same safety precautions as in the 12.4 demonstrations; also wear appropriate safety equipment for working with strong acids.

Neutralization reactions (15.3, pp. 343–344). Demonstrate the heat of neutralization by mixing equal volumes of 6 *M* HCl and 6 *M* NaOH in a small beaker or test tube; record the temperature change using a thermometer. Use appropriate safety precautions when preparing and mixing the caustic substances.

Reactions with carbonates / bicarbonates (15.3, p. 344). You may demonstrate the action of acid (vinegar, dilute HCl, or dilute H_2SO_4) on solid $CaCO_3$ or $NaHCO_3$ on a watch glass, or on a solution of

Na_2CO_3 or $NaHCO_3$. Do not add too much acid at once or vigorous effervescence and frothing will occur.

An interesting variation of this demonstration is to react a moderate amount of vinegar and baking soda in a large beaker and then immediately "pour" the invisible CO_2 produced over a lit candle (without spilling any of the liquid). If this is done properly, the flame should flicker and go out due to oxygen starvation (practice before class to master the technique; waiting too long will allow the CO_2 to diffuse away). Concentrated CO_2 can be poured in this manner because it is slightly denser than air (see section 1.3 Teacher Notes).

Reactions with metals and activity (15.3, pp. 344–345). You may demonstrate the differing activities of different metals (Table 15.7) by showing that dilute HCl (6 *M*) reacts with Zn or Mg but not with Cu. Show that dilute HCl does not react as vigorously with a clean piece of iron as it does with Zn or Mg because Fe is less active than Mg or Zn.

Equivalent masses (15.4, pp. 346–347). You can demonstrate the usefulness of equivalent masses and normality by showing that adding equal moles of acids and bases does not necessarily produce neutral solutions. Using a graduated cylinder or a pipet, measure equal volumes (equal moles) of 1.0 *M* HCl and 1.0 *M* NaOH into separate containers. Mix them and test with litmus or pH paper to show that the mixture is neutral. (You will need to have accurate volumes and concentrations to obtain a pH of 7, but it should be close.) Next, measure equal volumes (equal moles) of 1.0 *M* H_2SO_4 and 1.0 *M* NaOH into separate containers, as before, and mix them. Testing with litmus or pH paper will show the mixture very acidic. Add a second identical volume of 1.0 *M* NaOH and again test with litmus or pH paper; the mixture should be neutral or slightly basic. Discuss the utility of using equivalents rather than moles in neutralization reactions.

pH (15.5, pp. 348–349). If you have access to a pH meter, you may wish to test the pH of some common substances (see Table 15.8). Litmus or pH paper of appropriate range can also be used.

Acid-base indicators (15.5, pp. 350–351). Depending on the indicators you have available, you may wish to demonstrate that the "red" or "blue" of various indicators (Table 15.10) is not the same shade. Be sure students understand the purpose of a titration and the use of normality before doing Lab 24.

Hydrolysis and salts (15.7, pp. 355–357). Demonstrate, using pH paper or a pH meter (litmus is less satisfactory), that the solutions of various salts are not necessarily neutral [e.g., KF or NaF, KCl or NaCl, NH_4Cl *vs.* $NH_4C_2H_3O_2$, $Ca(C_2H_3O_2)_2$, $FeCl_3$, $NaC_2H_3O_2$, $NaHSO_3$, Na_2SO_4, $Al_2(SO_4)_3$]. Use freshly boiled and cooled deionized (or distilled) water; stopper tightly between boiling and use to prevent dissolution of atmospheric CO_2. Explain the hydrolysis reaction (if any) in each case, and relate your results to Table 15.10.

Buffers (15.7, pp. 357–359). You may demonstrate the buffering action of the salt of a weak acid added to a weak acid as follows. In two large test tubes (25 × 200 mm), place equal amounts of $CaCO_3$ (marble chips) about $^1/_2$" to 1" deep. To one sample, add about 10 mL of 1 *M* $NaC_2H_3O_2$; to the other add an equal volume of water. Then add 10 mL of 3 *M* $HC_2H_3O_2$ to each test tube. Note that the reaction rate is greater in the unbuffered solution due to a larger concentration of H_3O^+ for the reaction

$$CaCO_3(s) + 2\,H_3O^+(aq) \rightleftharpoons Ca^{2+}(aq) + 3\,H_2O(l) + CO_2(g)$$

Discuss the effect of $C_2H_3O_2^-$ (from $NaC_2H_3O_2$) on equation 15.36a and how it helps suppress the reaction with $CaCO_3$ in the buffered test tube (by pushing the equilibrium of this equation toward the left, thereby reducing the acidity of the solution).

Answers to Text Questions

Section Review 15.1 (p. 339)

Concept Review

1. Differentiate between the Arrhenius and Brønsted-Lowry definitions of an acid. *According to the Arrhenius definition, an acid is any substance that produces H^+ (or H_3O^+) ions when dissolved in water. According to the Brønsted-Lowry definition, an acid is any substance that can donate a proton (H^+) to another substance; water is not required.*
2. List three properties of acids and three of bases.
   acids: *sour taste; react with metals such as zinc to produce H_2; change blue litmus to red*
   bases: *bitter taste and slippery feel; react with acids to neutralize them; change red litmus to blue*
3. In what form do protons generally exist in aqueous solutions? *H_3O^+, the hydronium ion*

Chapter 15

4. What is an acidic anhydride? A basic anhydride? *An acidic anhydride is a nonmetal oxide which forms an acid when it reacts with water. A basic anhydride is a metal oxide which forms a basic solution when it reacts with water.*

Application

5. Identify the Brønsted-Lowry acid, base, and conjugate acid-base pairs in each of the following reactions.
   a. $H_2PO_4^-(aq) + HS_2O^-(aq) \rightleftharpoons H_3PO_4(aq) + SO_4^{2-}(aq)$

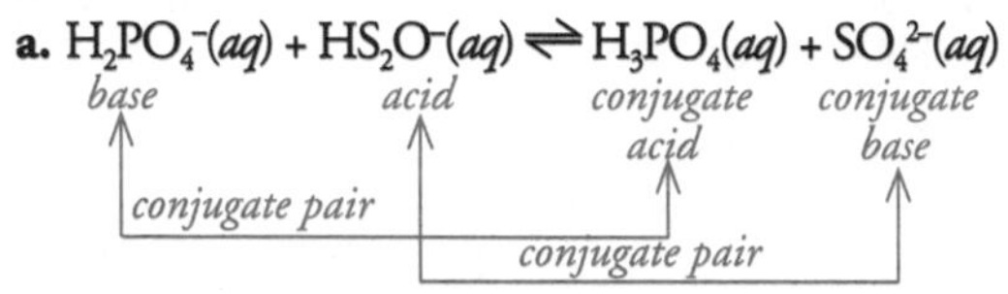

   b. $S^{2-}(aq) + H_2O(l) \rightleftharpoons HS^-(aq) + OH^-(aq)$

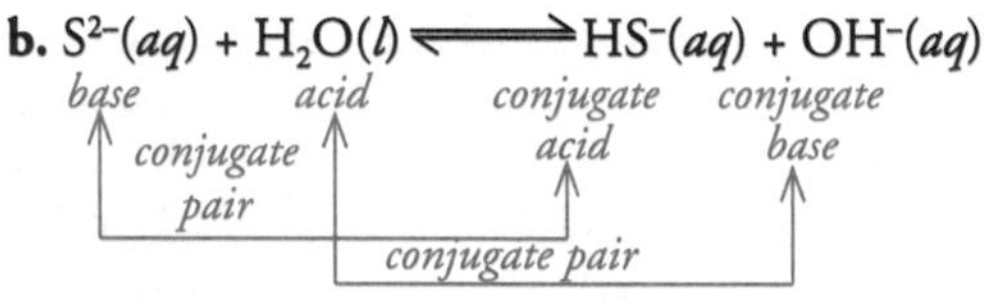

6. Name the following compounds as acids.
   a. H_2CrO_4 *chromic acid*
   b. H_2Te *hydrotelluric acid*
   c. $H_2C_2O_4$ ($C_2O_4^{2-}$ is oxalate) *oxalic acid*
   d. H_2S *hydrosulfuric acid*
   e. H_2SO_4 *sulfuric acid*
   f. H_3BO_3 (BO_3^{3-} is borate) *boric acid*
7. Identify each of the following acids as monoprotic, diprotic, or triprotic.
   a. HI *monoprotic*
   b. H_3BO_3 *triprotic*
   c. $H_2C_2O_4$ *diprotic*
   d. $HC_7H_5O_2$ *monoprotic*
   e. H_2SO_4 *diprotic*
   f. $HClO_4$ *monoprotic*
   g. HNO_3 *monoprotic*
   h. $HC_2H_3O_2$ *monoprotic*
8. Predict whether each of the following is an acidic or a basic anhydride.
   a. MgO *basic*
   b. N_2O_5 *acidic*
   c. P_4O_{10} *acidic*

Section Review 15.2 (p. 342)

Concept Review

1. Differentiate between a ***strong acid*** and a ***weak acid.*** *A strong acid ionizes essentially completely in aqueous solution to form H_3O^+, whereas a weak acid ionizes incompletely in aqueous solution.*
2. Differentiate between a weak acid and a dilute solution of a strong acid. *A weak acid is an acid that ionizes incompletely in aqueous solution. The term dilute, however, refers only to the concentration of the acid. Therefore, the acid in the dilute solution mentioned is still a strong acid, although its concentration has been decreased.*
3. From memory, give four examples of strong acids and three examples of strong bases.
   strong acids: *H_2SO_4, HCl, HNO_3, $HClO_4$, HBr, HI*
   strong bases: *NaOH, KOH, LiOH, $Ba(OH)_2$, $Ca(OH)_2$*
4. Explain the reasons for the following principle: the weaker the base in proton-transfer reactions, the stronger the conjugate acid. *The smaller the tendency for a substance to accept or attract a proton—i.e., the weaker the base—the larger the tendency of the protonated form to give up the proton it has—i.e., the stronger the acid.*

Application

5. Tell the direction of equilibrium for each of the following, using Table 15.6.
   a. $HClO_4(aq) + OH^-(aq) \rightleftharpoons H_2O(l) + ClO_4^-(aq)$
      right
   b. $NH_3(aq) + HSO_4^-(aq) \rightleftharpoons SO_4^{2-}(aq) + NH_4^+(aq)$
      right

Section Review 15.3 (p. 346)

Concept Review

1. What is meant by ***neutralization?*** *the complete reaction between an acid and a base to form a salt and water*
2. What is a salt? *A salt is an ionic compound composed of any cation except H^+ and any anion except OH^-; an ionic compound containing the cation of an aqueous base and the anion of an aqueous acid.*

Application

3. **a.** List the types of substances which are written in ionic form in an ionic equation. **b.** List the types of substances that are written in molecular form in an ionic equation.
   a. soluble salts, strong acids, strong bases
   b. weak acids, weak bases, soluble molecular substances, water-insoluble substances
4. Write net ionic equations for each of the following reactions which occur in aqueous solution. (Be sure to balance the equation first, if necessary!)
   a. $Na_2CO_3(aq) + CaCl_2(aq) \longrightarrow CaCO_3(s) + 2\ NaCl(aq)$
      $CO_3^{2-}(aq) + Ca^{2+}(aq) \longrightarrow CaCO_3(s)$

b. $HF(aq) + KOH(aq) \longrightarrow H_2O(l) + KF(aq)$
$HF(aq) + OH^-(aq) \longrightarrow H_2O(l) + F^-(aq)$

c. $NH_3(aq) + HCl(aq) \longrightarrow NH_4Cl(aq)$
$NH_3(g) + H^+(aq) \longrightarrow NH_4^+(aq)$

Section Review 15.4 (p. 348)

Concept Review

1. What is meant by the ***equivalent mass*** of an acid? Of a base? *The equivalent mass of an acid is the mass of the acid that will supply one mole of protons; the equivalent mass of a base is the mass of the base that will supply one mole of hydroxide ions*
2. Explain the difference between the normality of a solution and the molarity of a solution. *The normality of a solution is the concentration of a solution given in equivalents of solute per liter of solution. The molarity of a solution the number of moles of solute per liter of solution.*

Application

3. The label on a bottle of concentrated sulfuric acid reveals that its concentration is 18 *M*. What is the normality of this solution?
$$18\ mol\ H_2SO_4/L \times \frac{2\ eq\ H_2SO_4}{1\ mol\ H_2SO_4} = \mathbf{36\ N\ H_2SO_4}$$
4. Find the normality of an 18-M solution of hydrochloric acid.
$$18\ mol\ HCl/L \times \frac{1\ eq\ HCl}{1\ mol\ HCl} = \mathbf{18\ N\ HCl}$$

Section Review 15.5 (p. 352)

Concept Review

1. How do the relative concentrations of H_3O^+ and OH^- compare in pure water? *They are equal; water does ionize to a minimal extent, but the concentrations of hydroxide and hydronium ions produced are equal.*
2. What is the pH scale? *a measure of the concentration of H_3O^+ ions in a given solution*
3. At what pH is a substance considered neutral? *pH 7 (at 25° C)*
4. How are the pH and pOH scales related? *In any aqueous solution at 25° C, the sum of the pH and pOH will equal 14. Thus as one increases, the other must decrease.*
5. How is pH estimated by use of an acid-base indicator? *Answers will vary. pH indicators are organic acids or bases whose color changes with the pH of the solution. The indicator changes color when the substance's molecules dissociate at a particular pH. By noting the color change of the indicator, the pH of the solution can be estimated.*

Application

6. Tell whether each of the following solutions is acidic, basic, or neutral. (Recall that [*X*] refers to the concentration of substance *X* in moles per liter.)
   a. $[H_3O^+] = 1.0 \times 10^{-7}$
   $[OH^-] = 1.0 \times 10^{-7}$ *neutral*
   b. $[H_3O^+] = 1.1 \times 10^{-13}$
   $[OH^-] = 8.8 \times 10^{-2}$ *basic*
   c. $[H_3O^+] = 9.1 \times 10^{-6}$
   $[OH^-] = 1.1 \times 10^{-9}$ *acidic*
7. Using the data in Table 15.8, tell whether each of the following solutions is acidic, basic, or neutral.
   a. gastric juice *acidic*
   b. coffee *acidic*
   c. seawater *basic*
   d. soft drinks *acidic*
   e. blood *basic*
   f. lemon juice *acidic*
8. Tell what colors the indicators litmus, methyl orange, and phenolphthalein, respectively, would be in each of the following solutions. *(litmus = L; methyl orange = MO; phenolphthalein = P)*
   a. coffee *L—red; MO—yellow-orange; P—colorless*
   b. seawater *L—blue; MO—yellow-orange; P—pink*
   c. orange juice *L—red; MO—orange; P—colorless*
   d. blood *L—red-blue; MO—yellow-orange; P—colorless*
   e. lemon juice *L—red; MO—red; P—colorless*

Section Review 15.6 (p. 355)

Concept Review

1. What is ***titration***? How does the process allow a chemist to determine the concentration of a solution? *Titration is the gradual addition of a solution of accurately known concentration to a measured volume of solution of unknown concentration until the reaction is complete. Using the exact volume needed to neutralize the reaction, one can calculate the initial concentration.*
2. In a titration, what is the equivalence point? *the point at which equal numbers of moles of base and acid have reacted*

3. What is "acid rain"? *(wording may vary); rain that is more acidic than normal due to dissolved SO_2 or NO_x*

Application

4. 15.00 mL of a nitric acid solution is completely neutralized by 26.80 mL of 0.0950 *N* NaOH. Calculate the normality and molarity of the original solution.
   a. $V_bN_b = V_aN_a;\ N_a = \frac{V_bN_b}{V_a} = \frac{(26.80\ mL)(0.0950\ N)}{(15.00\ mL)} = \mathbf{0.170\ N\ HNO_3}$
   b. $0.170\ eq\ HNO_3/L \times \frac{1\ mol\ HNO_3}{1\ eq\ HNO_3} = \mathbf{0.170\ M\ HNO_3}$

Section Review 15.7 (p. 359)

Concept Review

1. Why are solutions of some salts acidic or basic instead of neutral? *A salt is acidic or basic when a reaction has occurred between the water molecules and an ion in the salt to produce OH^- or H_3O^+ ions (sometimes called hydrolysis since it involves the splitting of water molecules).*
2. What is the function of a buffer? *A buffer maintains a relatively constant pH by reacting with added strong acid or added strong base.*
3. Give one important example of the use of a buffer. *Answers will vary. One example is the buffers in the blood, which work to prevent fatal changes in blood pH.*

Application

4. Classify each of the following salts according to the types of acids and bases from which they may be considered to be derived (e.g., strong base—weak acid).
   a. NH_4NO_3 *weak base—strong acid*
   b. $KC_2H_3O_2$ *strong base—weak acid*
   c. $BaCl_2$ *strong base—strong acid*
   d. Na_3PO_4 *strong base—weak acid*
   e. K_2SO_4 *strong base—strong acid*
   f. $(NH_4)_2CO_3$ *weak base—weak acid*
   g. CaI_2 *strong base—strong acid*
   h. LiF *strong base—weak acid*
5. Tell whether aqueous solutions of each of the salts in question 4 would produce an acidic, basic, or neutral solution.
   a. acidic *e. neutral*
   b. basic *f. cannot be determined*
   c. neutral *g. neutral*
   d. basic *h. basic*
6. Aqueous solutions of which of the following combinations would be buffers?
   a. NH_3/NH_4NO_3
   b. HCl/NaCl
   c. $HC_2H_3O_2/NaC_2H_3O_2$
   d. NaH_2PO_4/Na_2HPO_4
   e. H_3PO_4/KH_2PO_4
   a, c, d, and e are all buffer solutions; all of these involve a weak acid/conjugate base or weak base/conjugate acid pair.

Chapter 15 Review (p. 361)

1. What ion is responsible for the properties of acidic solutions? Of basic solutions?
   acidic solutions: H^+ (or H_3O^+) ion
   basic solutions: OH^- ion
2. Distinguish between the Arrhenius and Brønsted-Lowry definitions of acids and bases. Which includes a wider range of substances? *Arrhenius defined an acid as a substance that produces H^+ when dissolved in water and a base as a substance that produces OH^- when dissolved in water. Brønsted-Lowry defines an acid as a substance that can donate a proton to another substance and a base as a substance that can accept a proton from some other substance. The Brønsted-Lowry definition includes a wider range of substances.*
3. Water can act as either an acid or a base in proton-transfer reactions.
   a. When it acts as a base, what is its conjugate acid? *H_3O^+*
   b. When it acts as an acid, what is its conjugate base? *OH^-*
4. Write formulas for the conjugate acids of each of the following bases.
   a. NH_3 *NH_4^+*
   b. HSO_4^- *H_2SO_4*
   c. HPO_4^{2-} *$H_2PO_4^-$*
   d. $C_2H_3O_2^-$ *$HC_2H_3O_2$*
5. Write formulas for the conjugate bases of each of the following acids.
   a. $HClO_4$ *ClO_4^-*
   b. H_2O *OH^-*
   c. HCN *CN^-*
   d. HPO_4^{2-} *PO_4^{3-}*
6. Name the following compounds as acids.
   a. HIO_3 (IO_3^- is iodate) *iodic acid*
   b. H_2Se *hydroselenic acid*
   c. H_4SiO_4 (SiO_4^{4-} is silicate) *silicic acid*
   d. HClO (ClO^- is hypochlorite) *hypochlorous acid*
   e. $HCHO_2$ (CHO_2^- is formate) *formic acid*
   f. H_3PO_2 (PO_2^{3-} is hypophosphate) *hypophosphoric acid*
   g. HI *hydroiodic acid*

7. Explain why acetic acid ($HC_2H_3O_2$) is *not* a polyprotic acid even though it contains four hydrogen atoms. *It contains only one acidic hydrogen; only one hydrogen atom can be ionized to form a proton. (The other hydrogen atoms are part of the acetate ion.)*
8. Distinguish between a ***strong*** acid and a ***concentrated*** acid. *The term "strong," when referring to an acid, tells us how completely it ionizes in aqueous solution. The concentration of an acid refers to the amount of acid in a given amount of solution.*
9. What term refers to a complete reaction between an acid and a base to form a salt and water? *neutralization*
10. Chemically speaking, what is a *salt?* How do salts differ from acids and bases? *Chemically speaking, a salt is an ionic compound composed of any cation except H^+ and any anion except OH^-. Salts differ from acids and bases in that soluble salts dissociate 100% into ions in aqueous solution; they are the products of neutralization (rather than the reactants); and they are ionic substances.*
11. What is an activity series? Why is hydrogen given such a prominent place in the series? *An activity series is a listing of metals, arranged in order of their ability to react with acids. Hydrogen serves as the dividing point between metals that will and will not react with acids.*
12. Write the net ionic equation for the reaction $HCl(aq) + NaOH(aq) \longrightarrow NaCl(aq) + H_2O(l)$

    $$H^+(aq) + OH^-(aq) \longrightarrow H_2O(l)$$
13. How many equivalent masses of NaOH would it take to completely neutralize 5 equivalent masses of a diprotic acid such as H_2SO_4? *ten*
14. How does the ***normality*** of an acid solution relate to the equivalent mass of the acid? *The normality of a solution is equal to the equivalents of solute per liters of solution.*
15. In your own words, explain why a 1-*M* HCl solution and a 1-*N* HCl solution have the same concentration, but a 1-*M* HCl solution and a 1-*N* H_2SO_4 solution do not. *The HCl solutions have the same* M *and* N *because they are both monoprotic acids; therefore* M = N. *The HCl and H_2SO_4 acids will have different* M *and* N *because HCl is monoprotic and H_2SO_4 diprotic; therefore, for diprotic acids,* N = 2 × M.
16. What is pH? Name three ways pH may be measured in the laboratory. *pH is a measure of the H_3O^+ molar concentration of a substance; it may be measured using a pH meter, acid-base indicators, universal indicator, or pH paper.*
17. In a laboratory titration, an 18.74-mL volume of a solution of HCl was neutralized by 27.08 mL of 0.0750 *N* NaOH. Calculate (a) the normality and (b) the molarity of the original HCl solution.

    normality:

    $$V_bN_b = V_aN_a$$

    $$(27.08\ mL)(0.0750\ N) = (18.74\ mL)(N_a)$$

    $$N_a = \frac{(27.08\ mL)(0.0750\ N)}{(18.74\ mL)} = \mathbf{0.108\ N}$$

    molarity:

    Since HCl is monoprotic, the normality is equal to the molarity = ***0.108M.***
18. Taking hydrolysis into account, predict whether each of the following solutions would be acidic, basic, or neutral.
    a. $NH_4Br(aq)$ *acidic*
    b. $KCl(aq)$ *neutral*
    c. $K_2CO_3(aq)$ *basic*
    d. $LiC_2H_3O_2(aq)$ *basic*

Chapter 15

Chapter 16 (pp. 362–381)
Oxidation-Reduction Reactions and Electrochemistry

16.1 Oxidation and Reduction Processes
16.2 Electrochemical Reactions
16.3 Voltaic Cells

Suggested Daily Pacing

138 **Check** homework.

Return and go over graded Test 10.

Introduce ch. 16, Oxidation-Reduction Reactions and Electrochemistry.

Discuss homework.

Teach pp. **363–366,** sec. **16.1** Oxidation and Reduction Processes.

Review lesson.

HW: Read pp. 367–371. Answer p. 371, questions 1–7. Read *Lab Manual* Lab 25 and complete Prelab Assignment.

139 **Give** "pop" reading quiz over pp. 367–371:

1. Where in the cell does oxidation occur? *the anode*
2. What is the process of passing an electric current through an electrolyte to bring about a nonspontaneous redox reaction? *electrolysis*
3. True or False: An electrolytic solution can conduct electrical charge. *true*
4. What process is used to form a thin coating of metal on an object using an electrolytic cell? *electroplating*
5. What is the flow of electric charge called? *electric current*

Check and discuss homework.

Review pp. 363–366.

Teach pp. **367–368,** sec. **16.2** Electrochemical Reactions, up to Electrolysis.

Review lesson.

Conduct Lab 25: Electrochemistry: Corrosion of Iron.

HW: Review pp. 368–371. Complete Lab 25 Report Sheet.

140 **Review** pp. 367–368.

Teach pp. **368–371,** sec. **16.2** (cont.).

Review lesson.

HW: Read pp. 372–375, up to Measuring Electrode Potentials. Answer p. 379, questions 1–4.

141 **Check** and discuss homework.

Review pp. 368–371.

Teach pp. **372–375,** sec. **16.3** Voltaic Cells, up to Measuring Electrode Potentials.

Review lesson.

HW: Read pp. 375–379. Answer p. 379, questions 5 and 6.

142 **Give Quiz 23** (over pp. 367–375).

Check and discuss homework.

Review pp. 372–375.

Teach pp. **375–379,** sec. **16.3** (cont.).

Review lesson.

HW: Read *Lab Manual* Lab 26 and complete Prelab Assignment.

143 **Check** and discuss homework.

Conduct Lab 26: Electrochemistry: The Voltaic Cell. Complete Lab 26 Report Sheet.

HW: Read pp. 382–387, up to The Nuclear Mass Defect. Answer p. 386, questions 1–4 and p. 390, questions 1 and 2.

Teacher Notes

Chapter 16 Overview. This chapter explores a broad category of chemical reactions called oxidation-reduction reactions—reactions that involve changes in the electron configurations of the reacting atoms.

The chapter opens with the basic concepts of oxidation and reduction, followed by a study of the differing strengths of various oxidizing and reducing agents. The flow of electric current in aqueous solutions is explained, followed by a discussion of electrolysis and electroplating. The chapter concludes with a detailed discussion of voltaic cells and how spontaneous redox reactions allow them to produce electric current.

Other oxidation-reduction mnemonics (16.1, p. 364). "LEO the lion says GER" is not the only oxidation-reduction mnemonic. Another is OIL RIG (Oxidation Is Loss of electrons; Reduction Is Gain of electrons).

Oxidizing/reducing agents (16.1, p. 364). Another analogous situation to clarify the terms reducing agent, reduction, etc., is to remind students that a bleaching agent brings about bleaching or whitening but it is not itself bleached or whitened.

Origin of the term *reduction* (16.1, p. 364). One might wonder at first why a *gain* of electrons is called *reduction.* Actually, the term *reduction* was used long before the discovery of electrons; it comes from the science of metallurgy (chapter 11). When an ore is chemically treated to separate the pure metal from the other substances in the ore, the ore is said to have been *reduced* to the metal. It was not until after the discovery of electrons that this process came to be associated with a gain of electrons.

Chemistry of photography (16.1, pp. 364–365). High-speed film commonly contains crystals of silver iodide rather than silver bromide; AgI is much more sensitive to light, producing a "faster" film. At the other end of the "speed spectrum," photographic *paper* commonly contains silver chloride, which is not very sensitive to light; the slow reaction allows longer (and therefore more easily regulated) exposure times when making prints from the developed negative.

Strong oxidizing/reducing agents (16.1, pp. 365–366). If students have a good understanding of what makes an acid or a base strong or weak, you should be able to use the same type of reasoning here: a strong oxidizing agent has a large tendency to act as an oxidizing agent, i.e., to gain electrons and get reduced.

Non-aqueous electrolytes (16.2, p. 367). Although the definition of electrolyte used in the text includes only electrolytes in aqueous solutions, many ionic substances become electrically conductive even in the absence of water if they are heated until they melt. For example, molten NaCl serves as the electrolyte in Fig. 16.4 even though it contains no water; the current flows because the Na^+ and Cl^- ions are free to move in the molten state. Another example is the molten mixture of aluminum salts used in the production of aluminum by electrolysis (Fig. 11.15). Nearly all electrolytes that we will encounter at everyday temperatures *are* aqueous solutions, however.

Electrolytic purification of copper (16.2, p. 371). The "anode sludge" produced by the electrolysis of copper contains many valuable minerals such as nickel, silver, and platinum-group metals. For this reason, the sludge is usually removed from the cell and further processed to extract these metals.

Voltaic cells (16.3, p. 372). Voltaic cells are named in honor of the Italian physicist Alessandro Volta (1745–1827), who invented an electric battery around 1800 (a silver-zinc battery using salt water as the electrolyte). In the past, voltaic cells have also been called *galvanic cells* after Italian anatomy professor Luigi Galvani (1737–1798), whose accidental observations of electrical effects in frog muscles led Volta to his discovery.

Sacrificial anodes (16.3, p. 374). In some outboard motors, the fin is not necessarily a magnesium anode, but may be painted steel or aluminum. In these motors, all the sacrificial anodes are located inside the motor's casing.

Calculating cell voltage (16.3, pp. 376–377). You may need to emphasize that the potentials given in Table 16.4 are *reduction* potentials; thus, in a redox reaction, one of them (the more negative one) must be reversed. Students should learn to use Table 18.6 to predict redox reaction products and E°_{cell} values.

If the value of E°_{cell} is *positive,* the reaction is spontaneous; an electrochemical cell using this reaction would be a voltaic cell. If the value of E°_{cell} is *negative,* the reaction is not spontaneous and will occur only if driven by an outside current; an electrochemical cell using this reaction would have to be an electrolytic cell.

Leaky batteries (16.3, p. 378). One weakness of the inexpensive Leclanché design is its tendency to leak electrolyte if stored for a long period of time in a discharged condition. Because the zinc anode is also the can that holds the electrolyte, the can gets thinner as the anode is used up. If a hole eventually develops at a thin spot in the zinc, the acidic electrolyte may leak out and corrode the battery contacts. Alkaline cells are much less likely to leak because the materials are contained within a stainless steel can that is not consumed as the cell discharges; they also use an electrolyte that is less corrosive.

Alkaline cells (16.3, p. 378). Generally, the faster a Leclanché or zinc-chloride cell is discharged, the less capacity the battery seems to have. An alkaline cell, on the other hand, maintains good capacity regardless of the discharge rate. Under very light loads (such as running a calculator), a "heavy duty" (zinc chloride) cell might last almost as long as an alkaline cell. However, the zinc chloride cell would deteriorate very quickly under heavier loads, whereas the alkaline cell would hold up much better. For this reason, alkaline cells are preferred over Leclanché and zinc chloride cells for moderate to heavy drain applications, such as portable stereos, radio-controlled model vehicles, and the like.

Lead-acid batteries (16.3, pp. 378–379). Since H_2O is less dense than H_2SO_4, as a battery gets discharged, the density of the electrolyte decreases. A battery hydrometer [hī·drŏm′ĕ·tẽr], which measures densities of aqueous solutions, may thus be used to determine the state of charge of a battery.

Other high-power batteries (16.3, pp. 378–379). Some of the most powerful primary batteries for their size were manufactured to power the electric motors of 1960s-vintage military torpedoes. Some torpedo battery packs using pumped seawater as both electrolyte and coolant could produce as much as 200,000 watts of power for a few minutes, sufficient to drive a 160-horsepower electric motor while still providing power for the torpedo's electronics. Such torpedoes could travel at speeds approaching 50 mph for 2–3 miles. Because of their limited endurance, battery-powered torpedoes were eventually replaced by much faster and longer-range versions (50–75 mph, 25 mi) powered by air-independent internal combustion engines burning high-energy compounds such as propylene glycol dinitrate $[C_3H_6O_2(NO_2)_2]$.

Lecture Demonstrations

Introducing redox reactions (16.1, pp. 363–365). Redox processes may be introduced by the following dramatic demonstration. Dissolve about 20 g $CuCl_2 \cdot 2\,H_2O$ in 175 mL H_2O in a 250-mL beaker. Tear a 4" × 4" piece of aluminum foil into pieces, or crumple it loosely and add it to the $CuCl_2$ solution. **CAUTION:** Reaction is highly exothermic; wear eye protection. Discuss the terms in this section as they apply to the reaction. (The Al was oxidized to Al^{3+} and the Cu^{2+} was reduced to Cu.)

A less dramatic demonstration is to scrape several notches around the rim of a post-1986 penny with a triangular file to reveal the zinc; then drop the penny into a beaker of 6-*M* HCl. **Caution:** HCl is a strong acid. Wear eye protection and take other precautions as appropriate. Hydrogen bubbles will appear from the exposed zinc as H^+ ions are reduced to H (forming H_2) and Zn is oxidized to Zn^{2+}. (If you let this reaction proceed several hours to a day or so, you will end up with a hollow, paper-thin copper shell; decant the acid, rinse the penny thoroughly in a beaker of water or 0.1-*M* $NaHCO_3$ and allow it to dry, and pass it around the class.

Activities of different metals (16.1, p. 366 *or* 16.3, p. 376). The relative activities (or differing reduction potentials) of several metals can be shown as follows:

Demonstrate that iron is more active (more easily oxidized) than nickel, copper, and silver by placing a clean, non-galvanized iron nail into each of three test tubes containing 0.1 *M* solutions of $NiCl_2$, $CuCl_2$, and $AgNO_3$, respectively (it may be helpful to clean the nails with steel wool first). The nails should be only about half submerged so that any reaction may be observed as a difference in the nail's appearance.

Similarly, place a strip of copper metal or a piece of heavy gauge copper wire into each of three test tubes containing 0.1 *M* solutions of $NiCl_2$, $FeCl_3$, and $AgNO_3$, respectively, to demonstrate that Cu is more active than Ag but less active than Ni and Fe. Relate the results to Table 16.2 and / or Table 16.4, depending on when the demonstration is performed.

Ask students to predict what would happen if a zinc strip were placed in $Pb(NO_3)_2$ and $Al_2(SO_4)_3$ solutions. Then demonstrate the actual results by using 0.1 *M* solutions of Pb $(NO_3)_2$ and $Al_2(SO_4)_3$; no reaction occurs with $Al_2(SO_4)_3$.

Electrolysis (16.2, pp. 368–370). One way to demonstrate electrolysis is to electrolyze a 0.5 *M* KI solution. Place a petri dish of the KI solution on an overhead projector; add several drops of 0.2% phenolphthalein solution and 1 mL of 1% starch solution. Connect two carbon rod electrodes to a 1.5-V lantern battery using alligator clip connectors (see Electroplating demonstration below for construction of homemade carbon electrodes). Iodine (I_2) forms at the anode, as indicated by the formation of a blue-black color with starch, and OH^- forms at the cathode, as indicated by a pink coloration due to the phenolphthalein. The reactions are:

anode: $2\,I^-(aq) \longrightarrow I_2(aq) + 2\,e^-$
cathode: $2\,H_2O(l) + 2\,e^- \longrightarrow 2\,OH^-(aq) + H_2(g)$

(If copper electrodes are used, omit the starch since I_2 reacts with Cu and it will not be detected.)

Electroplating (16.2, pp. 370–371). Electroplating may be demonstrated as follows. Prior to class time, shave back both ends of two wooden pencils, using a sharp knife or single-edged razor blade, to expose about 1 cm of pencil lead at each end; these serve as electrodes. Prepare about 100 mL of 0.50 *M* $CuCl_2$ (8.5 g $CuCl_2 \cdot 2\,H_2O$/100 mL solution) and place it in a 150-mL beaker. In class, connect two 1.5-V dry cells in series with copper wire, and connect the dry cell terminals to the pencils using alligator clip connectors, as shown in the figure below. Chlorine, detected by its odor, is produced at the positive electrode (anode), and copper metal plates onto the negative electrode (cathode). You may also wish to reverse the leads to show that the plated copper disappears from the pencil tip and plates onto the other electrode (now the cathode).

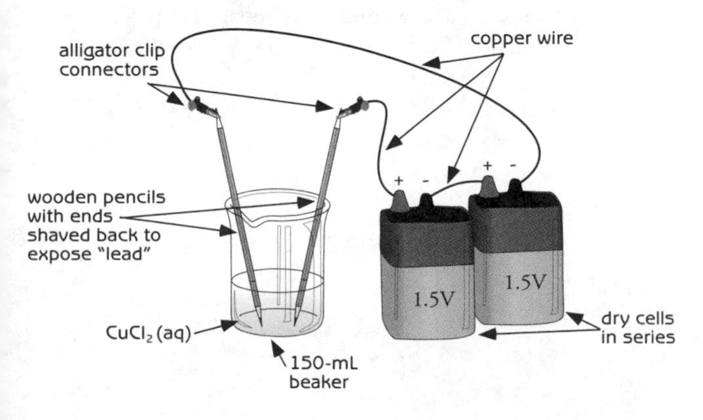

Voltaic cells (16.3, pp. 372–375). A type of voltaic cell called a *Daniell cell* may be constructed by placing a clean strip of copper in a 150-mL beaker containing 100 mL of 0.5 *M* $CuCl_2$ or $Cu(NO_3)_2$. Place a clean strip of zinc in a 150-mL beaker containing 100 mL of 0.5 *M* $Zn(NO_3)_2$; connect the strips to a voltmeter using alligator clip connectors. (Relatively inexpensive digital voltmeters / multimeters are available from electronics supply stores such as Radio Shack; analog and digital meters are also available from science supply companies.) Fill a U-shaped tube with 0.5 *M* $NaNO_3$ and plug the ends with cotton. Invert the U-tube so that it connects the two beakers. If no voltage registers, reverse the polarity. Discuss the reactions occurring in each beaker (see Fig. 16.11).

Chapter 16 Bibliography

Note: Internet sources are given **for the teacher's reference.** Address or content may have changed since this publication of this teacher guide. Be sure to thoroughly review the location and content of any site yourself and check your school policy before recommending the site to your students.

- Energizer® Technical Marketing Datasheets. <http://data.energizer.com>. Commercial site containing diagrams of various battery types and discussion of their chemistry.
- Linden, David, ed. *Handbook of Batteries.* New York: McGraw-Hill, 1995. The standard reference work on battery technology; includes thorough discussion of the chemistry, structure, and function of electrochemical cells, from ordinary dry cells to high-power molten salt designs.

Answers to Text Questions

Section Review 16.1 (p. 366)

Concept Review

1. What is a *redox reaction?* *an oxidation-reduction reaction—one involving a transfer of electrons*
2. Compare and contrast oxidation and reduction. *Oxidation is the process in which there is a loss of one or more electrons and reduction is the process in which there is a gain of one or more electrons. These two processes occur simultaneously.*
3. In a redox reaction, distinguish between the oxidizing agent and the substance that is oxidized. *The oxidizing agent is the substance that accepts electrons. The electrons accepted are those which have been given up by the reducing agent, thus causing the reducing agent to be oxidized.*

Application

4. Sodium metal reacts violently with chlorine gas (Cl_2) to form sodium chloride:

$$2\ Na(s) + Cl_2(g) \rightarrow 2\ NaCl(aq)$$

In this process, each sodium atom loses an electron and each chlorine atom gains an electron.

   a. Which element undergoes oxidation? *sodium*
   b. Which element undergoes reduction? *chlorine*
   c. Which element is the oxidizing agent? The reducing agent? *chlorine; sodium*

5. Which ion in each of the following pairs is the stronger *reducing* agent?

   a. Ni or I^- *Ni*
   b. Mn^{2+} or NO *NO*
   c. Al or K *K*
   d. Fe or Fe^{2+} *Fe*
   e. H_2 or SO_4^{2-} H_2

6. Beaker A contains a strip of nickel in a solution of aluminum sulfate, and beaker B contains a strip of aluminum in a solution of nickel sulfate. Tell what happens in each beaker and explain. *No reaction occurs in beaker A but the aluminum strip dissolves and nickel metal forms in beaker B. Al is a stronger reducing agent than Ni and Ni^{2+} is a stronger oxidizing agent than Al^{3+}; thus, Al is oxidized by Ni^{2+} rather than Ni getting oxidized by Al^{3+} (Ni^{2+} is below Al in Table 16.2).*

Section Review 16.2 (p. 371)

Concept Review

1. What constitutes an electric current? *the flow of electric charge, whether of electrons or ions*
2. Distinguish between electric current in a metal and electric current in an electrolyte solution. *Electric current in metals consists of a flow of electrons, whereas in an electrolyte it consists of a flow of ions.*
3. What is *electrolysis*? *the use of an electric current to bring about a nonspontaneous redox chemical reaction*

Application

4. **(a)** Explain the processes that occur at each electrode during the electrolysis of molten potassium iodide (KI). **(b)** Write the half-reactions for each and the net reaction. **(c)** Tell the direction of migration for each ion.

   a. Oxidation of I^- ions to form I_2 occurs at the anode(+); reduction of K^+ ions to form molten K occurs at the cathode (-).

   b. cathode: $2\ K^+ + 2\ e^- \longrightarrow 2\ K$
   anode: $2\ I^- \longrightarrow I_2 + 2e^-$
   net: $2\ I^- + 2\ K^+ \longrightarrow I_2 + 2\ K$

   c. Iodide ions (anions) migrate toward the anode and K^+ ions (cations) migrate toward the cathode.

5. Why cannot pure water be easily electrolyzed? *Pure water does not conduct an electric current significantly because it contains very few ions (i.e., it is a nonelectrolyte).*
6. Why cannot NaCl be used as an electrolyte in the electrolysis of water? *Cl^- ions would be oxidized at the anode instead of water since they are more easily oxidized than water; as a result, the electrolysis would produce chlorine gas instead of hydrogen.*
7. Why are metals such as silver and copper used for electroplating objects? *Answers will vary. Both are weaker reducing agents than hydrogen and their ions are more easily reduced than water; both are corrosion-resistant; some metals impart additional beauty to objects that are plated.*

Section Review 16.3 (p. 379)

Concept Review

1. What is a voltaic cell? *A voltaic cell is a device which converts the chemical potential energy of a spontaneous redox chemical reaction into electric energy.*
2. What does a metal's position in an activity series tell us about the chemical properties of that particular metal? *The closer to the top the metal is in the list, the more active the metal is and the stronger reducing agent the metal is. When two different metals are involved in a redox reaction, the metal higher in the list will be oxidized and give up electrons which will reduce the cation of the less active metal.*
3. What is the purpose of a salt bridge in a voltaic cell consisting of separate beakers? Why is a salt bridge unnecessary in a single-beaker voltaic cell in which the compartments are separated by a porous divider? *The purpose of a salt bridge here is to equalize the charges in the two beakers and thus prolong the life of the cell. The porous divider in a single-beaker cell serves the same function, making a salt bridge unnecessary.*
4. What is corrosion? *Corrosion is the deterioration of metals caused by electrochemical processes.*

Application

5. How might you perform an experiment to determine which metal in each pair below is the more active?
   a. Na or Fe **b.** Ag or Zn **c.** Cu or Hg
   Answers will vary. Some ideas:
   a. Place a strip of Fe in a Na^+ salt solution such as NaCl(aq); if no reaction occurs, Na is more active. (You cannot use Na metal in water since they react.)
   b. Place strips of Ag and Zn in separate beakers containing Zn^{2+} or Ag^+ ions, respectively; if Ag^{2+} reacts with Ag, Ag is more active and if Ag^+ reacts with Zn, Zn is more active.
   c. Place strips of Cu in Hg_2^{2+} salt solution; if no reaction, Hg is more active. Or place drops of Hg in Cu^{2+} salt solution; if no reaction, Cu is more active than Hg.
6. What does a negative voltage for a given half-cell indicate about the ease of reduction of the metal ion relative to the hydrogen ion, H^+? *It is more difficult to reduce than H^+.*

Chapter 16 Review (p. 381)

1. In each of the following pairs, choose the stronger *oxidizing agent.*
   a. Hg_2^{2+}, NO_3^- *NO_3^-*
   b. H_3O^+, Fe^{2+} *H_3O^+*
   c. I_2, Au^{3+} *Au^{3+}*
   d. Ca^{2+}, Mg^{2+} *Mg^{2+}*
2. In each of the following pairs, choose the stronger *reducing agent.*
   a. Hg, NO *Hg*
   b. H_2, Fe *Fe*
   c. I^-, Au *I^-*
   d. Ca, Mg *Ca*
3. Compare your answers for exercises 1 and 2. What conclusion could be drawn about the strengths of related pairs of oxidizing and reducing agents? *The stronger the oxidizing agent is, the weaker its reduced form is as a reducing agent.*
4. What is an electrolyte? *An electrolyte is a substance that dissociates or ionizes in water to produce ions which can conduct an electrical current.*
5. **(a)** If a truck's bumper is to be electroplated with chromium ("chrome"), which electrode must the bumper be? **(b)** What must be the composition of the other electrode?
   a. cathode (–)
   b. chromium
6. At what location in an electrochemical cell does oxidation occur? Where does reduction occur? *anode; cathode*
7. **(a)** Sketch a setup for the electroplating of a ring with gold; include all essential components and label them. **(b)** Write the equations for the reactions occurring at each electrode.
   a.

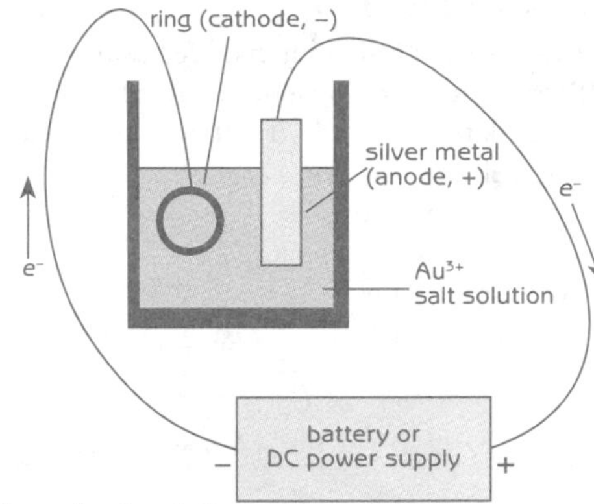

   b. cathode: *$Au^{3+} + 3e^- \longrightarrow Au$*
   anode: *$Au \longrightarrow Au^{3+} + 3e^-$*
8. **(a)** Distinguish between corrosion and rust.
   (b) Explain two methods of preventing the corrosion of iron.
   a. Corrosion refers to the deterioration of any metal by electrochemical processes, whereas rust refers to the result of iron corrosion—hydrated iron(III) oxide.
   b. Use a protective coating to exclude air and water from the iron surface; bring a more active metal than iron in contact with the iron.
9. Why does coating a metal with a more active metal help prevent corrosion? *When a metal is coated with a more active metal, the more active metal serves as the anode and is oxidized, thus protecting the less active metal from oxidation.*
10. Explain the reasons for the differences in signs for the cathode and anode in electrolytic and voltaic cells. *(Wording may vary.) The anode is positive in an electrolytic cell because electrons are being removed "forcibly" (it is electron-poor) but negative in a voltaic cell because electrons are "willingly" given up (it is electron-rich). The reverse applies to the cathode.*
11. What is meant by the ***standard electrode potential*** of a substance? How does this potential relate to the substance's position in an activity series? *The standard electrode potential of a substance is its electric potential (voltage) in a half-cell, relative to the standard hydrogen electrode. Hydrogen, a moderately active substance, has been arbitrarily given the standard electrode potential of zero volt. Any substance above hydrogen is more active (more negative) and will have a negative E°. Any substance below H is less active and will have a positive E°.*

12. If the values of $E°$ for the nickel, copper, gold, and hydrogen half-cells are –0.25 V, +0.34 V, +1.50 V, and 0.0 V, respectively, arrange these half-cells in order of *decreasing* ability to be reduced (beginning with the most easily reduced). *Au, Cu, H_2, Ni*

13. Are the ions that serve as carriers of charge in electrochemical cells *always* involved in the redox reactions at the electrodes? Explain. *No; it depends on their ease of oxidation or reduction relative to the other species present.*

14. For each of the following half-cell combinations, **(1)** write the reactions occurring in each half-cell, **(2)** write the overall reaction, **(3)** tell which half-cell is the anode and which is the cathode, and **(4)** calculate the standard cell potential. (Refer to Tables 16.2 and 16.6.)
    a. Cl^- / Cl_2 and Br^- / Br_2
    b. Cr / Cr^{3+} and Cd / Cd^{2+}
    c. Al / Al^{3+} and $Cr^{3+} / Cr_2O_7^{2-}$
    d. Ag / Ag^+ and F^- / F_2

a.		
ox. (anode):	$2\,Br^- \longrightarrow Br_2 + 2\,e^-$	$E° = -1.06\ V$
red. (cathode):	$Cl_2 + 2\,e^- \longrightarrow 2\,Cl^-$	$E° = +1.36\ V$
net:	$2\,Br^- + Cl_2 \longrightarrow Br_2 + 2\,Cl^-$	$E°_{cell} = +0.30\ V$

b.		
ox. (anode):	$Cr \longrightarrow Cr^{3+} + 3\,e^-$	$E° = +0.74\ V$
red. (cathode):	$Cd^{2+} + 2\,e^- \longrightarrow Cd$	$E° = -0.40\ V$
net:	$2\,Cr + 3\,Cd^{2+} \longrightarrow 2\,Cr^{3+} + 3\,Cd$	$E°_{cell} = +0.34\ V$

c.		
ox. (anode):	$Al \longrightarrow Al^{3+} + 3\,e^-$	$E° = +1.66\ V$
red. (cathode):	$Cr_2O_7^{2-} + 14\,H^+ + 6\,e^- \longrightarrow 2\,Cr^{3+} + 7\,H_2O$	$E° = +1.33\ V$
net:	$2\,Al + Cr_2O_7^{2-} + 14\,H^+ \longrightarrow 2\,Al^{3+} + 2\,Cr^{3+} + 7\,H_2O$	$E°_{cell} = +2.99\ V$

d.		
ox. (anode):	$Ag \longrightarrow Ag^+ + e^-$	$E° = -0.80\ V$
red. (cathode):	$F_2 + 2\,e^- \longrightarrow 2\,F^-$	$E° = +2.87\ V$
net:	$2\,Ag + F_2 \longrightarrow 2\,Ag^+ + 2\,F^-$	$E°_{cell} = +2.07\ V$

Chapter 17 (pp. 382–415)

Nuclear Chemistry

Suggested Daily Pacing

144 **Give** "pop" reading quiz over pp. 384–387:

1. What two particles are contained in the nucleus? *protons and neutrons*
2. Give the term for atoms of the same element that differ in their mass numbers. *isotopes*
3. Any unstable substance that tends to undergo nuclear decay is said to be __?__. *radioactive*
4. Who first discovered what would later be called radioactivity? *Henri Becquerel*
5. Give the term used to refer to any isotope of any element. *nuclide*

Check homework.

Introduce Ch. 17, Nuclear Chemistry using p. 383 and lecture demonstration located in Teacher Notes (Introducing Nuclear Chemistry [pp. 383–385]).

Discuss homework.

Teach pp. **384–387,** sec. **17.1** Radioactivity: Changes in the Nucleus—**17.2** Nuclear Stability, up to The Nuclear Mass Defect.

Review lesson.

HW: Read pp. 387–390, up to 17.3 Nuclear Reactions. Answer p. 390, questions 3–6.

145 **Check** and discuss homework.

Review pp. 384–387.

Teach pp. **387–390,** sec. **17.2** (cont.).

Review lesson.

HW: Read pp. 390–394, up to Half-Life: Rate of Decay. Answer p. 399, questions 1–3.

146 **Give** "pop" reading quiz over pp. 390–394:

1. What two numbers are always conserved in nuclear equations? *mass number and nuclear charge (atomic number)*

2–3. Give the four types of nuclear decay. *alpha decay, beta decay, gamma radiation, and neutron radiation*

4. Which kind of radiation is widely used in the treatment of cancer? *gamma radiation*
5. Which type of radiation is formed by electromagnetic waves of very high frequency and energy? *gamma radiation*

Check and discuss homework.

Review pp. 387–390.

Teach pp. **390–394,** sec. **17.3** Nuclear Reactions, up to Half-Life: Rate of Decay.

Review lesson.

HW: Read *Lab Manual* Lab 27 and complete PreLab Assignment.

147 **Check** and discuss homework.

Demonstrate Lab 27: Nuclear Chemistry.

HW: Complete Lab 27 Report Sheet. Read pp. 394–399. Answer p. 399, questions 4–9.

148 **Check** and discuss homework.

Review pp. 390–394.

Teach pp. **394–399,** sec. **17.3** (cont.).

Review lesson.

HW: Read *Lab Manual* Lab 28 and complete Prelab Assignment.

149 **Check** and discuss homework.

Conduct Lab 28: Radioactive Nuclear Decay and Half-Life.

HW: Complete Lab 28 Report Sheet. Read pp. 400–402, up to 17.5 Nuclear Fission and Fusion. Answer p. 402, questions 1–6.

150 **Give Quiz 24** (over pp. 386–399).

Check and discuss homework.

Review pp. 394–399.

Teach pp. **400–402,** sec. **17.4** Effects of Radiation on Matter.

Review lesson.

HW: Read pp. 402–406, up to Nuclear Power and the Environment. Answer p. 413, questions 1–3.

151 **Give** "pop" reading quiz over pp. 402–406:

1. Give the name for the process in which one atom splits into two or more smaller atoms. *nuclear fission*
2. The amount of an element that must be present at a given density in order for the nuclear reaction to be self-sustaining is the ___?___. *critical mass*
3. Name the process used to increase the percentage of a particular isotope. *enrichment*
4. What device does a nuclear plant use to produce heat? *nuclear reactor*
5. What part of the reactor slows neutrons down to allow for easier capture? *moderator*

Check and discuss homework.

Review pp. 400–402.

Teach pp. **402–406,** sec. **17.5** Nuclear Fission and Fusion, up to Nuclear Power and the Environment.

Review lesson.

HW: Read pp. 406–411, up to Special Applications of Nuclear Power. Answer p. 413, questions 4–8.

152 **Check** and discuss homework.

Review pp. 402–406.

Teach pp. **406–411,** sec. **17.5** (cont.), up to Special Applications of Nuclear Power.

Review lesson.

HW: Read pp. 411–413. Answer p. 413, questions 9 and 10.

153 **Give Quiz 25** (over pp. 400–407).

Check and discuss homework.

Review pp. 406–411.

Teach pp. **411–413,** sec. **17.5** (cont.).

Review lesson.

HW: Begin studying ch. 16–17 for Test 11 in les. 155. Answer p. 381, Review Exercises 1–2, 7, and 12–14; also answer p. 415, Review Exercises 4, 9–13, and 16.

154 **Check** and discuss homework.

Review ch. 16–17 for Test 11 in next lesson using Chapter Reviews on pp. 380–381 and 414–415 and Concept Review 6.

HW: Study ch. 16–17 for Test 11 in next lesson.

155 **Administer Test 11** over ch. 16–17.

HW: Read pp. 416–421. Answer p. 421, questions 1–6.

Teacher Notes

Chapter 17 Overview. This chapter introduces the important and fascinating science of nuclear chemistry, the study of reactions involving the nucleus. The chapter begins with the study of radioactivity, followed by a discussion of the potential energy present in an atom's nucleus. Nuclear reactions are then introduced, with a focus on the three main types of nuclear decay and the properties of the radiation they produce. Half-life and activity are discussed, followed by a brief introduction to bombardment reactions and their products. The effects of various types of radiation on matter, including living things, is studied along with some units of radiation measurement. The chapter concludes with a detailed study of fission and fusion reactions and their applications, ranging from civilian power generation to nuclear weapons.

Becquerel's discovery (17.1, p. 384). The radioactive compound studied by Becquerel was potassium uranyl sulfate, $K_2UO_2(SO_4)_2{\cdot}H_2O$.

Mass defects and molar amounts (17.2, p. 388). Although the text explains the mass defect on a "per atom" basis, the calculations also work with molar amounts:

$$\left.\begin{array}{l}\text{8 mol protons}\\\text{8 mol neutrons}\\\text{8 mol electrons}\end{array}\right\}\longrightarrow \text{1 mol } {}^{16}_{8}\text{O} + 1.23\times10^{13}\text{ J}$$

$$\mathbf{16.131920\ g \longrightarrow 15.994915\ g + 0.137\ g}$$

We can see that oxygen-16 is 0.137 grams (137 milligrams) per mole *lighter* than it should be according to the mass of its component particles. This is an easily measurable difference and shows just how large the mass defect is on the macroscopic scale.

You may wish to highlight the magnitude of the energy involved: assembling only 1 mole (~16 grams) of oxygen from its component particles would release as much energy as detonating 3000 tons of TNT.

Mass-energy conversion (17.2, p. 388). Although it is sometimes implied that nuclear reactions have the unique ability to "convert" mass to energy, we could say that the mass (as we have used the term) is not converted to anything; it is still there because energy has an associated "mass" according to $E = mc^2$. What has really occurred is that *potential mass-energy has been converted to kinetic mass-energy.*

Note that "mass defects" are not unique to nuclear reactions; *any* process in which the total energy of an object changes involves a mass defect. For example, the detonation of exactly 900 kg of TNT produces 899.999 999 954 kg of gaseous products and 0.046 mg of energy (4.187×10^9 J). Such tiny mass defects are not easily measured, however.

Smoke detectors and Am-241 (17.3, p. 391). A typical smoke detector contains about 0.2 mg of americium-241 dioxide (AmO_2), enough to produce 3000–30,000 alpha decays per second. At $1500 per gram, AmO_2 is nearly 200 times more expensive than gold, but only 30 cents' worth is required for each detector.

Beta-plus decay (17.3, p. 391). The text describes the most familiar type of beta decay, known as "beta-minus" decay (β^-) because an electron ("*e*-minus") is produced. However, a second form of beta decay, known as "beta-plus" decay (β^+), is also quite common. In β^+ decay, a proton turns into a neutron and emits a *positron* (${}^{0}_{1}e^+$, the antimatter counterpart of the electron) and a neutrino. (The name "beta-plus" comes from the sign of the positron.)

Beta-plus decay results in an atom with an atomic number one *lower* than the original element. For example, sodium-22 undergoes β^+ decay to form neon-22 according to the following reaction:

$${}^{22}_{11}\text{Na} \longrightarrow {}^{22}_{10}\text{Ne} + {}^{0}_{1}e^+$$

Note that the β^+ particle (positron) has a positive charge and is assigned an "atomic number" of 1 to comply with the rules for balancing nuclear equations (p. 390).

Tritium phosphors (17.3, p. 392). Tritium phosphorescent capsules should not be confused with "glow-in-the-dark" chemical paints. The former are powered by the beta decay of tritium and can glow for years without ever being exposed to light, whereas the latter glow only for a short time before they must be "recharged" by exposing them to light.

Gamma radiation from smoke detectors (17.3, p. 392). Household smoke detectors containing Am-241 also continuously emit low-intensity gamma radiation as a byproduct of the alpha decay process. However, the radiation exposure to household residents is less than 1 mrem/yr, a negligible amount.

Absorption of radiation (17.3, p. 393). Water is an excellent absorber of all forms of radiation, making it useful as radiation shielding. For example, highly radioactive spent fuel assemblies from nuclear reactors (Section 17.5) are commonly stored underwater for a year or two in indoor "storage pools" that look like Olympic-size swimming pools. The overlying water blocks radiation from the fuel, so that even at poolside the radiation level is very low.

Producing a beam of radiation (17.3, p. 394). Although a radioactive substance emits radiation equally in all directions, such radiation can be channeled (or *collimated*) by surrounding the radioactive substance with a radiation absorber such as a lead block with a hole in it (as shown in Fig. 17.10). In such an arrangement, only the radiation that is emitted in the direction of the hole escapes, resulting in a narrow beam of radiation that may be easily studied.

Radiometric dating (17.3, pp. 396–397). Evolutionists commonly use decay series such as the one in Fig. 17.13 to "date" rocks, usually assigning them very old ages. However, to use the half-life of an element to estimate the age of a sample, one must accurately know

(1) the half-life of the parent element;
(2) how much of the parent element remains in the sample;
(3) how much of the daughter element remains in the sample;
(4) how much of the parent element was originally in the sample;
(5) how much of the daughter element was originally in the sample;
(6) how much of the parent element entered or left the sample over time; and
(7) how much of the daughter element entered or left the sample over time.

Although 1–3 can be accurately measured, 4–7 cannot be measured and must be guessed at. Unfortunately, this leaves room for a scientist's worldview and presuppositions to determine which guesses are "reasonable," thereby affecting the "date" produced.

It should also be kept in mind that when God created the earth, it probably already contained quantities of what we might call "daughter" elements, so that the mere presence of these elements is not necessarily evidence of long geologic ages.

Ionizing *vs.* nonionizing radiation (17.4, p. 400). Ultraviolet light can also cause ionization under the right circumstances. However, lower-energy photons (such as microwaves) pose no danger of ionization. For this reason, microwave exposure from such devices as cordless / cellular phones, radio antennas, orbiting satellites, etc. is not considered by scientists to pose even a remote risk of cancer.

Radiation units (17.4, p. 401). The biological dose equivalent is obtained by multiplying the absorbed dose by a "quality factor," sometimes designated Q. Gamma rays have a Q of 1 (i.e., the dose equivalent equals the absorbed dose). Neutrons and heavy ions may have Q of up to 20 or more because they are more hazardous to living cells.

Conversion factors for radiation units may be found in Appendix A on p. 455 of the text.

Protecting cells from radiation (17.4, p. 402). To put cell damage from ionizing radiation in perspective, it is estimated that every cell of your body experiences some 70 *million* instances of oxidative damage to its DNA per year. Only five to eight of these "hits," or 0.00001%, can be attributed to ionizing radiation.[1] The vast majority come from your cells' own machinery (e.g., oxidative free radicals produced by metabolism in cell mitochondria).

Your cells do not die from this damage because God designed them with efficient DNA repair mechanisms to protect them from their own oxidative free radicals. These same mechanisms also serve to protect cells from reasonable levels of ionizing radiation (up to several thousand mrem/yr) without noticeable effects.

The DNA-repair mechanisms of some bacteria are extraordinarily efficient, allowing them to survive immense doses of radiation. The bacterium *Deinococcus radiodurans* can thrive indefinitely at dose rates of 6000 rads/hr, and can survive an acute dose of 1.5 million rads (~1.5 billion mrem) if given a few hours' respite afterward to repair the DNA damage.[2]

[1]Jaworowski, Zbigniew. "Radiation Risk and Ethics." *Physics Today* **52:**9, (September 1999), pp. 24–29; also available at <http://www.riskworld.com/Nreports/1999/jaworowski/NR99aa01.htm>.

[2]John Travis, "Meet the Superbug," *Science News* **154:**24 (12/12/1998), p. 376, archived at <http://www.sciencenews.org/sn_arc98/12_12_98/Bob1.htm>.

Background radiation (17.4, p. 402). In many regions of the world, people are exposed to far higher rates of background radiation than the U.S. average (up to several thousand mrem/yr), with no detectable ill effects. To put U.S. background levels in perspective, Sweden enacted a law in 1980 limiting radon exposure in existing homes to 2500 mrem/yr.

Radiation levels in space (17.4, p. 402). One of the most radioactive of all natural environments is the environment of space, due to high-energy charged particles from the sun and distant stars. Astronauts aboard a space shuttle in low earth orbit are exposed to about 0.2–10 mrad/hr depending on the altitude (up to 3400 mrem total for a 2-week mission). Dose rates increase with altitude due to charged particles trapped in the Earth's magnetic field, peaking at up to 90 rad/hr (90,000 mrad/hr) in the earth's Van Allen belts. Dose rates of several dozen rad/hr are also possible on the moon and in interplanetary space during solar storms.

Some of the most intense radiation in the Solar System is found between Jupiter and its moon Io, where high-energy ions trapped in Jupiter's intense magnetic field generate exposure rates of 2500–750,000 R/hr.

Energy produced by fission (17.5, p. 403). The fission of a uranium-235 atom releases a total of 200 MeV of energy, but only about 177 MeV is released immediately; the rest is released some time later when the unstable fission products decay.

Uranium-236 and fission (17.5, p. 403). When a uranium-235 nucleus absorbs a slow neutron, the reaction proceeds to fission (Fig. 17.17, eq. 17.12–13) about 86% of the time. In the other 14% of cases, the excited uranium-236 nucleus "de-excites" by emitting a high-energy gamma ray instead of fissioning, resulting in a long-lived atom of U-236 (an α emitter with a half-life of 23.7 million years).

Nuclear weapons discussion (17.5, pp. 404, 412). Nuclear weapons are highly controversial and have been a matter of intense debate for over 50 years. Although it is important for citizens to be knowledgeable about this issue, considerable exaggeration and distortion exists. The text and these teacher notes focus primarily on technical aspects of the subject, which provide a foundation for understanding, but there are other aspects involving moral and national security considerations that are far beyond the scope of a chemistry course. However, since these subjects may come up in class, the Chapter 17 Resource List contains resources that you can use for more information on this issue.

The first atomic bomb (17.5, p. 404). Because the July 16, 1945, nuclear test was code-named *Trinity* for security reasons, "Gadget" is sometimes referred to as the "Trinity device."

Kilotons and megatons (17.5, p. 404). One kiloton TNT equivalent (kT) is defined as exactly 10^{12} calories or 4.187×10^{12} joules. The yield of the Hiroshima bomb was approximately 12–15 kT; that of the Nagasaki bomb was 20–22 kT.

A large coal-fired electrical plant produces the equivalent of 1 kiloton TNT in heat energy every 28 minutes. However, a nuclear weapon releases this energy instantly rather than gradually.

Uranium enrichment (17.5, pp. 405–406). Uranium is enriched by removing unwanted uranium-238 to increase the percentage of ^{235}U. The excess ^{238}U removed during the enrichment process is known as *depleted uranium* because it is "depleted" of ^{235}U. Some uses of depleted uranium were discussed on p. 263.

Types of nuclear reactors (17.5, p. 406). The reactor shown in Fig. 17.23 and 17.24 is a U.S.-style pressurized-water reactor (PWR) using enriched UO_2 as fuel and H_2O as both coolant and moderator. (The water is pressurized to keep it in a liquid state.)

Although the PWR is the most common reactor type in the United States, several other reactor designs exist. Such reactors use a variety of fuels (uranium/thorium ceramics, unenriched UO_2, molten uranium salts) moderators (graphite, D_2O, or none at all) and coolants (CO_2, helium gas, molten salts, molten sodium, molten lithium, molten lead-bismuth alloy).

Why reactors cannot explode (17.5, pp. 406–407). Chain reactions in a nuclear reactor are gradual because the reactor is just barely critical and depends on a small percentage of delayed neutrons to keep the reaction going. When uranium-235 fissions, 99.5% of the neutrons produced are emitted immediately, but the other 0.5% are emitted only after a considerable delay (a few seconds to a few minutes). These are called *prompt neutrons* and *delayed neutrons,* respectively.

In a nuclear reactor, the fuel mass and neutron absorbers are adjusted so that the core is just barely critical, so that *prompt neutrons alone are not enough to sustain a chain reaction.* Delayed neutrons are required, but since they are emitted slowly, the chain reaction—and therefore changes in power output—are gradual. Delayed neutrons *cannot* produce a nuclear explosion because the reaction rate builds far too slowly.

A second reason reactors cannot undergo nuclear explosions is that the nuclear material is simply not concentrated enough. Even if a reactor is somehow made critical on prompt neutrons alone (as was Chernobyl), the resulting chain reaction is not vigorous enough to generate a nuclear explosion; the reaction breaks down due to thermal stress long before significant nuclear yield can be generated. The assembled core of an atomic bomb packs 2.5 to 5 critical masses into a sphere 3 inches or less in diameter; Chernobyl in its prompt-critical state represented only about 1.01 critical masses in a cylinder 35 feet across.

Loss of coolant accidents (17.5, p. 407). Even when a reactor is shut down, the decay of residual fission products continues to produce a significant amount of heat (known as *decay heat*) for some time. Thus, some degree of cooling must be maintained in the core at all times. In some reactors, natural convection is sufficient to keep the core from overheating, while others require backup cooling systems.

Comparing risks (17.5, p. 407). The 1989 Siberian pipeline explosion occurred when a broken pipeline filled a valley with thousands of tons of propane and butane that were later ignited by electrical sparks from a pair of passenger trains. As at Chernobyl, the cause was recklessness and negligence; the pipeline operators had noticed a large pressure drop in the pipeline (signaling a break), but had merely turned up the gas flow to compensate instead of checking for a leak.

Several notable disasters relevant to energy and chemical industries are shown below.

Selected Industrial and Power-Related Accidents

Year	Location	Description	Deaths
1966	Aberfan, Wales	coal storage pile collapse onto elementary school	144
1975	Henan Province, China	dam collapse	26,000–230,000
1978	San Carlos de la Rapito, Spain	tanker truck accident	180
1979	Three Mile Island, Pennsylvania	nuclear reactor accident	0
1979	Gujarati, India	dam collapse	5,000–15,000
1982	Caracas, Venezuela	explosion at oil-fired power plant	98
1984	Bhopal, India	rupture of chemical storage tank	2500
1984	Mexico City, Mexico	explosion of natural gas depot	452
1986	Chernobyl, Ukraine	nuclear reactor accident	44–200? (to date)
1988	Piper Alpha oil/gas platform, North Sea	explosion and fire	167
1989	Ural region, Siberia	propane explosion due to pipeline break	500

Chapter 17

Nuclear *vs.* coal (17.5, pp. 407, 410). The point of the nuclear-coal comparison is not to criticize coal, but to expose the myth that nuclear power is somehow inherently more dangerous than more familiar energy sources; coal is presently the primary source of electrical power in the United States. Coal and other fossil fuels are useful and viable sources of power (chapter 18), and are becoming increasingly clean due to modern pollution-control technology. Some fossil fuels, such as natural gas, are also notably cleaner than coal using present technology.

Note that even wind and solar power, if applied on a large (multi-gigawatt) scale, would likely have at least as significant an environmental impact due to their very low energy density, which would require huge tracts of pristine land to be razed and covered with solar collectors or windmills. Rooftop solar collectors would have less land-use impact, but would be extraordinarily expensive and would have trouble providing industrial-scale power.

Radiation deaths at Chernobyl (17.5, pp. 408–409). Many of the post-accident radiation deaths and injuries could have been avoided if the Soviet authorities had provided proper equipment. The early stages of the cleanup involved workers with minimal protection running out onto the roof of the reactor hall and adjacent buildings, picking up pieces of the shattered reactor core with shovels, and tossing them over the side or down the gaping hole in the roof, directly over the open, burning core. According to Zhores Medvedev in his book *Legacy of Chernobyl,*

> they considered the speed at which they ran to be their chief protection. Radiation fields in some parts of the roof of the machine hall were between 10,000 and 20,000 R/h [3–6 rads *per second!*] and one run of 30–50 seconds was considered permissible . . . One minute or less of great effort and hospital bed after for checks of the dose.[1]

A sense of the carelessness that characterized the early days of the cleanup was given by Russian official Gregory Medvedev:

> During my visit . . . I saw soldiers and officers picking up graphite [from the shattered reactor core] with their hands. . . . I opened the [car] door and pushed the radiometer almost onto a graphite block. 2000 roentgens [rads] per hour.[2]

[1]Zhores Medvedev, *Legacy of Chernobyl* (New York: Norton, 1992), 171.
[2]Gregory Medvedev, qt. in Zhores Medvedev, 168.

Chernobyl evacuations (17.5, pp. 408–409). More than 270,000 people were evicted from their homes by the Soviet government after the Chernobyl accident to protect them from alleged radiation dangers. However, in much of the evacuation zone, the increase in radiation levels over the next decade averaged only 60–600 mrem/yr, comparable to natural background levels. By comparison, 5000 mrem/yr above background is considered acceptable for nuclear workers in the U.S., and 500 mrem/yr above background is considered safe even for children. In retrospect, forced evacuation from some of these areas may have been a significant overreaction.

Three Mile Island (17.5, p. 409). The Three Mile Island accident was ultimately caused by a faulty pressure relief valve in the primary loop (Fig. 17.25). Following an unscheduled reactor shutdown, this valve opened as designed to released excess pressure in the primary loop. Unfortunately, the valve stuck open, but a broken sensor led operators to believe the valve had closed as designed. The open valve allowed coolant to flow out of the system into an overflow tank (and eventually the containment building basement). Meanwhile, the confused operators became convinced that there was too *much* coolant in the system rather than too little, leading them to shut down the emergency core cooling system. As the water level in the core dropped, the core became uncovered and overheated, melting the exposed fuel.

The average radiation exposure to people nearest the plant during the accident was between 1.2 and 8 mrem, although a lone fisherman directly downwind from the plant *may* have received as much as 37 mrem (considered the maximum possible off-site dose).

Pro-nuclear scientist Dr. Peter Beckmann once speculated that the Three Mile Island accident resulted in approximately 300 premature deaths between 1979 and 1985—not from nuclear radiation, but from coal-related accidents and pollution that occurred because the lost electrical capacity had to be made up by coal-fired plants.[3]

[3]Peter Beckmann, "A Shared Nuclear Secret" (1988), <http://www.powerup.com.au/~dominion/ff/p05.htm>.

Fuel reprocessing in the U.S. (17.5, p. 410). Although no reprocessing is presently taking place in the U.S., spent nuclear fuel can be reprocessed at any point in the future as long as it remains accessible. If the fuel is reprocessed, the leftover waste that would need to be stored in a repository amounts to only 1 cubic meter per 1000-MW reactor per year.[4]

[4]John McCarthy, "Facts from Cohen and Others: How Long Will Nuclear Energy Last?" <http://www-formal.stanford.edu/jmc/progress/cohen.html>.

Uranium—a billion year supply (17.5, p. 411). Some antinuclear activists have claimed that a nuclear-fission-based economy is unsustainable because the world will "run out" of uranium in 50 years or so at present rates of consumption. While it is true that the uranium recoverable *at or below the current market price* will possibly run out in 50 years, vast quantities of uranium would still be recoverable at a slightly higher price. Since fuel cost is a minuscule part of the cost of running a reactor, nuclear power could remain competitive even at many times the present uranium price.

Professor Bernard Cohen has estimated that a uranium-based nuclear power industry could remain a competitive and practical source of electricity for ***5 billion years*** using fuel recycling and breeder reactors,[5] and he does not even take into account the earth's huge thorium reserves, which are even more extensive than uranium. Dr. Cohen's calculations seem reasonable, but it is clear that even if he overestimates the uranium supply a thousandfold, nuclear power would still be viable for millions of years from a fuel-supply standpoint. Thus, the claim that nuclear power plants may run out of fuel in a few decades is simply not credible.

[5]John McCarthy, "Facts from Cohen and Others: How Long Will Nuclear Energy Last?" <http://www-formal.stanford.edu/jmc/progress/cohen.html>.

Naval reactors (17.5, p. 411). At present, every seagoing submarine in the U.S. Navy is nuclear powered. Not only does nuclear power make the submarine independent of oxygen for propulsion, the abundant electrical power it provides allows the submarine to make its own oxygen and drinking water from seawater, enabling the vessel to remain submerged (and therefore hidden) for months at a time. Nuclear power also allows the submarine to travel at high speed under water (as fast as 40 to 50 mph, depending on the design) for sustained periods.

Unlike commercial reactors, most naval reactors use very highly enriched uranium—up to 97.65% ^{235}U—fashioned into uranium/zirconium (or zirconium hydride) alloy plates containing about 15% U. The high enrichment allows the reactor to be very small for a given power output (important in a submarine) and also allows the reactor to run for as long as 40 years without refueling. U.S. naval reactors are also designed to be extremely safe, since they are in close proximity to the crew and must be robust enough to withstand battle damage. Interestingly, the reactors used in modern submarines do not use coolant pumps; the coolant is circulated by natural convection, making the submarine much quieter and more difficult to detect.

Special reactors: nuclear rockets (17.5, p. 411). In the nuclear rocket in Fig. 17.25c, liquid hydrogen from the large tank passes through the core of the nuclear reactor, becomes very hot, and expands out the back of the reactor under tremendous pressure, producing thrust in the opposite direction. Because of the high exhaust temperature and resulting high gas velocity, the rocket design pictured can produce about twice as much total thrust per pound of fuel as the best chemical rockets. Some advanced gas-core reactor designs could potentially outperform the best chemical rockets by a factor of 20, conceivably making manned trips to the outer planets possible.

Interestingly, nuclear rocket technology is not new; it was developed in the 1960s as part of a program called NERVA (Nuclear Engine for Rocket Vehicle Application). Although several powerful rocket engines were built and tested, the project was sidelined during the Apollo program in order to land a man on the moon as soon as possible regardless of the long-term consequences. In 1969, NASA canceled a proposed mission to Mars, and the NERVA program followed in 1972. Some engineers are presently studying the feasibility of reviving the NERVA program to power a future mission to Mars.

Enewetak atoll (17.5, p. 412). Enewetak [ĕn′*e*·wē′täk] atoll is located at the northwest tip of the Marshall Islands in the western Pacific.

Largest H-bomb (17.5, p. 412). The gigantic Soviet H-bomb mentioned in the text was manufactured in the 1960s at the personal request of Nikita Khrushchev. Dubbed *Tsar Bomba* ("King of Bombs"), this 60,000-lb device had a design yield of over 100 megatons (100,000 kilotons) of TNT. It was a three-stage design, essentially using a very large (5–10 megaton) H-bomb as the *primary* of a gigantic main fusion stage. A Tsar Bomba prototype—with its uranium third-stage tamper replaced by lead to reduce the yield to "only" 50 megatons—was tested over Novaya Zemlya Island in the Soviet Arctic on October 30, 1961. When the bomb was detonated, its main fusion stage briefly produced more than $^1/_{80}$ of the entire power output of the sun, even at the reduced yield. Several Tsar Bombas (in their 100+ megaton configuration) were built and stockpiled by the Soviet Union, but were retired after only a few years; they were simply too heavy and powerful to be practical.

The largest nuclear weapon ever built by the U.S. was the Mk-17/Mk-24 bomb, with a reported yield of 15–20 megatons. These unwieldy 42,000-lb giants were introduced in 1954 and retired in 1957.

H-bomb yields (17.5, p. 412). Contrary to the writings of some disarmament activists, the vast majority of modern nuclear weapons (both U.S. and Russian) have yields in the range of 150–550 kilotons, *not* 20–50 megatons (see table). As of 1999, the only U.S. design in active service with a yield of more than 475 kT was the B-83 strategic bomb, a 2400-lb, 1200-kT design comprising 10% or less of the U.S. arsenal. Most Russian warheads have a 550-kT yield.

U.S. Nuclear Weapons (currently in service)

W-76 (Trident C-4 SLBM)[1]	100 kT
W-78 (Minuteman III ICBM)	350 kT
W-80 (Tomahawk cruise missile)	5–150 kT[3]
W-87 (Minuteman III ICBM)[2]	300 or 475 kT
W-88 (Trident D-5 SLBM)	475 kT
B-61 bomb	0.3–340 kT[3]
B-83 bomb	10?–1200 kT[3]

[1]SLBM = submarine-launched ballistic missile; ICBM = intercontinental ballistic missile.
[2]W-87 previously equipped MX (Peacekeeper) ICBM, but MX was scrapped under START II treaty.
[3]Yield can be varied on command.

H-bomb diagram (17.5, p. 412). Note the very small size and weight of the W-80 (Fig. 17.26) compared to the early atomic bomb in Fig. 17.19. The W-80 is used in nuclear versions of the Tomahawk cruise missile.

How it works. When the primary is detonated (as in Fig. 17.20), thermal energy from the blazing plutonium sphere passes through openings in the blast shield into the secondary chamber, where it is absorbed by the surface of the heavy uranium shell (tamper) surrounding the fusion fuel. Heated to millions of degrees, the tamper's surface explosively vaporizes, driving the rest of the tamper inward with extreme force (~500 million tons per square inch). As the tamper collapses inward at more than a million mph, the fusion fuel (LiD, a ceramiclike solid) is compressed to more than 30 times the density of lead. The hollow plutonium "sparkplug" at the core of the fusion fuel is also compressed to immense densities (~1000 g/cm^3), making it supercritical and initiating a rapid fission chain reaction. Trapped between the crushing pressure of the tamper and the rapidly heating "sparkplug," the fusion fuel quickly reaches the "ignition point" of 54 million °F (30 million K) and begins a rapid fusion burn, halting the implosion and increasing the core temperature of the secondary to more than 600 million °F (350 million K). Additional energy is released as high-energy fusion neutrons fission the remnants of the uranium tamper. The entire detonation takes less than a millisecond, though the fireball persists for several seconds before rising and cooling to form a mushroom-shaped cloud.

Although Fig. 17.26 is externally accurate, keep in mind that it is a simplified diagram and is not necessarily representative of modern warheads internally. For example, the most advanced warheads of several nations are known to use watermelon-shaped primaries and spherical secondaries, resulting in a more compact device for a given yield; it is possible that the W-80 may incorporate some of these features as well.

The "neutron bomb" (17.5, p. 412). By careful design, it is possible to design a very small H-bomb (~1 kT) in which a large portion of the energy released exits the bomb as high-energy neutrons rather than blast energy and radiant heat (making it potentially useful as an antimissile or antitank weapon). Such a device, often called a *neutron bomb* or *enhanced-radiation warhead,* typically consists of a very small fission primary and a spherical secondary containing deuterium-tritium gas or LiD/LiT; no fission "sparkplug" is used. The secondary tamper consists of a heavy but nonfissionable material such as tungsten.

The American W-79-0 neutron warhead for a nuclear artillery shell measured about 7" × 15", had a total yield of 1 kT, and was triggered by a 0.25-kT primary. The last U.S. neutron weapons were retired by the early 1990s, although work on 0.01–1 kT neutron warheads continues in other nations.

Nuclear war: myth and reality (17.5, p. 412). Although the subject of nuclear war is far beyond the scope of this text, the following information is provided in case the subject comes up in class.

Although an all-out nuclear war between two superpowers would be horrific for the countries involved, be aware that a great deal of exaggeration also exists about the subject of nuclear weapons and nuclear war (i.e., that there are enough weapons to kill everyone on earth several times over, remove the crust of the earth, etc.). See the Resource List at end of this chapter for a variety of sources on the subject.

In 1999, the world's entire nuclear arsenal had a combined yield of about 5000 megatons, or 5 million kilotons, of which 2800 megatons belonged to Russia and 1850 megatons to the United States.[1] To put this figure into perspective, 5000 megatons detonated simultaneously in one spot would produce a crater roughly 10 miles across and 1–2 miles deep; if spread worldwide, the resulting fallout would result in an average radiation dose of 2.1 rem (2100 mrem) over the next 2–3 years.[2] If all these weapons were targeted at cities (most are not), and every city suffered a subsequent firestorm (many would not), the resulting smoke could cause temperatures in the Northern Hemisphere to drop by 6–12 °F for 10–30 days before returning to normal.[3]

Although averaging radiation effects globally ignores the untold suffering that would occur in hard-hit areas, it demonstrates that

> no matter what the losses to those areas might be, it is certain that human and other life on Earth would survive even an all-out global nuclear war.[4]

Another important fact to be aware of is that although U.S. and Russian nuclear strategy from the 1940s through the 1960s emphasized attacking civilian cities, later strategies have emphasized attacking *military installations*[5] (although cities in close proximity to military targets would certainly suffer grievous damage, and fallout would be a grave danger for hundreds of miles downwind).

It is estimated that in an all-out nuclear war between the United States and the Soviet Union at the peak of the Cold War, about 5% of the land area in the lower 48 U.S. states would have been subjected to blast pressures that would have destroyed or seriously damaged most homes.[6] Although untold suffering would occur in these regions, blast and fire damage outside these areas would have been minimal. However, fallout (radioactive bomb residue that settles out as dust) could cause millions of additional fatalities in areas downwind from the explosions unless the population evacuated or took shelter. If such a war occurred now, the affected land area would undoubtedly be far smaller, since nuclear arsenals today are less than half what they were during the 1980s.

Although weapons effects at relatively close range (1–4 miles for a typical H-bomb) can be horrific, effects at a distance of several miles are often exaggerated. For example, if a 550-kiloton thermonuclear warhead—the most common size in the Russian arsenal—were detonated 7 miles away from us at the most effective altitude, we would initially see an intense flash of white light (like a camera flash or magnesium flare, only far brighter) lasting for 3–4 seconds. A person in direct line of sight from the fireball would also feel intense heat for 3–4 seconds (like standing too close to a fire), but would probably not be burned at this distance. Thirty seconds after the initial flash, we would experience a sudden blast of intense thunder, a feeling of increased air pressure (+1.8 psi), and a 60-mph gust of wind. Windows would be shattered, houses might suffer structural damage (cracked boards, doors blown in, etc.), and lightweight objects would be blown around. The overpressure and wind would last about three seconds, followed by one or two seconds of slightly reduced pressure and a weaker wind blowing back toward the detonation point as the thunder died away. At this distance, the most dangerous aspects of the explosion would be flying glass from broken windows; fires started by the explosion; and radioactive fallout (condensed bomb debris that falls as dust, which could arrive in only a few hours depending on atmospheric conditions).[7]

The radius of near-total destruction (5-psi blast overpressure) for a 550-kT H-bomb is 2.3 miles if the weapon is detonated at ground level and 3.5 miles if it is detonated at the optimum altitude to maximize blast effect.

[1]Total yield at the peak of the Cold War was about 13,000 megatons.
[2]Zbigniew Jaworowski, "Radiation Risk and Ethics," *Physics Today* **52**:9 (September 1999), pp. 24–29, accessed at <http://www.riskworld.com/Nreports/1999/jaworowski/NR99aa01.htm>. Note that doses in areas of heavy fallout would be far higher, and doses elsewhere could be considerably lower.
[3]Stephen H. Schneider and Starley L. Thompson, "Nuclear Winter Reappraised," *Foreign Affairs,* summer 1986, pp. 993–995; "The Nuclear Winter Debate," *Foreign Affairs* fall 1986, pp. 174–175.
[4]Jaworowski.
[5]See *A Fighting Chance: The Moral Use of Nuclear Weapons* (San Francisco: Ignatius, 1988), 91. Note that this applies primarily to the United States and Russia; other nations with smaller nuclear arsenals (e.g., Communist China) do explicitly target civilian cities, but with far fewer warheads.
[6]Cresson Kearny, "The Dangers from Nuclear Weapons: Myths and Facts" (1998), <http://www.oism.org/nwss/s73p912.htm>.
[7]Sources: *Nuclear Bomb Effects Computer* (Washington, D.C.: Lovelace Biomedical and Environmental Research Institute/U.S. Department of Energy, 1977); Samuel Glasstone and Philip J. Dolan, *The Effects of Nuclear Weapons* (Washington, D.C.: U.S. Department of Defense/U.S. Department of Energy, 1977); U.S. Defense Nuclear Agency, "Nuclear Weapons Effects" (computer program), archived at <http://www.fas.org/nuke/hew/Library/Nukesims.html>.

Tokamak (17.5, p. 413). *Tokamak* [tô′ka·măk′: Fig. 17.28] is a Russian acronym for the phrase "toroidal chamber, axial magnetic field." (*Toroidal* refers to a doughnut shape.)

Fusion wastes (17.5, p. 413). Four pounds of helium is approximately the amount that would be needed to fill a 13-ft-diameter weather balloon at sea level.

Other methods of controlled fusion (17.5, p. 413). In this chapter, we have focused primarily on high-temperature, high-pressure fusion, which is the most straightforward from a theoretical standpoint. There are other methods that can be used to achieve fusion, including *muon-catalyzed fusion* and *soniluminescent fusion.* However, neither of these techniques seems capable of providing industrial-scale power.

Fusion and the environmental movement (17.5, p. 413). One would think that a power plant that ran on seawater and emitted only helium would be heartily embraced by environmentalists, but this is not the case. Many activists are against ***all*** industrial technology, clean or not. Consider the following quotations from prominent environmentalists:

> Giving society cheap, abundant energy . . . would be the equivalent of giving an idiot child a machine gun.
> —Paul Ehrlich, author of *The Population Bomb* and *The End of Affluence,* quoted in "An Ecologist's Perspective on Nuclear Power," Federation of American Scientists Public Issue Report, May/June 1978; also quoted in Paul Ciotti, "Fear of Fusion: What If It Works?", *Los Angeles Times,* April 19, 1989, Section 5, p. 1.

The only real good technology is no technology at all. Technology is taxation without representation, imposed by our elitist species [humans] upon the rest of the natural world.

—John Shuttleworth, author of Friends of the Earth manual, quoted in John McCarthy, "Quotations," <http://www-formal.stanford.edu/pub/jmc/progress/quotes.html>.

[Regarding the possible success of fusion research:] It's the worst thing that could happen to our planet.

—Jeremy Rifkin, quoted in Paul Ciotti, "Fear of Fusion: What If It Works?", *Los Angeles Times*, April 19, 1989, Section 5, p. 1.

Lecture Demonstrations

Introducing nuclear chemistry (17.1, pp. 383–385). Because nuclear radiation cannot be sensed directly and is generally not well understood by the media or the population at large, many students will come into this chapter with severe misconceptions about nuclear chemistry. Common misconceptions include the belief that radioactive materials glow in the dark; that radiation is somehow artificial; or that all radiation (even at very low levels) is highly dangerous. For this reason, the following suggestions are provided.

One idea is to bring in some common radioactive materials to pass around the class. Possibilities include the following:

Natural radioactivity:

- piece of granite (1000 radioactive decays per second per kilogram from natural radioactive uranium, thorium, and other elements; each decay produces nuclear radiation)
- small bag of phosphate or superphosphate fertilizer (5000 decays per second per kilogram from radium, radon, polonium, and lead-210)
- small clay flowerpot containing soil (uranium, thorium, radium, radon, polonium, etc.)
- a piece of coal (contains uranium, thorium, radon-222, carbon-14, and various radioactive decay products)
- 1-lb bag of coffee (450 decays per second, from various minerals)
- a loaf of bread (70 decays per second, mostly from carbon-14 and potassium-40)
- an old lantern mantle, if you can find one (older mantles contained enough radioactive thorium oxide to discharge an electroscope at close range from alpha emissions)

Artificial radioactivity:

- battery-operated household smoke detector (30,000 decays per second from americium-241, a synthetic alpha and gamma emitter; note the universal radiation symbol inside);
- tritium-containing watch, if you have one.

Darken the classroom and point out the fact that none of the substances glow (except the tritium watch, which is glowing because it contains phosphorescent compounds that are excited by nuclear radiation).

You might also point out that you, the teacher, are radioactive (2000–3000 decays per second for an average-sized adult, from naturally radioactive carbon and potassium); your students are similarly radioactive. The air you are breathing is mildly radioactive (it contains traces of radon-222, a radioactive noble gas emitted by the earth). Even the sky can be thought of as "radioactive"; as you teach, high-energy nuclear radiation from distant stars (cosmic rays) is streaming into your classroom through the ceiling.

If you have access to a low-range Geiger counter or other survey meter—available from various equipment suppliers and scientific supply companies—you can use it to convincingly demonstrate that some of these materials are, indeed, radioactive. (More concentrated sources such as thorium-containing lantern mantles give higher count rates than bread or people, of course. Note that most inexpensive meters detect only beta and gamma radiation. See Lab 27 for more information.)

Conclude by reassuring your students that natural levels of radiation are not harmful; God *made* the earth radioactive, and equipped every cell of our bodies with mechanisms to handle it.

Uses of radiation (17.3, pp. 391–392). Obtain an ordinary household smoke detector containing Am-241 and pass it around the class with the plastic faceplate removed so that students can see the ion chamber containing the radioactive material. (You may even wish to demonstrate the detector's operation by lighting a match, immediately extinguishing it, and letting the smoke rise up into the ion chamber from a distance of a few inches.) Point out that the alpha radiation is safely contained by the enclosure, and that the gamma radiation is of such low intensity that it is completely harmless.

If you have access to a Geiger counter or other survey meter, you may wish to try to obtain a count rate from the ion chamber (put the window of the Geiger tube as close as possible to the chamber to intercept as many gammas as possible). Try this before class to make sure the increased count rate is obvious.

If you have a tritium-containing watch, dim the classroom lights and pass it around the class.

Measuring activity (17.3, p. 396). If you obtained a household smoke detector for the previous demonstration, examine the ion chamber to see if it contains an activity label. For example, in the photo of the smoke detector on p. 391 Fig. 17.6, the label "contains .09 microcuries americium-241" may be seen just beneath the universal radiation symbol. This particular label tells us that the smoke detector contains enough americium-241 to produce an activity of 0.09 microcuries, or 3300 Bq (3300 decays per second). If your smoke detector has a similar label, point it out to the class and have them calculate the decay rate in terms of the number of decays per second (Bq).

Nuclear power plants (17.5, pp. 405–410). After completing section 17.5, you might consider arranging a field trip to a nuclear power plant if one is located in your area. Most plants are happy to arrange tours by school groups, though advance notice is often requested.

Chapter 17 Bibliography

Note: Internet sources are given **for the teacher's reference.** Address or content may have changed since this publication of this teacher guide. Be sure to thoroughly review the location and content of any site yourself and check your school policy before recommending the site to your students.

Health effects of radiation:

- Jaworowski, Zbigniew. "Radiation Risk and Ethics." *Physics Today* **52**:9, (September 1999), pp. 24–29; also available at <http://www.riskworld.com/Nreports/1999/jaworowski/NR99aa01.htm>. An excellent overview of radiation safety, comparing natural vs. artificial radiation levels and evaluating the safety of low levels of radiation.

Nuclear power:

- Cohen, Bernard. *The Nuclear Energy Option.* New York: Plenum Press, 1990. A thorough discussion of all aspects of the nuclear power issue from a pro-nuclear perspective; written by a nuclear physicist unaffiliated with the nuclear industry or the government.
- Hore-Lacy, Ian, and Hubery, Ron. *Nuclear Electricity.* 5th ed. Melbourne, Australia: Uranium Information Centre, 1999. Full text online at <http://www.uic.com.au/ne.htm>. A thorough overview of a broad spectrum of nuclear power issues. Topics include uranium mining and processing; technical, safety, and environmental aspects of nuclear power generation; disposal of nuclear wastes; nuclear weapons proliferation; nuclear *vs.* coal; and nuclear *vs.* "renewables." Includes glossary and appendices.
- McCarthy, John. "Frequently Asked Questions about Nuclear Energy." <http://www-formal.stanford.edu/jmc/progress/nuclear-faq.html>. Pro-nuclear site highlighting the sustainability of nuclear power.
- Rhodes, Richard. *Nuclear Renewal: Common Sense About Energy* (New York: Whittle Books/Viking Penguin, 1993). A brief, balanced, and highly readable overview of the history of the nuclear industry, the bureaucratic mismanagement that has brought it to its present impasse, and its hopes for the future. The U.S. nuclear industry is compared with the French and Japanese industries; the Fermi 1, Three Mile Island, and Chernobyl accidents are discussed. Costs, environmental impacts, and risks of various forms of power generation are compared.

Nuclear fusion:

- Fowler, T. Kenneth. *The Fusion Quest.* Baltimore: Johns Hopkins University Press, 1997. A somewhat technical overview of the progress of fusion research from the beginnings of the field through the mid-1990s, although some of the more recent developments in the field are not covered.
- Heeter, Robert F., ed. "Answers to Frequently Asked Questions about Fusion Research." <http://FusEdWeb.pppl.gov/FAQ/fusion-faq.html>. Introductory and advanced material on nuclear fusion research; prepared and maintained by the Princeton Plasma Physics Laboratory.

Nuclear weapons:

- Hansen, Chuck. *U.S. Nuclear Weapons: The Secret History.* Arlington, Texas/New York: Aerofax/Crown Publishers, 1988. Encyclopedia of U.S. nuclear tests, weapons, and delivery systems; includes brief overview of nuclear weapons physics, numerous nuclear test photos, and declassified photos, specifications, and diagrams of particular designs.
- Kearny, Cresson. "The Dangers from Nuclear Weapons: Myths and Facts" (1998). <http://www.oism.org/nwss/s73p912.htm> (accessed 4/14/2000). Extract from an online civil-defense manual, originally written by a research engineer at Oak Ridge National Laboratory. Discusses some of the common misunderstandings regarding nuclear weapons effects.
- Martino, Joseph P. *A Fighting Chance: The Moral Use of Nuclear Weapons.* San Francisco: Ignatius Press, 1988. Book written from a conservative perspective exploring the morality of nuclear weapons; he concludes that their use against military targets is moral and justifiable, but intentional targeting of civilians would contradict Biblical teaching. Although Martino appears to be Catholic, his observations are equally applicable from a Bible-believing perspective.
- Sublette, Carey. *Nuclear Weapons Frequently Asked Questions* (1999). <http://www.fas.org/nuke/hew/Nwfaq/Nfaq0.html> (accessed 4/14/2000). A comprehensive explanation of the physics of how nuclear weapons work, the history of nuclear weapons development, and devices presently in service. Some material in the Effects section (regarding low-level radiation exposure and "nuclear winter") may be somewhat less reliable.

Answers to Text Questions

Section Review 17.1 (p. 386)

1. What is *nuclear chemistry?* *the study of reactions involving the nucleus*
2. What contribution(s) did Becquerel make to the study of nuclear chemistry? How did the Curies contribute? *Becquerel discovered radioactivity when experimenting with a fluorescent mineral that happened to contain uranium. Pierre and Marie Curie discovered that several elements exhibit this behavior and called the phenomenon radioactivity. (They also discovered two new radioactive elements: polonium and radium.)*
3. What is *nuclear radiation?* *subatomic particles or electromagnetic waves emitted by an atomic nucleus during a nuclear reaction*
4. What is meant when an isotope is described as *radioactive?* *The atomic nucleus has a tendency to*

break apart. Anytime a nucleus breaks up, either particles or electromagnetic waves may be radiated at high speeds from the nucleus.

Section Review 17.2 (p. 390)

1. From the standpoint of nuclear chemistry, what is the function of the strong nuclear force? *The strong nuclear force holds the nucleus together.*
2. What is ***radioactive decay?*** *the conversion of one type of nucleus into another in a spontaneous nuclear reaction*
3. What is the ***nuclear mass defect?*** How is the "missing" mass accounted for? *(Wording will vary.) The term refers to the fact that the mass of every atom is measurably less than the total mass of its individual particles. It is accounted for by taking into account the "mass" of the energy that would be released when forming a nucleus from its parts.*
4. Define ***nuclear binding energy.*** How does this energy relate to the nuclear mass defect? *the amount of energy necessary to break up a nucleus into its component nucleons; it represents an amount of energy equivalent to the mass defect.*
5. Why is binding energy per nucleon a useful measure of nuclear stability? *As a rule, the higher the binding energy per nucleon, the more strongly the nucleus is held together.*
6. Which isotope has the highest binding energy per nucleon: $^{14}_{7}N$, $^{56}_{26}Fe$, or $^{64}_{30}Zn$? *$^{56}_{26}Fe$*

Section Review 17.3 (p. 399)

1. Name the three types of nuclear decay and write one symbol for each.
   alpha decay (α, $^{4}_{2}\alpha$, $^{4}_{2}He$, or $^{4}_{2}He^{2+}$)
   beta decay (β, $^{0}_{-1}\beta$, $^{0}_{-1}e^{-}$, or $^{0}_{-1}e$)
   gamma radiation (γ, $^{0}_{0}\gamma$)
2. Which type of radiation (alpha, beta, or gamma)
   - **a.** consists of high-speed electrons? *beta*
   - **b.** consists of electromagnetic waves? *gamma*
   - **c.** consists of high-speed helium ions? *alpha*
   - **d.** reduces atomic number by 2 and mass number by 4? *alpha*
   - **e.** increases atomic number? *beta*
   - **f.** does not affect atomic number or atomic mass? *gamma*
   - **g.** is stopped by a sheet of paper? *alpha*
3. Name one use each of alpha, beta, gamma, and neutron radiation.
   - **a.** alpha radiation *smoke detectors*
   - **b.** beta radiation *self-luminous watches, exit signs, firearm sights*
   - **c.** gamma radiation *cancer treatment*
   - **d.** neutron radiation *production of transuranium elements; treatment of cancer*
4. What is the ***half-life*** of a radioactive substance? *The half-life of a radioactive substance can be defined as the length of time it takes for one half of a radioactive substance to decay into a new substance; it is a measure of the stability of the substance.*
5. If you started with 32 grams of a substance having a half-life of 1 year, how much of the original substance would remain after 2 years? 4 years? *8 grams; 2 grams*
6. What is the ***activity*** of a radioactive substance? *the amount or rate of decay occurring in a radioactive substance*
7. A sample of a radioactive substance undergoes 18.5 billion nuclear disintegrations per second. What is its activity in becquerels? In curies? *18.5 billion Bq; 0.500 Ci*
8. What is a ***radioactive decay*** series? *a chain of isotopes linked by nuclear decay, beginning with an unstable isotope and ending with a stable isotope*
9. How may particle accelerators be used to induce nuclear reactions that would not otherwise occur? *Answers may vary. If particles are accelerated to high speeds and energies and then collided with other particles, nuclear reactions may occur.*

Section Review 17.4 (p. 402)

1. Why are neutrons considered ionizing radiation, even though they cannot directly cause ionization? *Neutrons are considered ionizing radiation because the neutrons indirectly cause ionization by reacting with target nuclei to form alpha-, beta-, or gamma-emitting isotopes.*
2. Why are cells of the gastrointestinal tract and bone marrow more susceptible to radiation damage than brain or muscle cells? *The cells in these areas are rapidly reproducing; cells are most susceptible to radiation damage when they are dividing (reproducing).*
3. Why would different precautions be required when handling alpha or beta emitters than when

handling gamma emitters? *Alpha radiation is stopped by the skin and beta radiation can be prevented by proper clothing, whereas gamma rays are much more penetrating. Alpha and beta emitters become much more dangerous if ingested or inhaled.*

4. How is nuclear radiation detected? *Nuclear radiation is easily detected because of its ability to knock electrons loose from atoms. (Detectors include small, gas-filled chambers, fluorescent liquids or crystals, or even semiconductor chips.)*
5. What units are used to measure radiation exposure? Which unit(s) takes into account the differing effects of radiation on living things? *radiation exposure: rad, rem, gray, sievert biological effect: rem and sievert*
6. The Three Mile Island nuclear accident in 1979 exposed the surrounding population to an average radiation dose of 1.2 millirem. Knowing what you know about natural background radiation, do you think this would be a harmful dose? Why or why not? *(Answers may vary.) No; this amount is very small compared to the 200–400 millirems of radiation Americans are exposed to each year, mostly from natural sources, with no apparent harm.*

Section Review 17.5 (p. 413)

1. What is *nuclear fission?* Who coined this term? *Nuclear fission is the cleavage of heavy nuclei into two or more smaller nuclei. The term was coined by Lise Meitner.*
2. What is a nuclear *chain reaction?* *(Wording may vary.) A nuclear chain reaction occurs when a nucleus undergoes fission, releasing neutrons that cause other atoms to fission, which in turn cause additional fissions, and so on.*
3. What is meant by the *critical mass* of a fissionable substance? *the amount of fissionable material at a given density that is necessary for a self-sustaining nuclear chain reaction to occur*
4. What is the purpose of the moderator in a nuclear reactor? The coolant? The control rods? The containment vessel? *Wording may vary.*
   - *moderator: slows neutrons for easier capture by fissionable atoms*
   - *coolant carries heat out of the core; keeps core from overheating*
   - *control rods: control the reaction rate by absorbing some of the neutrons*
   - *containment vessel: designed to prevent the emission of dangerous levels of radiation into the environment in the event of an accident*
5. Can a nuclear reactor explode like an atomic bomb? Why or why not? *No; a reactor is just barely critical and occupies a large volume. In addition, reactors in the United States use fuel with a high percentage of nonfissionable ^{238}U; this fuel does not have sufficient percentage of ^{235}U to produce an explosive reaction.*
6. What is a loss of coolant accident? A meltdown? What precautions are taken to prevent such occurrences in nuclear power plants? *(Wording will vary.) An accident involving loss of coolant occurs when some type of breakdown prevents sufficient coolant from reaching the core and the core overheats. A meltdown occurs when the fuel melts right through the bottom of the pressure vessel. Nuclear power plants (especially in developed countries) have multiple backup systems, with additional automated systems, to provide adequate coolant to ward off overheating. Even if a meltdown were to occur, the containment vessel is designed to prevent the emission of dangerous levels of radiation.*
7. What term refers to the recycling of spent nuclear fuel? *reprocessing*
8. What is a ***breeder reactor?*** How can it possibly produce more fuel than it uses without violating the laws of thermodynamics? *A breeder reactor is a nuclear reactor that produces more fissionable material than it consumes. It does not violate the laws of thermodynamics because it does not create fuel from nowhere; rather, it converts preexisting nonfissionable material into fissionable material.*
9. Name three uses of nuclear reactors besides the production of electricity. *powering ships, submarines, etc.; can be used to power spacecraft, rocket engines, etc.*
10. What is *nuclear fusion?* How does it differ from nuclear fission? *Nuclear fusion is the combining of small nuclei into larger ones, whereas nuclear fission is the splitting of heavy nuclei into two or more smaller nuclei.*

Chapter 17 Review (p. 415)

1. Define ***nuclide.*** *any isotope of any element*
2. What is ***radioactive decay?*** *the conversion of one type of nucleus into another in a spontaneous nuclear reaction*
3. Name the three types of nuclear decay. *alpha, beta, and gamma decay*
4. If you started with 100 grams of a substance having a half-life of 2.5 hours, how much of the original

substance would remain after 5 hours? 7.5 hours? *25 grams; 12.5 grams*

5. If a radioactive substance has an extremely long half-life, would you expect its activity to be high or low? *low*

6. Name two units used to measure activity. *becquerel (Bq) and curie (Ci)*

7. What term refers to the elements beyond uranium ($Z > 92$)? *transuranium elements*

8. What are the transuranium elements? Which transuranium elements occur in large quantities in the earth's crust? *elements beyond uranium in the periodic table, almost exclusively produced by artificial bombardment reactions; none of them occur naturally in large quantities.*

9. What is ***ionizing radiation***? *any form of radiation capable of causing ionization*

10. Why are alpha emitters more dangerous when ingested or inhaled than when they are simply deposited on the skin? *Alpha rays cannot penetrate the skin, but can cause damage if they come into direct contact with susceptible tissues via ingestion or inhalation.*

11. On average, does most radiation exposure come from artificial sources or from natural sources? Explain. *Over 80% of the average American's exposure to radiation comes from natural sources. The earth emits the majority of the radiation, as well as cosmic rays, rocks and soil, and radiation occurring naturally in the body.*

12. Why is fuel for nuclear power plants commonly ***enriched*** in uranium-235? *Natural uranium consists of about 99.3% U-238 and 0.3% U-235, but only U-235 is fissionable under the conditions found in a nuclear reactor. Consequently, the uranium is usually enriched in U-235 to make a critical mass easier to achieve.*

13. Compare and contrast nuclear fission reactions with fusion reactions. *Nuclear fission is the breaking apart of a nucleus into smaller nuclei, whereas nuclear fusion is the joining of the nuclei of lighter atoms to form the nucleus of a heavier atom. Both processes release tremendous amounts of energy.*

14. Is nuclear power the only form of power generation that presents risk? What risks might be posed by other forms of power generation, including solar and wind power? *(Answers will vary.) Of course not. Mining accidents, gas explosions, floods from collapsed dams, and transportation accidents are just a few risks. Solar and wind power pose potential risks as well: construction accidents (because such a large quantity needed, due to low power density), maintenance accidents (falls when cleaning, clearing snow, etc.), use of large quantities of toxic heavy metals in solar cell manufacture, transportation accidents, possible collapse of wind towers, damage to wildlife due to large amount of land required, etc.).*

15. Why are fusion reactions also called ***thermonuclear reactions***? *because of the extremely high temperatures involved*

16. As a form of power generation, what advantages might nuclear fusion offer? *Fusion fuels are abundant in nature, a fusion reactor would produce very little waste, and products of the fusion process are much less radioactive than fission products.*

17. Do you think the production of nuclear waste should be considered an insurmountable obstacle to the continued development of nuclear power? What about the danger of nuclear accidents? Explain your answer. *(Answers will vary.) Probably not. The waste produced is minimal compared to the waste produced by other power generation methods. Nuclear waste can be recycled (as it is in other countries). Although there is always a possibility of accidents, nuclear power can be considered at least as safe as the alternatives, and possibly safer.*

18. The half-life of $^{85}_{36}Kr$ is 10.76 yr. What mass of a 14.0-mg sample of $^{85}_{36}K$ produced on the day of your birth would remain when you are 32 yr, 102 days old?

32 yr, 102 da = 32.38 yr

$$32.38\ yr \times \frac{1\ t_{1/2}}{10.76\ yr} = 3\ t_{1/2} \qquad \frac{1}{2} \times \frac{1}{2} \times \frac{1}{2} = \frac{1}{8}$$

$$\text{mass remaining} = 14.0\ mg \times \frac{1}{8} = \mathbf{1.75\ mg}$$

Chapter 18 (pp. 416–453)
Organic Chemistry

Suggested Daily Pacing

156
Check homework.

Return and go over graded Test 11.

Introduce ch. 18, Organic Chemistry.

Discuss homework.

Teach pp. **417–421,** introduction and sec. **18.1** Introduction to Organic Chemistry.

Review lesson.

HW: Read pp. 421–424, up to Alkenes.

157
Give "pop" reading quiz over pp. 421–424:

1. What type of covalent bond does an alkene contain? *double*
2. What is another name for the alkane series? *paraffin series*
3. True or False: Alkanes are considered very reactive. *false*
4. What are organic compounds called that contain only hydrogen and carbon? *hydrocarbons*
5. What word ending is used to identify an alkane? *-ane*

Review pp. 417–421.

Teach pp. **421–424,** sec. **18.2** Hydrocarbons, up to Alkenes.

Review lesson.

HW: Read pp. 424–427. Answer p. 432, questions 1–4.

158
Check and discuss homework.

Review pp. 421–424.

Teach pp. **424–427,** sec. **18.2** (cont.).

Review lesson.

HW: Read pp. 428–431. Answer p. 432, question 5.

159
Check and discuss homework.

Review pp. 424–427.

Teach pp. **428–431,** sec. **18.2** (cont.).

Review lesson.

Give Quiz 26 (over pp. 421–431).

HW: Read pp. 432–434, up to Aldehydes and Ketones. Answer p. 438, questions 1–3. Read *Lab Manual* Lab 29 and complete Prelab Assignment.

160
Check and discuss homework.

Review pp. 428–431.

Teach pp. **432–434,** sec. **18.3** Substituted Hydrocarbons, up to Aldehydes and Ketones.

Conduct Lab 29 (Part I): Observation of Substituted Hydrocarbons.

Review lesson.

HW: Complete Lab 29 Report Sheet (Part I). Read pp. 434–438. Answer p. 438, questions 4–9.

161
Check and discuss homework.

Review pp. 432–434.

Teach pp. **434–436,** sec. **18.3** (cont.), up to Amines.

Conduct Lab 29 (Parts II–III): Observation of Substituted Hydrocarbons.

Teach pp. **436–438,** sec. **18.3** (cont.).

Review lesson.

HW: Complete Lab 29 Report Sheet (Parts II–III). Read pp. 439–443, up to 18.5 Biochemistry. Answer p. 443, questions 1–6.

162 **Give Quiz 27** (over pp. 432–438).

Check and discuss homework.

Review pp. 434–438.

Teach pp. **439–443,** sec. **18.4** Polymer Chemistry.

Review lesson.

HW: Read *Lab Manual* Lab 30 and complete Prelab Assignment.

163 **Check** and discuss homework.

Conduct Lab 30: Oxidation of an Aldehyde.

HW: Complete Lab 30 Report Sheet. Read pp. 443–447, up to Fats. Answer p. 449, questions 1–6.

164 **Check** and discuss homework.

Review pp. 439–443.

Teach pp. **443–447,** sec. **18.5** Biochemistry, up to Fats.

Review lesson.

HW: Read pp. 447–449. Answer p. 449, questions 7–9.

165 **Check** and discuss homework.

Review pp. 443–447.

Teach pp. **447–449,** sec. **18.5** (cont.).

Review lesson.

Review ch. 18 for Test 12 (Final Exam) in les. 170.

HW: Begin studying ch. 1–18 for Test 12 (Final Exam) in les. 170.

Note: Assign 10–15 items from ch. 1–5 Chapter Reviews.

166 **Check** and discuss homework.

Review ch. 1–5 for Test 12 (Final Exam) in les. 170, using important concepts from Chapter Reviews 1–5.

HW: Continue studying ch. 1–18 for Test 12 (Final Exam) in lesson 170.

Note: Assign 10–15 items from ch. 6–9 Chapter Reviews.

167 **Check** and discuss homework.

Review ch. 6–9 for Test 12 (Final Exam) in les. 170, using important concepts from Chapter Reviews 6–9.

HW: Continue studying ch. 1–18 for Test 12 (Final Exam) in lesson 170.

Note: Assign 10–15 items from ch. 10–14 Chapter Reviews.

168 **Check** and discuss homework.

Review ch. 10–14 for Test 12 (Final Exam) in les. 170, using important concepts from Chapter Reviews 10–14.

HW: Continue studying ch. 1–18 for Test 12 (Final Exam) in lesson 170.

Note: Assign 10–15 items from ch. 15–18 Chapter Reviews.

169 **Check** and discuss homework.

Review ch. 15–18 for Test 12 (Final Exam) in next lesson, using important concepts from Chapter Reviews 15–18.

HW: Study ch. 1–18 for Test 12 (Final Exam) in next lesson.

170 **Administer Test 12** (Final Exam) over ch. 1–18.

Teacher Notes

Chapter 18 Overview. This final chapter explores the world of organic chemistry, one of the largest and fastest-growing fields of chemistry today. Beginning with a brief introduction to organic compounds in general, the chapter then focuses on the properties, sources, and uses of hydrocarbons. Substituted hydrocarbons are then discussed, followed by a survey of polymer chemistry and its applications in everyday life. The chapter concludes with a glimpse of biochemistry, the chemistry of life, revealing God's design in His living creations.

General properties of organic compounds (18.1, p. 418). Note that the properties of organic compounds listed on p. 418 are *general* principles; there are exceptions. For example, although the majority of organic compounds are insoluble in water, there are some that are *very* soluble (including many alcohols and carbohydrates). Likewise, although organic molecules tend to be nonpolar, a few are polar. Although most organic compounds react relatively slowly, some react very rapidly.

Condensed structural formulas (p. 419). Note that in a molecule such as $CH_3CH_2CH_3$, the *carbons* are bonded to each other in a chain, though it may not appear so. You may find it helpful to demonstrate on the chalkboard how a condensed structural formula relates to a structural formula. Note also that when writing condensed structural formulas, CH_3– is the same as H_3C–.

Other aromatic compounds (18.2, p. 426). Benzene and its derivatives are not the only compounds having the aromatic ring structure. Certain organic anions having five- or seven-carbon rings are aromatic, as are several members of a class of hydrocarbons called *annulenes.* A number of non-hydrocarbon substances also have an aromatic ring structure, including *pyridine* (a component of several alkaloids, including nicotine), the pesticide *furan,* and the molecules *pyrrole, pyrimidine,* and *purine,* which are found in a wide variety of biological molecules. Even common *graphite* is an aromatic compound; structurally, graphite can be thought of as a giant polycyclic aromatic hydrocarbon:

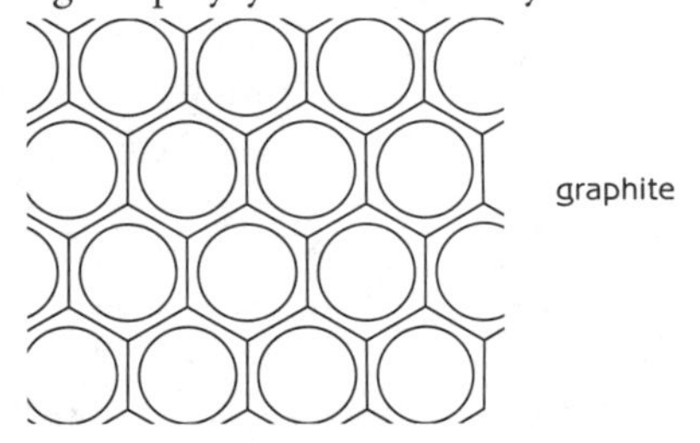

Oil platform photo (18.2, p. 428). The oil platform on p. 428 is located in the Gulf of Mexico (about 80 miles south of Mobile, Alabama) where the water is more than 3200 feet deep. The platform can produce about 60,000 barrels of oil and 200 million cubic feet of natural gas per day from several undersea wells. The gas and oil are pumped to shore via a network of pipelines on the ocean floor.

Fossil fuels and the "energy crisis" (18.2, pp. 428–429). Since the late 1960s, alarmists have been issuing dire predictions that the world is going to "run out" of oil in 20 years, coal in 50 years, etc. In fact, by dividing proven reserves by the annual rate of consumption, one can predict that nearly any given fuel will "run out" in a few decades. However, such predictions are based upon a fundamental misunderstanding of the term "proven reserves." The proven reserve is not the total amount available; rather, it is the amount of coal or oil ***recoverable at or below the current market price, with present technology, and without further exploration.*** It should be obvious that there is much more coal and oil that is either (1) recoverable at a slightly higher cost, (2) will become recoverable as technology improves, and (3) that will be added to proven reserves as soon as someone bothers to search for it. For example, proven oil reserves were estimated at 10 years' supply in 1914; 13 years' supply in 1951; and 43 years' supply in 1999. (Note that proven reserves are continuously increasing, not decreasing, due to technology improvements.)

It is presently estimated that *even if limited to today's extraction technologies,* at least 150 years' worth of petroleum, 200 years' worth of natural gas, and 2000 years' worth of coal are available and accessible at relatively low cost in the earth's crust, plus vast quantities of other fossil fuels (e.g., orimulsion, tar sands, oil shale, etc.).[1] It should be obvious from these figures that the world is not going to "run out" of fossil fuels anytime soon, even if consumption increases dramatically. Also keep in mind that if the price of fossil fuels rises very much due to increasing scarcity, nuclear power—with total energy reserves measured in millions or even billions of years (chapter 17)—will quickly take their place.

[1]Robert L. Bradley Jr., "The Increasing Sustainability of Conventional Energy" (April 22, 1999), <http://www.cato.org/pubs/pas/pa341txt.pdf>, pp. 3–5.

"Renewable" energy *vs.* fossil fuels (18.2, pp. 430–431). Many environmentalists have called for the phaseout of fossil fuels and internal combustion engines, to be replaced by what they term "renewable" resources such as solar power and wind power. However, sunlight and wind are far too diffuse to be practical for large-scale power generation in the foreseeable future; to meet even a large fraction of the current electrical needs of the United States, many thousands of square miles of land would have to be covered with hordes of windmills and solar panels, at vast expense and with devastating environmental impact.

According to a Cato Institute study, a single large fossil-fuel-powered plant (the Teesside natural-gas-fired plant in England, rated at 1875 MW) "produces more electricity each year than the world's millions of solar panels and 30,000 wind turbines combined—and on fewer than 25 acres of land."[2] The same could be said for many large nuclear power stations.

[2]Ibid., p. 19.

Methanol toxicity (18.3, p. 433). Methanol is the active ingredient in most formulations of windshield washer fluid.

One reason that methanol is so toxic is that in attempting to break it down, body cells convert methanol into formaldehyde (the active ingredient in embalming fluid), which is in turn converted to formic acid (the active ingredient in fire ant stings). Although the long-term damage done by formaldehyde is undoubtedly serious, the formic acid causes greater short-term effects as it upsets the body's ability to maintain proper blood pH, often leading to death by metabolic acidosis. These metabolic byproducts are also extremely toxic to the cells of the optic nerve, often leading to permanent blindness through the death of those cells even if the victim survives.

Formaldehyde (18.3, p. 434). Formaldehyde is sometimes called *methanal.* A preservative solution containing formaldehyde dissolved in alcohol is known by the trade name *formalin.*

Ketones (18.3, p. 434). Note that the names of ketones are characterized by an *-one* ending.

Acetaminophen (18.3, p. 438). The actual chemical name of the amide known as acetaminophen (Tylenol®) is *N-acetyl-para-aminophenol,* or APAP; acetaminophen is the "generic" trade name for APAP in the United States. In Europe and Australia, APAP is known by the generic trade name *paracetamol* instead.

Types of polyethylene (18.4, p. 439). Polyethylene consisting of highly branched molecules is known as *low-density polyethylene,* or LDPE; polyethylene consisting of unbranched (linear) polyethylene is known as *high-density polyethylene* (HDPE) and is more heat stable. Spectra®, manufactured by Allied Signal, is called *high-molecular-weight polyethylene* (HMWPE) and consists of linear polyethylene molecules of high molecular weight; its great strength is demonstrated in Fig. 18.19c. Uses of each type (LDPE, HDPE, HMWPE) are given in Table 18.9 on p. 442.

Lecture Demonstrations

Organic *vs.* inorganic properties (18.1, p. 418). Display a variety of inorganic and organic substances (or materials containing organic compounds) and discuss the differences given in Table 18.1 (e.g., use NaCl, Al foil, I_2, $CuSO_4 \cdot 5\ H_2O$; ethyl alcohol, benzene, naphthalene, bottle of CO_2). You may wish to demonstrate (1) combustibility by heating a small amount of several substances in a test tube (e.g. sugar *vs.* I_2); (2) solubility differences using NaCl or KCl in H_2O *vs.* in petroleum ether or cyclohexane; (3) structural differences by testing the conductivity of molten NaCl *vs.* paraffin, or solutions of NaCl *vs.* ethanol; and (4) rate of a precipitation reaction (immediate) *vs.* fermentation or saponification.

Alcohols (18.3, pp. 432–434). You may wish to display several common materials containing alcohols when teaching this section. See Fig. 18.14 for ideas; look for an *-ol* ending on names of ingredients.

Tests for aldehydes and ketones (18.3, p. 434). You can demonstrate Benedict's and / or Tollens's tests by comparing the results with acetone (no reaction) and an aldehyde such as formaldehyde (a 1% glucose solution will also work well). (Students will perform these tests themselves in Lab 29.)

1. *Benedict's reagent:* May be purchased from a supplier, or prepared as follows. Dissolve 61.0 g sodium citrate dihydrate and 35 g Na_2CO_3 (anhydrous) in 280 mL H_2O with heating and stirring; filter if necessary. Add, while stirring, a solution of 6.1 g $CuSO_4 \cdot 5\ H_2O$ in 35 mL H_2O; dilute to 350 mL. Place 5 mL of Benedict's solution into each of two test tubes. Add 1 mL acetone to one and 1 mL aldehyde to the other; heat in a boiling water bath for 3–5 minutes. Formation of a reddish precipitate (Cu_2O) is a positive test for the aldehyde functional group.

2. *Tollens's reagent:* To a *clean* test tube add 4 mL of 5% $AgNO_3$; add 2 drops of 5% NaOH and mix (dark brown Ag_2O forms). Add 5% NH_3 (17 mL conc. NH_3 /100 mL solution) drop by drop with constant mixing until the precipitate is *almost* all dissolved. Use this solution within 15 minutes; *do not store.*

Divide the Tollens's reagent into two equal portions in *clean* test tubes. To one tube add 3 drops acetone and to the other tube add 3 drops aldehyde. If no mirror forms or no precipitate forms within a few minutes, place them in a hot water bath. A positive test for the aldehyde functional group is indicated by a silver mirror or a black precipitate of silver. Silver mirrors in test tubes may be cleaned by dissolving them in a small amount of HNO_3. *Do not allow to stand* since explosive products can from. Dispose of the contents and rinsed mirror waste in a waste container. Add 6-*M* HNO_3 in a 1:1 ratio and store for disposal (check current regulations).

Esters (18.3, pp. 435–436). Demonstrate esterification by placing 6 mL of each alcohol and 6 mL of each acid listed below in a test tube; add about 20 drops concentrated H_2SO_4, mix, and heat in a boiling water bath for 8–10 minutes. The layer which forms on top is the ester. Place several drops of each ester on filter paper circles to pass among the students; see if they can identify the odor (each of the esters below are produced naturally by well-known plants).

acetic acid + *n*-pentyl (amyl) alcohol .... (bananas)
acetic acid + *n*-octyl alcohol (l-octanol) ... (oranges)
butyric acid + ethanol.......................... (pineapples)

butyric acid + methanol............................(apples)
butyric acid + *n*-pentyl alcohol .... (apricots)
salicylic acid (1 g) + methanol .... (wintergreen)

Polymer chemistry (18.4, pp. 439–443). You may wish to have examples of various polymers on hand as you teach; see Table 18.9 and Fig. 18.19–24 for ideas.

Polymerization of nylon (18.4, pp. 440–441). If you wish, you can demonstrate the synthesis of nylon-6,10 as follows. Just prior to class, *in a fume hood,* dissolve 3.0 g 1,6-diaminohexane (hexamethylenediamine) and 1.0 g NaOH in 50 mL H_2O in a 250-mL beaker. In a separate beaker, dissolve 1.5–2.0 mL sebacoyl chloride in 50 mL hexane (cyclohexane may be substituted). **CAUTION:** 1,6-diaminohexane and sebacoyl chloride are toxic, corrosive, and irritating to the eyes, skin, and respiratory system; NaOH is caustic and can cause burns. Wear eye protection, long gloves with sleeve protectors, and work in a fume hood. 1,6-diaminohexane decomposes readily at room temperature and must be stored in a tightly sealed jar in an approved chemical refrigerator (*not* a food refrigerator). If such storage facilities are not available, order the chemical just in time to perform the demonstration; use the chemical immediately; and discard any excess using approved disposal procedures. Keep containers tightly covered when not in use.

In class, *slowly* pour the sebacoyl chloride solution down the side of the 250-mL beaker while it is tilted, so that it forms a second layer atop the diaminohexane solution. Using a forceps, grasp the center of the film that has formed at the interface and *slowly* pull it from the beaker. You may wish to wind the nylon polymer on a windlass fashioned from glass tubing or on a large beaker which has a paper towel taped around it. *Do not handle the polymer* until it has been thoroughly washed with water or ethyl alcohol. Washed and dried pieces may be distributed to students. Demonstrate the stretchy nature of the nylon strand.

Any remaining reactants should be stirred together to form nylon which should be washed before being discarded in the trash basket. Neutralize remaining solvents with $NaHSO_4$ if basic or $NaHCO_3$ if acidic, and flush them down the sink with water.

Biochemistry (18.5, pp. 443–449). The modern science of biochemistry increasingly overlaps the field of *molecular biology*—the study of how living cells work at the molecular level. For a sense of how some cellular biochemical processes operate, you may wish to consult *Biology: God's Living Creation* (A Beka Book, 1997), pp. 40–42. The illustration of the machinery of photosynthesis (p. 41, Fig. 2.10) may help reinforce the concept that the cell is not a simple bag of chemicals; it is a complex collection of intricate "molecular machines."

For a more in-depth look at biochemical processes, you may wish to consult an up-to-date biochemistry or molecular biology textbook.

Carbohydrates (18.5, pp. 445–446). You can demonstrate why carbohydrates were once thought to be hydrates of carbon by repeating the reaction of concentrated H_2SO_4 with sucrose (see Chapter 10 Lecture Demonstrations). Alternatively, you may heat a small amount of sucrose in an old test tube using a Bunsen burner and point out the formation of water at the neck of the test tube.

Chapter 18 Resource List

Note: Internet sources are given **for the teacher's reference.** Address or content may have changed since this publication of this teacher guide. Be sure to thoroughly review the location and content of any site yourself and check your school policy before recommending the site to your students.

Hydrocarbons / substituted hydrocarbons:

- CambridgeSoft Chemfinder <www.chemfinder.com>. Searchable database of hundreds of thousands of organic and inorganic chemicals; gives structural formula, molecular formula, and physical data for each chemical.

Petroleum and energy issues:

- Robert L. Bradley Jr., "The Increasing Sustainability of Conventional Energy" (April 22, 1999), <http://www.cato.org/pubs/pas/pa341txt.pdf>. Interesting article favorably comparing the drawbacks and benefits of fossil fuels compared to "renewable" energy sources; discusses the abundance of fossil fuels and speculates about their future.

Polymer chemistry:

- "Polymers Up Close and Personal." <http://www.psrc.usm.edu/macrog/floor2.htm>. Detailed resource on the chemistry of a wide variety of polymers, from aramids to polyketones; produced by the University of Southern Mississippi Department of Polymer Chemistry.

Biochemistry:

- Rasmol Home Page <http://www.umass.edu/microbio/rasmol/>. Home page, supported in part by the National Science Foundation, from which the free molecular modeling program *Rasmol* can be downloaded (versions are available for a wide range of computing platforms, including Windows, Macintosh, and Unix). Instructions for using various sources of .pdb files are also found on this site.
- RCSB Protein Data Bank. <http://www.rcsb.org/pdb/>. Repository of downloadable molecular coordinate files (.pdb format) of several thousand proteins, such as the ones pictured on pp. 315 and 445, that can be viewed using the Rasmol molecular modeling program (above).

Answers to Text Questions

Section Review 18.1 (p. 421)

1. List three ways in which organic compounds differ as a class from inorganic compounds. *They burn in air; exist principally as gases, liquids, or low-melting solids; form covalent compounds; are nonpolar; are insoluble to slightly soluble in water; and have low reaction rates.*
2. Why are organic compounds generally insoluble in water? *Their molecules are often nonpolar and water is polar; "like dissolves like."*
3. What is wrong with each of the following structural formulas?

   a.
```
H
 \
  C=H
 /
H
```
   Hydrogen can form only 1 covalent bond, not 2.

   b.
```
H   H
 \ /
  C
  |
  H
```
   Carbon forms 4 covalent bonds, not 3.

   c.
```
    H
 H\ | /H
    C
   / \
  H   H
```
   Carbon can form no more than 4 covalent bonds.

4. What is meant when two different molecules are said to be *isomers?* *They are compounds with the same molecular formula but different arrangements of atoms (different structures).*
5. Why can the simple structural formula of an organic molecule be somewhat misleading as to the true shape of the molecule? *The molecule is not always flat as shown; molecules written with 90-degree angles may actually be tetrahedral in shape, etc.*
6. What term describes various arrangements of atoms and bonds that give distinct physical and chemical properties to molecules in which they are found? *functional group*

Section Review 18.2 (p. 432)

1. Distinguish between saturated and unsaturated hydrocarbons. Which group includes alkenes? Alkanes? *Saturated hydrocarbons contain only single carbon-carbon bonds and cannot hold additional atoms without breaking the chain; unsaturated hydrocarbons contain double or triple carbon-carbon bonds and may accommodate additional atoms without breaking the chain. Alkenes are considered unsaturated hydrocarbons and alkanes are considered saturated hydrocarbons.*
2. Which group of hydrocarbons is sometimes referred to as the ***paraffin series?*** The ***olefin series?*** *alkanes; alkenes*
3. Which of the following names indicate alkene functional groups?
   a. 1,3-butadiene (used to make synthetic rubber)
   b. β-carotene (pigment in carrots)
   c. cyclopropane (an anesthetic)
   d. styrene (used to manufacture polystyrene plastics)
   ***a, b,** and **d;** the suffix -ene indicates that the substance is not an alkene*
4. Which of these names would be correct for the following structural formula?
```
   H  H  H  H  H
   |  |  |  |  |     H
H—C—C—C—C—C=C/
   |  |  |  |  |     \
   H  H  H  H  H      H
```
   a. 5-hexene
   b. 1-hexene
   c. hexene ***b.** 1-hexene*
   d. 1-hexyne
   e. 5-hexyne
5. What natural source is the primary source of hydrocarbons? Name three uses for hydrocarbons. *petroleum; used as fuel, as raw material in the synthesis of plastics, lubricants, synthetic rubber, medication, and numerous other materials*

Section Review 18.3 (p. 438)

1. What are substituted hydrocarbons? *Substituted hydrocarbons can be thought of as hydrocarbons that have had one or more hydrogen atoms replaced by different atoms or functional groups.*
2. How do alcohols and phenols differ? ***Alcohols** are organic compounds that have had one or more hydrogen atoms replaced by an –OH (hydroxyl) group. **Phenols** are a particular type of alcohol in which the hydroxyl group(s) are attached directly to an aromatic (benzene) ring.*
3. What common name is given to methanol? To ethanol? *"wood alcohol"; "grain alcohol"*
4. What type of substituted hydrocarbon results when a carboxylic acid reacts with an alcohol? *esters*
5. Name two classes of substituted hydrocarbons that contain nitrogen atoms in the functional group. *amines and amides*

6. List two uses of each of the following (see Table 18.6).
   a. ethanol *solvent; antiseptic; fuel; synthesis of ether; medicines; (alcoholic beverages)*
   b. methanol *solvent; fuel; gas line antifreeze; synthesis of formaldehyde; windshield-washer fluid*
   c. glycerol *manufacture of cellophane, drugs, cosmetics and explosives; sweetener*
   d. phenol *antiseptic; disinfectant; manufacture of plastics; fibers, and drugs*
   e. acetone *nail polish remover; plastics; paints; varnishes; metal cleaner; synthesizer of many organic compounds*
   f. formaldehyde *preservation of specimens; germicide; disinfectant; manufacture of rayon; plastics; and adhesives*
7. What is an alkaloid? *An alkaloid is an amine that occurs naturally in plants.*
8. List two alkaloids and their physiological effects. (see Table 18.7).
   Any two of the following:
   nicotine—short-term stimulant in small doses, but toxic in large doses
   caffeine—mild stimulant
   morphine—relief of severe pain; addictive if misused
9. List three substances that are classed as amides. *Amides mentioned in the text include nylon; acetaminophen; several antibiotics such as penicillin; phenobarbital; and diazepam*

Section Review 18.4 (p. 443)

1. To what broad group of organic compounds do plastics and synthetic fibers belong? *polymers*
2. Name three common vinyl polymers. *polyethylene, polytetrafluoroethylene (Teflon®), polyvinyl chloride (PVC), and polystyrene (see Table 18.9 for others)*
3. What class of polymers contains repeated ester groups? Name three common products composed of this type of polymer. *polyesters; clothing, soda bottles, some helium balloons, computer diskettes, etc.*
4. What term refers to aromatic polyamide polymers? Name one well-known polymer from this group. *aramids; Kevlar®*
5. Name two uses of polycarbonates and two uses of polyurethanes.
   polycarbonates*—shatterproof windows, eyeglass lenses, baby bottles*
   polyurethanes*—skate wheels, furniture padding, elastic clothing fibers*
6. How is a silicone different from an organic polymer? *A silicone is composed of silicon-oxygen chains rather than carbon chains.*

Section Review 18.5 (p. 449)

1. How has the science of biochemistry changed since it was first established? *The science of biochemistry was begun as a small branch of organic chemistry, but was soon expanded once scientists began to discover the complexity and immensity of the subject area.*
2. What is an amino acid? What is the relationship between amino acids and proteins? *An amino acid is a molecule containing an amine group and a carboxylic acid group that are both attached to the same carbon atom. Every protein is a polymer of many amino acid molecules.*
3. From a chemical perspective, what is a carbohydrate? *A carbohydrate is an aldehyde or ketone that contains multiple hydroxyl (alcohol) groups.*
4. Distinguish between monosaccharides, disaccharides, and polysaccharides and give an example of each.
   monosaccharides*—contain 3–8 carbon atoms per molecule; glucose, fructose*
   disaccharides*—form by the linking together of two monosaccharide molecules; sucrose, lactose, maltose*
   polysaccharides*—polymers of monosaccarides; amylose (plant starch)*
5. Why is glucose not stored as separate molecules in an organism? *The osmotic pressure created by separate storage would cause the cells to burst.*
6. What polysaccharide is a major component of wood and cotton? *cellulose*
7. What is the most basic type of lipid molecule? What functional group does this molecule possess? *fatty acid; carboxyl group*
8. What type of biological molecule results from an esterification reaction between three fatty acid molecules and a trihydroxy alcohol? *triglyceride (fat)*
9. What term refers to the salt of a fatty acid? Why are these compounds useful? *soaps; Since soap has both a nonpolar and a polar region, it can be used to wash away nonpolar or oily dirt with water.*

Chapter 18 Review (pp. 452–453)

1. Define *organic chemistry.* *the study of compounds containing carbon*
2. Give three reasons why carbon can form such a wide variety of compounds. *forms four strong covalent bonds; may bond to itself to form rings or chains of carbon atoms; may form double or triple bonds to itself or with other elements; can be bonded in various arrangements*
3. Distinguish between cyclic and aliphatic hydrocarbons. *Aliphatic hydrocarbons consist of open chains of carbon atoms (either straight or branched), while cyclic hydrocarbons contain ring-shaped groups of carbon atoms.*
4. Distinguish between alkanes, alkenes, and alkynes.
   ***Alkanes**—aliphatic hydrocarbons containing only single covalent bonds between carbon atoms*
   ***Alkenes**—aliphatic hydrocarbons containing one or more double covalent bonds between carbon atoms*
   ***Alkynes**—aliphatic hydrocarbons containing one or more triple covalent bonds between carbon atoms*
5. What is an aromatic hydrocarbon? *a cyclic hydrocarbon containing delocalized electrons ("resonance" structures)*
6. What is the difference between an alkane and an alkyl group? *An alkane is an aliphatic hydrocarbon containing only single bonds between carbon atoms. An alkyl group is a fragment obtained by removing a hydrogen atom from a simple alkane. The resulting alkyl group must be attached to another atom (often a carbon chain) and cannot "stand alone."*
7. What term refers to the reaction of a hydrocarbon with oxygen? *combustion*
8. Write the balanced equation for the combustion of liquid pentane.
   $C_5H_{12}(l) + 8\ O_2(g) \longrightarrow 5\ CO_2(g) + 6\ H_2O(g)$
9. Classify each of the following molecules as an alkane, alkene, alkyne, or aromatic hydrocarbon.

   a. (cyclohexane ring)$-CH_2CH_3$ ***alkane***

   b. $CH_3CH_2-C(CH_3)_2-CH_2C{\equiv}CCH_3$ ***alkyne***

   c. $CH_3-C(CH_3)_2-CH_2CH{=}CH_2$ ***alkene***

   d. 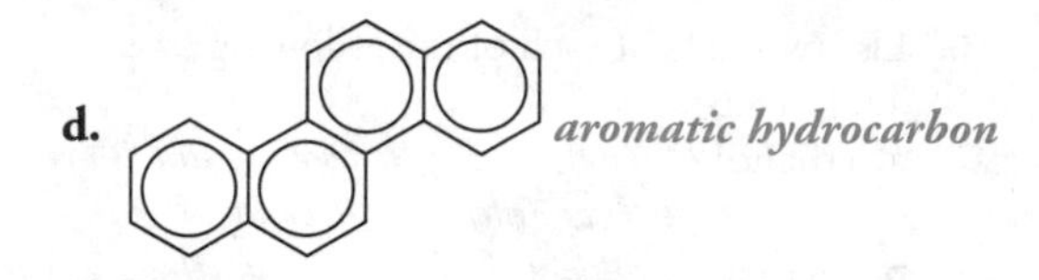 ***aromatic hydrocarbon***

10. List five important uses of benzene. *used as a solvent in certain adhesives; used in the production of explosives such as TNT and in the manufacture of plastics, paints, synthetic rubber, polyester fibers, and other chemicals; and in the enriching of gasoline*
11. What is a PAH? *polycyclic aromatic hydrocarbon*
12. What is petroleum? *Petroleum is a complex mixture of different types of hydrocarbons, ranging from very heavy alkanes to lightweight aromatics and dissolved gases.*
13. Why can fractional distillation be used to separate the different constituents of petroleum? *because the individual components or fractions of the mixture have different boiling points*
14. Why is the process of cracking used on some petroleum distillates? *to increase the amount of crude oil that distills as gasoline*
15. What class of organic compounds is characterized by the hydroxyl functional group (–OH)? *the alcohols*
16. To which group of substituted hydrocarbons does formaldehyde belong? Acetone? *aldehydes; ketones*
17. Classify each of the following molecules as alcohol, aldehyde, ketone, carboxylic acid, ester, amine, or amide:

    a. $H-CH_2-C({=}O)H$ (H–C(H)(H)–C(=O)–H) ***aldehyde*** *(acetaldehyde)*

    b. $H-CH_2-C({=}O)NH_2$ (H–C(H)(H)–C(=O)–NH_2) ***amide*** *(acetamide)*

    c. $CH_3-C({=}O)-CH_3$ ***ketone*** *(acetone)*

    d. H–C(H)(H)–N(H)–C(H)(H)–H ***amine*** *(dimethylamine)*

    e. $CH_3CH_2CH_2-C({=}O)-O-CH_3$ ***ester*** *(methyl butyrate)*

    f. $CH_3CH_2C({=}O)OH$ ***carboxylic acid*** *(propionic acid)*

    g. CH_3CH_2OH ***alcohol*** *(ethanol)*

18. List two carboxylic acids along with their formulas and sources.

See ***Table 18.16*** *for answers.*

19. Differentiate between amines and amides by drawing each functional group.

amine: —N— (with a bond down from N) *amide:* —C(=O)—N—

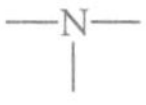

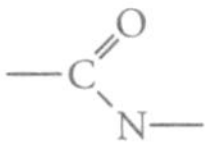

20. How do the properties of carboxylic acids differ from those of inorganic acids? *Carboxylic acids, or organic acids, are generally weak and ionize only slightly in water to produce* H_3O^+.

21. What term refers to large organic molecules composed of repeating units of smaller molecules? *polymers*

22. What term refers to the process by which many monomers may be linked together to form a single large molecule? *polymerization*

23. What is a silicone? *any of a group of versatile inorganic polymers based on long chains of silicon and oxygen*

24. What is a protein? *a polymer of amino acids*

25. What is a carbohydrate? *aldehyde or ketone molecules containing multiple hydroxyl (alcohol) groups*

26. What term refers to relatively simple carbohydrates containing up to a dozen or so carbon atoms? *sugar*

27. What group of biological organic compounds includes fats, oils, and waxes? *lipids*

28. Distinguish between *fat* and *fatty acid.* *A fatty acid, the most basic lipid, is a carboxylic acid molecule consisting of a chain of 12–20 carbon atoms with a carboxyl group at one end. A fat molecule, or triglyceride, results when three fatty acids react with glycerin.*

29. Do oils consist primarily of saturated or unsaturated fatty acids? Explain. *Oils, fats that are liquid at room temperature, consist primarily of unsaturated fatty acids. Unsaturated fatty acids, which contain one or more double bonds, do not stack well because the double bonds "kink" the chains, usually causing the fat to be liquid at room temperature.*

30. Classify each of the following molecules as an amine, amide, carboxylic acid, amino acid, or ester.

a. 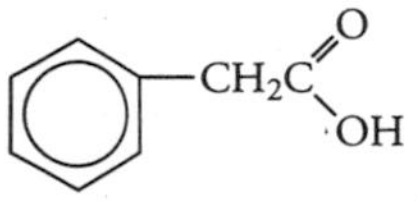 C_6H_5–$CH_2C(=O)OH$ ***carboxylic acid***

b. 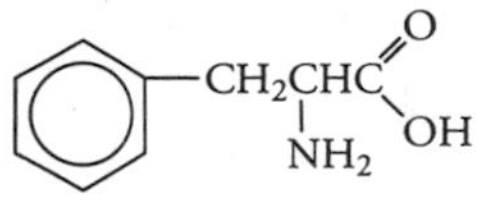 C_6H_5–$CH_2CH(NH_2)C(=O)OH$ ***amino acid***

c. 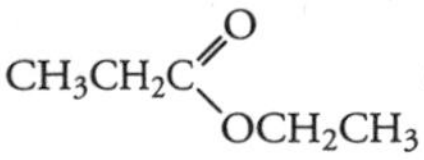 $CH_3CH_2C(=O)OCH_2CH_3$ ***ester***

d. 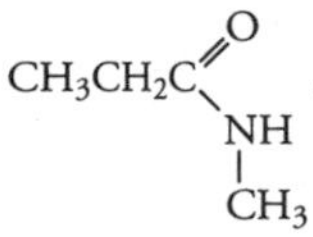 $CH_3CH_2C(=O)NHCH_3$ ***amide***

e. 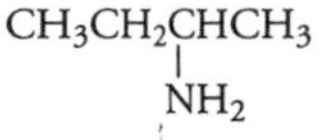 $CH_3CH_2CH(NH_2)CH_3$ ***amine***

31. Write the balanced equation for the combustion of hexane.

$2\ C_6H_{14} + 19\ O_2 \longrightarrow 12\ CO_2 + 14\ H_2O$

32. What is the general empirical formula for a carbohydrate? $C_x(H_2O)_y$

33. What is a soap? *a salt of a fatty acid*

Chapter 18